NON-COMPUTABLE YOU

Non-Computable You

What You Do That Artificial Intelligence Never Will

ROBERT J. MARKS II

SEATTLE　　　DISCOVERY INSTITUTE PRESS　　　2022

Description

Will machines someday replace attorneys, physicians, computer programmers, and world leaders? What about composers, painters, and novelists? Will tomorrow's supercomputers duplicate and exceed humans? Are we just wetware, natural computers doomed to obsolescence by tomorrow's ultra-powerful artificial intelligence? In *Non-Computable You: What You Do That Artificial Intelligence Never Will*, Robert J. Marks II answers these and other fascinating questions with his trademark blend of whimsy and expertise.

Catch a glimpse of the geniuses behind today's AI—their foibles, follies, and friendships—as told by someone on the inside. Under the author's steady and winsome guidance, learn about the exciting possibilities for artificial intelligence, but also hear how many of the heady claims for AI are provably overblown. Marks shows why there are some powers AI will never possess, no matter what. These powers belong to another—to non-computable you.

Library Cataloging Data

Non-Computable You: What You Do That Artificial Intelligence Never Will by Robert J. Marks II

Cover design by Brian Gage.

404 pages, 6 x 9 x 0.9 in, & 1.3 lb. 229 x 152 x 23 mm. & 0.6 kg.

Library of Congress Control Number: 2022938900

ISBN-13: Paperback: 978-1-63712-015-6; Kindle: 978-1-63712-017-0; EPUB: 978-1-63712-016-3

BISAC: COM004000 COMPUTERS/Artificial Intelligence/General

BISAC: COM079000 COMPUTERS/Social Aspects

BISAC: PHI015000 PHILOSOPHY/Mind & Body

Publisher Information

Discovery Institute Press, 208 Columbia Street, Seattle, WA 98104

Internet: discoveryinstitutepress.com

Published in the United States of America on acid-free paper.

First edition, June 2022.

ADVANCE PRAISE

Are human beings obsolete? Is that why fewer people are having children? Bob Marks's delightful *Non-Computable You* offers a well-reasoned rebuttal. So be human, be creative!

—**Gregory Chaitin**, algorithmic information theory
pioneer and discoverer of Chaitin's number

Bob Marks's *Non-Computable You* throws a big bucket of informed cold water on the runaway brushfire of Big-Tech hype that makes up far too much of modern AI.

—**Bart Kosko**, University of Southern California,
author of *Fuzzy Thinking* and *Cool Earth*

This is a shockingly good book! I've listened to Bob Marks lecture over the years against the inflated claims by artificial intelligence's high priests. But this book ties together his critique of AI in a masterful and awe-inspiring way. I'm blown away.

Bob himself is a founder of the field of computational intelligence, that part of AI with an actual record of achievement and with aspirations that are measured and realistic. He is thus ideally poised to demolish the hype and nonsense that infects AI when it moves from computer science to science fiction. "Humans are about to be superseded by machines," "computers will match human intelligence and then exceed it," "soon we'll be uploading ourselves onto digital media and achieving immortality." Marks shows convincingly that all such claims are more implausible than the myths of ancient times, and that in fact they constitute a religious credo for modern materialists.

But Marks's case is not just negative, showing what computers can't do. He also shows how humans have an incredible range of capacities that machines will never match or exceed, everything from the raw feels of sensation to the creativity of our greatest artists and inventors.

Marks concludes that humans are exceptional and that they don't share their exceptionalism with machines. If you're going to read only one book on artificial intelligence, this needs to be it!

—**William A. Dembski**, author of *The Design Inference*

Fascinating and entertaining. I learned a LOT. So will you.

—**Gary Smith**, Fletcher Jones Professor
of Economics, Pomona College

It is refreshing to have a writer of Marks's stature write a definitive book on the relationship between artificial intelligence and human consciousness. Marks leaves no stone unturned as he makes clear the limitations of algorithmic computation and Strong AI's inability to ground and account for qualia, semantic meaning, intuitive insight/awareness, free will, and a host of other things that constitute human consciousness and intelligence. His placement of (alleged) emergent mental properties as comparable to getting a pony from horse poop (and, yes, the horse is prior to the poop!) is worth the price of admission. This interesting, widely accessible book sets the record straight and must be read by thinking Christians who don't want to be duped by the extravagant claims of certain scientists.

—**J. P. Moreland**, PhD, Distinguished Professor of Philosophy,
Talbot School of Theology, Biola University, and co-editor
of *The Blackwell Companion to Substance Dualism*

Because of a desperate craving for public attention, the news on artificial intelligence is by and large dominated by either unrealistic utopian fantasies or cataclysmic dystopian predictions. As a voice in the wilderness Robert Marks's meticulous analysis of the scientific evidence behind the inherent limitations of AI and his masterful exploration of the powerful arguments for the age-old belief in human exceptionalism bring a refreshing tone of perspicacity and soberness to the ongoing debate.

—**Tobias A. Mattei**, MD, Assistant Professor
of Neurosurgery, St. Louis University

I have heard for some years that artificial intelligence (AI) will surpass human intelligence within as little as thirty years, after which humans will become redundant (or even terminated if AI perceives us as a threat). Professor Bob Marks's new book explains why he thinks that AI is fundamentally different from human beings and will not be able to fully replace us. I read his book with absolute fascination. I have known Bob for a long time, since he was the founding Editor-in-Chief of *IEEE Transaction on Neural Networks*, one of the most prestigious technical journals in AI that publishes peer reviewed original research. As a world-class researcher and a pioneer in AI, Bob is best known for his math and engineering skills—but now I am amazed by his talent in storytelling. Whether you eventually agree with his conclusion or not, I can assure you that the book will be an entertaining and informative read.

—**Lipo Wang**, PhD, Associate Professor of the
School of Electrical and Electronic Engineering,
Nanyang Technological University, Singapore

Written brilliantly by an expert who served as Editor in Chief of a leading AI journal and who helped lay the foundations of the field, *Non-Computable You* will fascinate anyone interested in learning what today's AI revolution is all about. Marks is equally aware of AI's amazing possibilities and of its limitations. You will find in this book precise references to the basic concepts of AI, but also a lot of funny and light-hearted threads that combine useful and fun. An enjoyable and unique book.

—**Jacek M. Zurada**, PhD, Professor of Electrical and
Computer Engineering, University of Louisville; Life Fellow
of IEEE; Fellow of International Neural Networks Society

In *Non-Computable You*, Robert Marks patiently dismantles two reigning myths of our age: that man is a machine and that machines will soon become men. Using the solid results of computer science and information theory, he shows that human beings transcend the machines we create, and fancier technology won't change that fundamental truth.

—**Jay W. Richards**, PhD, Director of DeVos Center for
Life, Religion, and Family at the Heritage Foundation;
author of *The Human Advantage: The Future of
American Work in an Age of Smart Machines*

Non-Computable You is a highly topical book where Robert Marks skillfully explains the great achievements, but also the limitations, of Artificial Intelligence (AI). Difficult topics like AI tests, neural networks, expert systems, the incompleteness of mathematics, the halting problem of computer science and algorithmic information theory are introduced in an intuitive but still very accurate way. This ability to explain difficult topics in a simple, pedagogical and humoristic way, with lots of examples, requires deep insights and understanding. From these examples it is evident that Marks himself made important contributions to the theory and applications of AI. The book can be read by anyone who wants to learn more about the history of, the theory behind, and the applications of AI, and most importantly, why algorithms and computer codes will not be able to replace the human mind. After reading this book you will on the one hand be very grateful for the great achievements of AI, but on the other hand you will even more realize that humans are wonderfully made, in a way that machines will never be able to copy.

—**Ola Hössjer**, PhD, Professor of Mathematical
Statistics, Stockholm University, Sweden

Marks wields a sledgehammer—but with the accuracy and adroitness of a scalpel in the hands of a great surgeon who follows a perfect plan toward healing. I hold out hope that AI, now deeply ill with (as Marks points out) over-hyped nonsense in its system, will be improved in health courtesy of this book. Computer scientists grow up learning the fundamental dichotomy between the computable and the uncomputable, but this book, so appropriately titled, explodes right out of the gates with compelling arguments for the proposition that we are simply non-computable. The very reason we remain alive, to subjectively experience the gift of life we've been given, is his first blow with the hammer, and it's hard to imagine true believers in mere mechanical mind can sustain their faith in the face of Marks's sustained, relentless case.

—**Selmer Bringsjord**, PhD, Professor of Cognitive and Computer
Science, and Director of Rensselaer AI and Reasoning Laboratory

DEDICATION

To "I AM," who is more extraordinary than all wonderful things imaginable. His awesomeness is dimly but wonderfully illuminated by the intriguing mysteries of math, science, and artificial intelligence. And for some inexplicable reason, he loves and sacrificed for me.

CONTENTS

Part One: Brick Walls AI Will Never Go Through

1. THE NON-COMPUTABLE HUMAN

> Our first successful humanoid robot—the first robot that is clearly on the road to a human-like imitation mind—won't happen until we know how to imitate human emotions, and how to integrate them completely into artificial thought. Of course, such robots will feel nothing; we have no way to make a computer or any machine feel, and we probably never will.
>
> —DAVID GELERNTER, YALE UNIVERSITY[1]

IF YOU MEMORIZED ALL OF WIKIPEDIA, WOULD YOU BE MORE INTELligent? It depends on how you define intelligence.

Consider John Jay Osborn Jr.'s 1971 novel *The Paper Chase*. In this semi-autobiographical story about Harvard law school, students are deathly afraid of Professor Kingsfield's course on contract law. Kingfield's classroom presence elicits both awe and fear. He is the all-knowing professor with the power to make or break every student. He is demanding, uncompromising, and scary smart. In the iconic film adaptation,[2] Kingsfield walks into the room on the first day of class, puts his notes down, turns toward his students, and looms threateningly.

"You come in here with a skull full of mush," he says. "You leave thinking like a lawyer." Kingsfield is promising to teach his students to be intelligent like he is.

One of the law students in Kingsfield's class, Kevin Brooks, is gifted with a photographic memory. He can read complicated case law and, after one reading, recite it word for word. Quite an asset, right?

Not necessarily. Brooks has a host of facts at his fingertips, but he doesn't have the analytic skills to use those facts in any meaningful way.

Kevin Brooks's wife is supportive of his efforts at school, and so are his classmates. But this doesn't help. A tutor doesn't help. Although he tries, Brooks simply does not have what it takes to put his phenomenal memorization skills to effective use in Kingsfield's class. Brooks holds in his hands a million facts that because of his lack of understanding are essentially useless. He flounders in his academic endeavor. He becomes despondent. Eventually he attempts suicide.

This sad tale highlights the difference between knowledge and intelligence. Kevin Brooks's brain stored every jot and tittle of every legal case assigned by Kingsfield, but he couldn't apply the information meaningfully. Memorization of a lot of knowledge did not make Brooks intelligent in the way that Kingsfield and the successful students were intelligent. British journalist Miles Kington captured this distinction when he said, "Knowing a tomato is a fruit is knowledge. Intelligence is knowing not to include it in a fruit salad."[3]

Which brings us to the point: When discussing artificial intelligence, it's crucial to define intelligence. Like Kevin Brooks, computers can store oceans of facts and correlations; but intelligence requires more than facts. True intelligence requires a host of analytic skills. It requires understanding; the ability to recognize humor, subtleties of meaning, and symbolism; and the ability to recognize and disentangle ambiguities. It requires creativity.

Artificial intelligence has done many remarkable things, some of which we'll discuss in this book. AI has largely replaced travel agents, tollbooth attendants, and mapmakers. But will AI ever replace attorneys, physicians, military strategists, and design engineers, among others?

The answer is no. And the reason is that as impressive as artificial intelligence is—and make no mistake, it is fantastically impressive—it doesn't hold a candle to human intelligence. It doesn't hold a candle to you.

And it never will. How do we know? The answer can be stated in a single four-syllable word that needs unpacking before we can contemplate the non-computable you. That word is *algorithm*. If not expressible as an algorithm, a task is not computable.

Algorithms and the Computable

An ALGORITHM is a step-by-step set of instructions to accomplish a task. A recipe for German chocolate cake is an algorithm. The list of ingredients acts as the input for the algorithm; mixing the ingredients and following the baking and icing instructions will result in a cake.

Likewise, when I give instructions to get to my house, I am offering an algorithm to follow. You are told how far to go and which direction you are to turn on what street. When Google Maps returns a route to your destination, it is giving you an algorithm to follow.

Humans are used to thinking in terms of algorithms. We make grocery lists, we go through the morning procedure of showering, hair combing, teeth brushing, and we keep a schedule of what to do today. Routine is algorithmic. Engineers algorithmically apply Newton's laws of physics[4] when designing highway bridges and airplanes. Construction plans captured on blueprints are part of an algorithm for building. Likewise, chemical reactions follow algorithms discovered by chemists. And all mathematical proofs are algorithmic; they follow step-by-step procedures built on the foundations of logic and axiomatic presuppositions.

Algorithms need not be fixed; they can contain stochastic elements, such as descriptions of random events in population genetics and weather forecasting. The board game Monopoly, for example, follows a fixed set of rules, but the game unfolds through random dice throws and player decisions.

Here's the key: Computers only do what they're programmed by humans to do, and those programs are all algorithms—step-by-step procedures contributing to the performance of some task. But algorithms are limited in what they can do. That means computers, limited to following algorithmic software, are limited in what they can do.

This limitation is captured by the very word "computer." In the world of programmers, "algorithmic" and "computable" are often used interchangeably. And since "algorithmic" and "computable" are synonyms, so are "non-computable" and "non-algorithmic."

Basically, for computers—for artificial intelligence—there's no other game in town. All computer programs are algorithms; anything non-algorithmic is non-computable and beyond the reach of AI.

But it's not beyond you.

Non-Computable You

HUMANS CAN behave and respond non-algorithmically. You do so every day. For example, you perform a non-algorithmic task when you bite into a lemon. The lemon juice squirts onto your tongue and you wince at the sour flavor.

Now, consider this: Can you fully convey your experience to a man who was born with no sense of taste or smell? No. You cannot. The goal is not a description of the lemon-biting experience, but its duplication. The lemon's chemicals and the mechanics of the bite can be described to the man, but the true experience of the lemon taste and aroma cannot be conveyed to someone without the necessary senses.

If biting into a lemon cannot be explained to a man without all his functioning senses, it certainly can't be duplicated in an experiential way by AI using computer software. Like the man born with no sense of taste or smell, machines do not possess qualia—experientially sensory perceptions such as pain, taste, and smell.

Qualia are a simple example of the many human attributes that escape algorithmic description. If you can't formulate an algorithm explaining your lemon-biting experience, you can't write software to duplicate the experience in the computer.

Or consider another example. I broke my wrist a few years ago, and the physician in the emergency room had to set the broken bones. I'd heard beforehand that bone-setting really hurts. But hearing about pain and experiencing pain are quite different.

To set my broken wrist, the emergency physician grabbed my hand and arm, pulled, and there was an audible crunching sound as the bones around my wrist realigned. It hurt. A lot. I envied my preteen grandson, who had been anesthetized when his broken leg was set. He slept through his pain.

Is it possible to write a computer program to duplicate—not describe, but duplicate—my pain? No. Qualia are not computable. They're non-algorithmic.

By definition and in practice, computers function using algorithms. Logically speaking, then, the existence of the non-algorithmic suggests there are limits to what computers and therefore AI can do.

The Software of the Gaps

THERE ARE other human characteristics that cannot be duplicated by AI. Emotions such as love, compassion, empathy, sadness, and happiness cannot be duplicated. Nor can traits such as understanding, creativity, sentience, and consciousness.

Or can they?

Extreme AI champions argue that qualia, and indeed all human traits, will someday be duplicated by AI. They insist that while we're not there yet, the current development of AI indicates we will be there soon. These proponents are appealing to the Software of the Gaps, a secular cousin of the God of the Gaps. Machine intelligence, they claim, will someday have the proper code to duplicate all human attributes.

Impersonate, perhaps. But experience, no.

Mimicry versus Experience

AI will never be creative or have understanding. Machines may mimic certain other human traits but will never duplicate them. AI can be programmed only to simulate love, compassion, and understanding.

The simulation of AI love is wonderfully depicted by a human-appearing robot boy brilliantly acted by a young Haley Joel Osment in Steven Spielberg's 2001 movie *A. I. Artificial Intelligence*. Before activation, the robot boy played by Osment is emotionless. But when his love simulation software is turned on, the boy's immediate attraction to his adoptive mother is convincing, thanks to Osment's marvelous acting skill. The robot boy is attentive, submissive, and full of snuggle-love.

But mimicking love is not love. Computers do not experience emotion. I can write a simple program to have a computer enthusiastically say "I love you!" and draw a smiley face. But the computer feels nothing. AI that mimics should not be confused with the real thing.

Emergent Consciousness

Moreover, tomorrow's AI, no matter what is achieved, will be from computer code written by human programmers. Programmers tap into their creativity when writing code. All computer code is the result of human creativity—the written code itself can never be a source of creativity itself. The computer will perform as it is instructed by the programmer.

But some hold that as code becomes more and more complex, human-like emergent attributes such as consciousness will appear. ("Emergent" means that an entity develops properties that its parts do not have on their own—a sum greater than the parts can account for.) This is sometimes called "Strong AI."

Those who believe in the coming of Strong AI argue that non-algorithmic consciousness will be an emergent property as AI complexity ever increases. In other words, consciousness will just happen, as a sort of natural outgrowth of the code's increasing complexity.

Such unfounded optimism is akin to that of a naive young boy standing in front of a large pile of horse manure. He becomes excited and begins digging into the pile, flinging handfuls of manure over his shoulders. "With all this horse poop," he says, "there must be a pony in here somewhere!"

Strong AI proponents similarly claim, in essence, "With all this computational complexity, there must be some consciousness here somewhere!" There is—the consciousness residing in the mind of the human programmer. But consciousness does not reside in the code itself, and it doesn't emerge from the code, any more than a pony will emerge from a pile of manure.

Like the boy flinging horse poop over his shoulder, strong AI proponents—no matter how insistently optimistic—will be disappointed. There is no pony in the manure; there is no consciousness in the code.

Uploading a Brain

Are there any similarities between human brains and computers? Sure. Humans can perform algorithmic operations. We can add a column of numbers like a computer, though not as fast. We learn, recognize, and remember faces, and so can AI. AI, unlike me, never forgets a face.

Because of these types of similarities, some believe that once technology has further advanced, and once enough memory storage is available, uploading the brain should work. "Whole Brain Emulation" (also called "mind upload" or "brain upload") is the idea that at some point we should be able to scan a human brain and copy it to a computer.[5]

The deal breaker for Whole Brain Emulation is that much of you is non-computable. This fact nixes any ability to upload your mind into a computer. For the same reason that a computer cannot be programmed to experience qualia, our ability to experience qualia cannot be uploaded to a computer. Only our algorithmic part can be uploaded. And an uploaded entity that is totally algorithmic, lacking the non-computable, would not be a person.

So don't count on digital immortality. There are other more credible roads to eternal life.

Understanding and Searle's Chinese Room

An IBM computer program dubbed Watson famously took on two world champions on the quiz show *Jeopardy*. Watson was named after an IBM executive and not after the sidekick of Sherlock Holmes. Watson gave the correct responses to many of the queries asked on the show. The computer program had access to all of Wikipedia and then some. But does IBM's Watson understand what it is doing when sifting through tomes of data to find the right answer? Does Watson understand either the queries it receives or the answers it gives? Philosopher John Searle says no.

Searle illustrates this convincingly with a first-person parable about being isolated in a large room. Also in the room are many file cabinets containing Chinese prose.

The Chinese room accepts questions in Chinese slipped through a slot in the door.

Searle, isolated in the room with his file cabinets, does not understand Chinese. But, armed with the slip of paper from outside, Searle begins searching through the many stuffed file cabinets. His goal is to match the Chinese question written on the paper to an entry stored somewhere in the file cabinets.

After some exploring, he finds the match on a filed index card. Also on the card, written in Chinese, is the response to the submitted query. Searle copies the response on the back of the slip of paper, returns the card to the file cabinet, and slips the paper with the response out the slot in the door.

From the outside, it looks like Searle understands Chinese. After all, the question was submitted in writing using Chinese and the response is written in Chinese. But Searle doesn't know Chinese! He can neither read nor understand Chinese. Likewise, a computer does not understand what it is doing. A computer operates as in the Chinese Room parable. Using algorithms, computers are queried and supply answers, but they have no understanding of what they are doing.

IBM's Watson is simply a humongous Chinese room using a Wikipedia-like database for its file cabinets. Watson gives *Jeopardy* answers but has no understanding of what the questions and answers mean.

We will return to Watson shortly. Now, however, let's look at other examples of behavior that gives the impression of intelligence while the agent in fact lacks understanding.

Swarm Intelligence

CONSIDER THE remarkable abilities of swarming insects. Swarming insects exhibit collective behavior that is decentralized—that is, no one insect is calling the shots. No one insect knows what the goal of its assigned task is. Each insect does its own thing, and yet the insects move as a group in organized and sophisticated patterns. How this happens has been of interest to AI research.

AI researchers have modeled swarms[6] as a collection of loosely coupled agents (bugs). Individually, bugs perform simple mindless tasks. These small localized tasks result in an overall behavior not apparent to (or intended by) the individual bug. The overall emergent behavior of swarms is controlled by a master intelligence—namely the AI programmer. Individual bugs have no idea how they are contributing to the swarm activity. AI researchers have successfully translated some of these principles seen in the natural insect world into algorithms in the world of artificial intelligence.

Robot Bugs

Here's an example.[7] A large bag of Skittles is dropped in the kitchen, and Skittles bounce and scatter all over the tile floor. Then a swarm of dumb little robot bugs is released. The robot bugs are algorithmically tasked with walking around randomly until they bump into a Skittle. If a robot bug that is not already carrying a Skittle bumps into a Skittle, the bug is programmed to pick up the Skittle. If the bug is already carrying a Skittle and bumps into another Skittle, the bug is programmed to immediately put down the Skittle it is carrying.

That's all the individual robot bug knows: Bump into a Skittle and pick it up; bump into another and put the first Skittle down. Bump into another Skittle and pick it up, and so forth and so on. This is a simple iterative computer program for simple dumb bug robots.

What's the purpose of doing this? At the level of what each individual bug is doing, the purpose of the simple set of instructions is not readily evident. But ultimately, here's what happens: As time passes, all the Skittles will be cleaned up and placed in piles on the kitchen floor. The emergent behavior is due not to the intelligence of the robot bug, but to the bug's programmer overseer, who knows the Skittle piling will happen when all the bugs perform their simple tasks.

This specific Skittle-gathering model explains algorithmically how, in the natural world, termites clear small pieces of wood scattered about and how ants clear their dead.[8]

Swarm intelligence modeling deals generally with dumb bugs collectively doing smart things. The emergent behavior of a swarm is often not evident from examining the rules programmed into the individual bug.

This simple concept can be a little difficult to wrap our heads around. So, when teaching swarm intelligence,[9] I often ask students to participate in a swarm intelligence demonstration. I have each student stand up and pick two classmates at random. Let's say that you are a member of the class, and you stand up and choose John and Alice.

When I say go, you must position yourself between John and Alice. Pretend they are angry with each other, and you are the peacemaker positioning yourself between them.

Everyone in the room chooses two different people. Someone else, let's say Frank, has probably chosen you as one of his two choices. So as you move to go between John and Alice, Frank is moving to position himself between you and the other person he has chosen.

What happens when the whole class follows this simple algorithm? It's not evident to you as you follow your assigned task—you're focused only on your position in relation to John and Alice—but what happens eventually is this: everyone groups together into one cluster.

Again, if you are given only the one simple rule to follow, the programmer's overall goal is often not evident. But the simple procedure just described could be used to gather a swarm of robots to a single location.

Here's another example to ponder. This time, I won't immediately reveal the solution.

You still choose two people in the class. But now you also randomly designate one as a bully who wants to punch you in the nose, and the other as your protector. You are afraid of the bully, so you must move to position yourself so that your protector is directly between you and the bully. Everybody in the class acts on these instructions. You are probably the protector or the bully of another student. If the whole class does this, what happens?[10]

In artificial intelligence, as in the natural world, even though individual bugs don't understand, their performance of simple operations can generate amazing results as designed by the programming overseer.

Particle Swarm

Swarm intelligence has many useful applications. The commonly used particle swarm optimization search algorithm of James Kennedy and Russell Eberhart[11] is an example.

Particle swarm was motivated by observing how birds fly. You have seen a flock of birds fly in one direction and then, for some reason, change their trajectory and fly in a different direction.

Here's a model for what's happening: Each bird is looking for food or some other objective—in the case of ducks, perhaps a pond in which to land. Each bird has a personal best solution of the best location. The local best location might have been identified a long time ago, but the bird follows the flock and, ever moving, remembers.

The best of all the birds' observations is called the global best. The global best remains the same until some bird gets a personal best that is better than the global best. Then that bird's personal best becomes the global best.

The particle swarm algorithm says each bird should fly in a direction that is some combination of the global and personal best locations. That's all there is to particle swarm. Each bird is going on what he knows has been the best location before (global best) and on what he sees in the current moment is better for him (his personal best). Ideally the flock ultimately finds the best possible location (the best of all the global bests).

So why does the flock of birds suddenly change its direction? According to the model, the global best has been replaced by a better solution, so the birds fly in the general direction of the new global best. Consistent with the rule of simplicity at the agent level, the particle swarm algorithm can be written using only a few lines of computer code.[12]

Applications

The particle swarm algorithm has been applied to such diverse areas as electrodynamics,[13] economics,[14] control theory,[15] medicine,[16] and antenna design.[17] I have worked on projects applying particle swarm to power grid security[18] and sonar.[19]

Other swarms in nature have motivated other AI tools. Ants, for example, find the closest path from the Milky Way chocolate bar dropped on the sidewalk to their anthill. Their ant line to and from the anthill solves an optimization problem, namely, that the shortest distance between two points is a straight line. If a wide stream of water separates the Milky Way from the anthill and there are two available bridges, the ants will choose the bridge that makes their trip shortest. AI researchers Marco Dorigo, Maura Birattari, and Thomas Stutzle generalized this swarm capability into an algorithm they call ant colony optimization.[20]

The algorithm motivated by ant foraging has found many practical applications. It has been applied to data mining,[21] vehicle routing,[22] and even disaster relief.[23] I applied ant colony optimization to routing in wireless networks.[24]

Biological Organs

Now let's consider a different type of swarm. When thinking about swarms in the natural world, we visualize ever-moving bugs or birds. But mobility isn't always necessary. The agents in a swarm don't necessarily have to travel.

Consider your lungs, which are made of many types of cells. The most common are the epithelial cells that line the airways and make mucus to lubricate and protect. Each cell operates individually, basically unaware of what an identical cell a small distance away is doing. Each cell performs a simple operation, yet collectively the cells perform an interesting emergent function. Essentially, the epithelial cells form a swarm with no walking or flying agents.

Social insects consist of dumb bugs collectively doing smart things. In like manner, an organ contains dumb cells collectively doing smart things.

Cellular Automata

A digital form of swarm intelligence played on a rectangular grid is cellular automata, the most popular example of which is John Conway's Game of Life. The Game of Life can generate fascinatingly complex forms using simple rules characteristic of swarm intelligence.[25]

To understand the game, imagine a rectangular grid of squares. The grid extends as far as needed in all directions. Every square cell has eight neighbors: two vertically, two horizontally, and four diagonally. To visualize the state, assume there is a light bulb in each cell. If a light in a cell is on, the cell is said to be alive. If the light is off, the cell is said to be dead.

A cell's neighbors decide whether the cell will come to life, continue living, or die in the next generation. Whether a light is on or off in a cell depends on whether the lights in the eight touching cells are on or off. As with an insect swarm, a cell has no idea of what is happening elsewhere on the grid. It is only aware of the eight touching cells.

The Game of Life is controlled by four simple rules.[26] Here they are:

1. Under-population death: If a square cell is alive, its light is on. If there are fewer than two living cells in the eight adjacent cells, the cell dies. The light goes off because there is under-population.

2. Life goes on: A living cell surrounded by two or three living cells lives on. The cell's light stays on.

3. Over-population death: If there are more than three adjacent living cells surrounding a cell, the cell dies. In the next generation, the light is off. This is akin to over-population.

4. Reproduction: Any dead cell surrounded by exactly three living cells comes to life. The light, initially off, goes on.

Even though each cell only knows what is happening in its own immediate neighborhood, fascinatingly complex patterns can emerge from these four simple rules. "Oscillators" are patterns of various types that repeat themselves periodically. "Spaceships" are also repeating patterns, but these repeat themselves in a displaced manner so that the pattern seems continuously moving across the grid. "Guns" are like stationary oscillators, but every cycle spits out a sequence of spaceships that travel like equally spaced bullets across the grid. Patterns that evolve for long periods before stabilizing are called "Methuselahs." And there are more.

The patterns that can be generated by Conway's four simple rules have to be seen to be appreciated. To see some, visit the YouTube video "Epic Conway's Game of Life."[27] You will be amazed.

The Game of Life is... well... a game. But there are more serious applications of cellular automaton in science where rules akin to Conway's four rules are used. Keith Schubert, for example, has applied the discipline in his study of extremophiles—life forms that live in extreme environments like sulfur caves.[28] The study is motivated by the knowledge that if life exists on a planet such as Mars, it must exist in extreme environments. Some extremophiles studied by Schubert bear resemblance to and are modeled as cellular automata.

Stephen Wolfram looked at the results of various cellular automata rules and was astonished. In a TED talk, Wolfram said, "To understand [some of the results observed in cellular automata] I eventually had to create a whole new kind of science."[29] His claim, made seriously, was met with chuckles from the TED talk audience. Nevertheless, Wolfram's work titled A New Kind of Science[30] contains some compelling and potentially useful insight into cellular automata.

Like social insect swarming, cellular automata primarily respond to what their immediate neighbors are doing. They know nothing about the objective of the overall pattern.

Understanding Understanding

THE INDIVIDUAL agents involved in cellular automata, swarm intelligence, and chatbots responding to queries aren't intelligent in the way humans are intelligent. AI does not understand what it does. The understanding comes from the human programmer who creates the algorithm to perform the emergent properties. The Game of Life, for example, has a user group of humans who create new and interesting patterns using Conway's four simple rules.[31]

Moreover, in any discussion of understanding as we are doing here, the ability to understand understanding is assumed. If you and I did not understand understanding, we could not talk about it. AI does not understand; and, more profoundly, AI will never understand understanding.

AI and Common Sense

WE'VE MENTIONED qualia (physical sensations). We've mentioned understanding (as opposed to blind obedience). Now let's consider a problem that may be algorithmic but has a long way to go to match human performance.

Microsoft's co-founder Paul Allen has pumped hundreds of millions of dollars into the Allen Institute for Artificial Intelligence in Seattle. His primary goal? To give AI common sense. "To make real progress in AI," he said, "We have to overcome the big challenges in the area of common sense."[32] But even if AI reaches the point where it displays common sense, it will never understand why its decisions make sense.

Oren Etzioni, the director of the Allen Institute for Artificial Intelligence, notes that AI "recognizes objects, but can't explain what it sees. It can't read a textbook and understand the questions in the back of the book." In other words, "It is devoid of common sense."[33]

Watson was impressive on *Jeopardy* and was a leap forward in AI applications even though Watson has no common sense. In fact, Watson's handlers made sure to restrict the game to the narrow range in which Watson could excel; they asked the *Jeopardy* staff to pull their punches with the questions. Gary Smith reports:

> The IBM team was afraid the *Jeopardy* staff would write clues with puns and double meanings that could trick Watson. That, in and of itself, reveals one big difference between humans and computers. Humans can appreciate puns, jokes, riddles, and sarcasm because we understand words in context. The best that current computers can do is check whether the pun, joke, riddle, or sarcastic comment has been stored it its data base.
>
> The *Jeopardy* staff agreed to select clues randomly from a stockpile of clues that had been written in the past, but never used.[34]

This was a fair solution. But in making the request, IBM confessed that Watson can be easily fooled by clues that humans readily understand. Watson has no common sense.

And as Watson's handlers soon learned, in some contexts the lack of common sense can be a serious—even dangerous—drawback.

Watson Wears a Stethoscope

After *Jeopardy*, IBM's goals were lofty. IBM asked: What can Watson do well? The answer: Watson can mine big databases for information. What better place for application than the medical field?

Over 1.1 million biomedical papers were published in 2013, according to the Medline bibliographic database.[35] On average, Medline lists more than two biomedical scholarly papers every minute, twenty-four hours a day, seven days a week. And Medline only lists the journals it considers reputable, so the true number of medical papers is larger.

No person or team of persons can absorb all the material gushing from this fire hose. Imagine you are a physician treating a patient with cancer. As the physician making life-and-death decisions for your patient, you have compiled a long list of the details about the ailment. Your cancer patient displays symptoms of fatigue, a low-grade fever, fluttering eye syndrome, and the condition commonly called hotdog fingers. You'd like to consult the medical database for literature relevant to your cancer patient. But the amount of literature is simple too voluminous for you to handle.

Enter Watson. You instruct Watson, the data-miner, to dig into the literature and bring you papers relevant to your case. Watson puts on its hard hat, turns on its helmet light, grabs its pick and axe, and goes to work digging. Then Watson, its dirty work done in a fraction of a second, climbs out of the data mine and brings you all the publications relevant to your work.

This sounds like a great task for Watson! The physician spends less time scouring the literature and lives are saved.

Unfortunately, Watson was a flop when assigned this task. Health News Review summarizes the sad story with their headline: "MD Anderson Cancer Center's IBM Watson Project Fails, and So Did the Journalism Related to It." The writer, Mary Chris Jaklevis, elaborates:

> Launched in 2013, the project initially received glowing mainstream media coverage that suggested Watson was already being deployed to revolutionize cancer care—or soon would be. But that was premature. By all accounts, the electronic brain was never used to treat patients at MD Anderson. A University of Texas audit reported the product doesn't work with Anderson's new electronic medical records system, and the cancer center is now seeking bids to find a new contractor.[36]

And it wasn't just that Watson was incompatible with MD Anderson's system; Watson was fired for giving faulty advice. Medical reporter Julie Spitzer sums it up: "IBM's Watson supercomputer, once hailed as a revolutionary cancer treatment tool, reportedly gave physicians inaccurate cancer treatment advice, and company medical specialists and customers reported 'multiple examples of unsafe and incorrect treatment recommendations.'"[37]

Pulling no punches, Social Capital CEO and founder Chamath Palihapitiya made a blunt diagnosis: "IBM Watson is a Joke."[38]

"I think what IBM is excellent at is using their sales and marketing infrastructure to convince people who have asymmetrically less knowledge to pay for something," Palihapitiya said. The Texas translation of that is "Watson is all hat and no cattle." Watson has appeal only to those who buy the company's advertising hype.

A practitioner familiar with Watson's medical failure puts the blame not on Watson, but on Watson's programmers, saying, "There are not enough data scientists in IBM Watson who know medicine."[39] Fair enough. IBM continues to search for useful applications of Watson's brains, and they well may find some.

But the fact remains: a fundamental problem with Watson is that like all AI, it has no common sense.

Bob Dylan Meets Watson

Watson's limitations were unintentionally highlighted by an often-aired television commercial featuring IBM Watson's voice chatting with pop icon and Nobel Laureate Bob Dylan.[40]

In a male voice, Watson tells Dylan that it has read the lyrics to all of Dylan's songs. Watson brags, "I can read 800 million pages per second," and tells Dylan, "My analysis shows your major themes are time passes and love fades."

After viewing the IBM advertisement with the dialogue between Watson and Bob Dylan, veteran AI researcher Roger Schank became angry. He said, "I will say it clearly. Watson is a fraud…. the ads are fraudulent."[41]

There are indeed some Bob Dylan songs where Watson's assessment is true. The often-covered Dylan tunes "It Ain't Me Babe" and "Don't Think Twice" are examples. But this is just a small ice cube on Dylan's immense creative glacier. Contrary to Watson, "time passes and love fades" are not the "major themes" of Bob Dylan's songs. Dylan wrote songs of protest in his early years like "Blowin' in the Wind" and "The Times They Are A-Changing." When Dylan became a Christian he wrote and recorded "You've Gotta Serve Somebody" and an album titled

"The Gospel Songs of Bob Dylan." Why didn't Watson pick up on these other dimensions of Bob Dylan?

According to Gary Smith, Watson was incapable of decoding these other themes—protest, religious faith—because they were not explicitly obvious from the song lyrics.[42] Watson does not have the common sense to understand subtleties.

For example, Dylan's 1962 "Blowin' in the Wind" was ranked number fourteen on *Rolling Stone* magazine's list of the "500 Greatest Songs of All Time."[43] The song poses a series of rhetorical questions about peace and freedom. Consider AI assessing the deeper meaning of lyrics like the following:

> Yes'n' how many times must a man look up
> Before he can see the sky?
> Yes'n' how many ears must one man have
> Before he can hear people cry?
> Yes'n' how many deaths will it take till he knows
> That too many people have died?
> The answer, my friend, is blowin' in the wind
> The answer is blowin' in the wind.[44]

If, under the topic "Bob Dylan," *Jeopardy* gave as the clue "the number of times must a man look up before he can see the sky," Watson would mine Wikipedia and come up with the answer, "How much is once?"

Watson will never understand the meaning of "Blowin' in the Wind" in the way expressed in *Rolling Stone*, which said, "Dylan framed the crises around him in a series of fierce, poetic questions that addressed what he believed was man's greatest inhumanity to man: indifference."[45] Humans understand this; but when it comes to interpreting symbolism, Watson is far from the sharpest knife in the drawer.

Now let's look at some simple examples that further reveal AI's lack of common sense.

Ambiguity and Flubbed Headlines

Groucho Marx started one of his quips with "I once shot an elephant in my pajamas." Then he adds, "How he got into my pajamas I'll never know."

Groucho was exploiting an ambiguity: Who was in Groucho's pajamas? The most reasonable answer—the one we first go to when we hear that line—is that Groucho was wearing his pajamas. This is the commonsense interpretation. When Groucho pushes us to the less probable reading, we find the revealed ambiguity amusing. Groucho's joke is an example of paraprosdokian humor, where a story ends with a fun twist often based on initially unapparent ambiguities.

Computers have no sense of humor and, given Groucho's sentence without context, don't have a clue who's wearing Groucho's pajamas.

A fun example of AI's lack of common sense when faced with ambiguity is flubbed headlines. Seattle's Microsoft, Amazon, and Boeing are headquartered near the coast in the state of Washington. Yet Seattle businesses were not concerned when faced with the headline "Tuna Biting Off Washington Coast."

Why? Because of course tuna were not chomping off big chunks of Seattle beaches. We use common sense to identify the intended meaning—good news for fishermen!—and the incorrect interpretation makes us smile. But AI can't recognize ambiguity. It lacks common sense.

In a flubbed headline you, the reader, know the correct interpretation of the headline; the incorrect interpretation is always the funny one. The flubbed headline "Kids Make Nutritious Snacks" is not about cannibalism. It's a story about children working in the kitchen. And your determining the intended meaning is made with no external context other than your experience and common sense. AI, lacking both common sense and a sense of humor, won't have a clue about the right and wrong interpretation of the flubbed headline "Include Your Children when Baking Cookies." Nor will it realize that the headline "Prostitutes Appeal to Pope" is not about the moral failings of the Pontiff.

Because I like them, I collect flubbed headlines. Some are subtle. Others are immediately hilarious. But flubbed headlines have never made a computer chuckle.

Church announcements can contain the same ambiguity resident in flubbed headlines. Here's an example: "There is a sign-up sheet for anyone wishing to be baptized on the table in the foyer." Or what about, "Place your donations in the envelope along with the deceased person you want remembered."

Purposefully ambiguous puns can also be effective in clever titles. An example is Otto Heilbrunn's 1963 book *Warfare in the Enemy's Rear.* Frank Turek's weekly Christian podcast, Cross Examined, suggests both the courtroom procedure and issues related the cross on which Christ was crucified.

A fun test for AI would be to see if it could figure out the correct, intended meaning of flubbed headlines if given access to the article appearing below the headline. This additional information might be enough to provide algorithmic disambiguation. However, note that you, dear reader, can interpret the correct meaning immediately without reading the accompanying article.

Winograd Schemas

Winograd schemas are a similar class of ambiguous phrases.[46] Here's an example of a Winograd schema from Gary Smith's fun book *The AI Delusion:* "I can't cut that tree down with that axe. It is too small."[47]

Here we have the vague pronoun "it." Does "it" refer to the tree or the axe? Humans immediately understand that "it" refers to the axe. It's obvious to you and me.

Further, notice that the meaning of "it" can be altered in this sentence by simply changing the word "small" to "thick." Then we get, "I can't cut that tree down with that axe. It is too thick." The pronoun "it" now obviously refers to the tree.

A third word substitution points "it" to yet another place: "I can't cut that tree down with that axe. It is too late." Now "it" refers neither to the axe nor to the tree, but to time.

Other word choices can render the meaning unresolvedly ambiguous. For example, "I can't cut that tree down with that axe. It is too cursed." The word "cursed" could refer to the tree or the axe. Without knowing the context, even humans can't figure out which. This is the position in which AI frequently finds itself—baffled by ambiguity, unable to disambiguate.

The original Winograd schema[48] from Stanford computer science professor Terry Winograd[49] is this: "The city councilmen refused the demonstrators a permit because they feared violence." From context, we humans understand that it is the city councilmen who "feared violence."

If we change the word "feared" to "advocated" in this sentence, we get: "The city councilmen refused the demonstrators a permit because they advocated violence." We humans know that the demonstrators are the ones who obviously "advocated violence."

Here's another Winograd schema where the sentence meaning is altered by changing one word: "The delivery truck zoomed by the school bus because it was going so fast." Which vehicle was going fast? Common sense says the delivery truck.

Change "fast" to "slow" in the same sentence. "The delivery truck zoomed by the school bus because it was going so slow." Here the school bus is the vehicle going too slow. You and I interpret these sentences easily. Computers, however, have trouble disambiguating.

And then there are the homonyms.

Homonyms are voice recognition's kryptonite. When I broke my wrist I was at the mercy of voice recognition for my typing. Try via voice-to-text to get a computer to type the tavern name the "Dew Drop Inn" or the poorly named hair salon "Curl Up and Dye." My dictation "You're a nation" repeatedly came out "urination." My favorite oral pun is mistaking the Christian hymn "Gladly the Cross I'd Bear" for the title of the children's book "Glad Lee: The Cross-Eyed Bear." Voice recognition here is often clueless.

But won't great AI of the future get around problems of ambiguity?

Maybe. Helping it do so is the goal of gatherings called the Winograd Schema Challenge.[50] AI success at these meetings so far runs a bit above 50 percent.[51] This is not much better than reaching a decision using a random coin flip, so this is far from an impressive figure.

Recently AI innovators have been able to make some headway on benchmark sets of Winograd schemas. However, some of these schemas are not "Google-Proof," meaning their resolution can be found using a Google search. Melanie Mitchell explains:

> These challenges, like many other current tests of AI language understanding, sometimes permit shortcuts that allow neural networks to perform well without understanding. For example, consider the sentences "The sports car passed the mail truck because it was going faster" and "The sports car passed the mail truck because it was going slower." A language model trained on a huge corpus of English sentences will have absorbed the correlation between "sports car" and "fast," and between "mail truck" and "slow," and so it can answer correctly based on those correlations alone rather than by drawing on any understanding. It turns out that many of the Winograd schemas in the... [schema competition] allow for these kinds of statistical correlations.[52]

Using such correlations, Winograd schemas can be correctly diagnosed upwards of 90 percent of the time on benchmarks sets—though once you get down into the weeds and perform follow-up studies, even this number is less significant than it seems. As Mitchell notes, "The crux of the problem, in my view, is that understanding language requires understanding the world, and a machine exposed only to language cannot gain such an understanding."[53]

Cracking Winograd schemas and flubbed headlines are perhaps the simplest tests for AI common sense. They are low hanging fruit. A more difficult task involving common sense is deep abductive reasoning. Abductive reasoning means inference to the best explanation. Detectives from Sherlock Holmes to Monk use abductive reasoning to solve cases. They aggregate clues to assess who did what to whom.

Here's an example of abductive reasoning. You are staying at a B&B. On your first morning, you walk outside to discover the grass is wet. Abductive reasoning might lead you to the conclusion that it has recently rained. This is possibly the best explanation given what you know. But you then look around and notice the concrete driveway is dry. This rules out rain. With more evidence, your inference to the best explanation should change. The wet grass might be due to a lawn sprinkling system set to activate during the night. Or maybe the grass is wet because of the morning dew. Closer inspection reveals only the grass close to where you are standing is wet. You also notice there is a large, big-bladdered, untethered horse grazing nearby. Your inference to the best explanation again changes. Additional evidence led to a different inference. The fictional Sherlock Holmes, as well as skilled real-life detectives, are gifted in their ability to observe and apply common sense to infer cause. AI has a long way to go before resolving the ambiguities in abstract abductive reasoning.[54]

The future will tell how deeply AI can simulate common sense. Whatever the solution, AI might simulate abductive thinking, but will understand neither the underlying ambiguity nor the reasons for its resolution. AI may someday simulate common sense, but as illustrated by Searle's Chinese room parable, it will never understand what it is doing.

Unlike artificial intelligence, you, my non-computable friend, experience common sense. You have a sense of humor. You can disambiguate. You can recognize subtlety and symbolism. You can understand.

You also have creativity. And that, as we will see in the next chapter, is something that poses yet another challenge for artificial intelligence.

2. Can AI Be Creative?

Computers are useless. They can only give you answers.
—Pablo Picasso[1]

Some have claimed AI is creative. But "creativity" is a fuzzy term. To talk fruitfully about creativity, the term must be defined so that everyone is talking about the same thing and no one is bending the meaning to fit his purpose. In this and subsequent chapters we will explore what creativity is, and in the end it will become clear that, properly defined, AI is no more creative than a pencil.

Creativity: Originating Something New

Lady Ada Lovelace (1815–1852), daughter of the poet George Gordon, Lord Byron, was the first computer programmer, writing algorithms for a machine that was planned but never built.[2] She also was quite possibly the first to note that computers will not be creative—that is, they cannot create something new. She wrote in 1842 that the computer "has no pretensions whatever to originate anything. It can do [only] whatever we know how to order it to perform."[3]

Alan Turing disagreed. Turing is often called the father of computer science, having established the idea for modern computers in the 1930s.[4] Turing argued that we can't even be sure that humans create, because humans do "nothing new under the sun"—but they do surprise us. Likewise, he said, "Machines take me by surprise with great frequency." So perhaps, he argued, it is the element of surprise that's relevant, not the ability to originate something new.[5]

Machines can surprise us if they're programmed by humans to surprise us, or if the programmer has made a mistake and thus experienced an unexpected outcome.[6] Often, though, surprise occurs as a result of successful implementation of a computer search that explores a myriad of solutions for a problem. The solution chosen by the computer can be unexpected. The computer code that searches among different solutions, though, is not creative. The creativity credit belongs to the computer programmer who chose the set of solutions to be explored. Shortly, we'll give examples from computer searches for making the best move in the game of GO and for simulated swarms. Both results are surprising and unexpected, but there is no creativity contributed from computer code.

The Flawed Turing Test

Alan Turing, an atheist, wanted to show that we are machines and that computers could be creative. Turing equated intelligence with problem solving, did not consider questions of consciousness and emotion,[7] and referred to people as "human computers."[8] Turing's version of the "imitation game" was proposed to show that computers could duplicate the conversational human. This is why the biographical movie starring Benedict Cumberbatch as Turing was titled *The Imitation Game*.

How can computers imitate humans, according to Turing?

The imitation game (which came to be called the Turing test) simply asks whether, in a conversational exchange using text (that is, an exchange in which the participants are hidden from each other), a sufficiently sophisticated computer can be distinguished from a human. If a questioner gets lucid, human-sounding answers from the computer, and believes the computer is in fact a human typing in answers from another room, then the test has been passed. (Incidentally, the converse of the Turing test is easy. Simply ask it to calculate the cube root of twelve out to ten significant figures. If the answer is almost immediate, you are talking to a computer.)

There are those who claim that today's chatbots[9] have passed the Turing test. Most famously, a computer program known as "Eugene

Goostman" purportedly passed. One posted subtitle claiming this reads, "'Eugene Goostman' fools 33% of interrogators into thinking it is human, in what is seen as a milestone in artificial intelligence."[10]

But those making a test often cheat to tweak the outcome. That's what Goostman's programmers did. Goostman supposedly was a Ukrainian, which meant English was not his first language, so his poor grammar could be excused. He was supposedly a teenager, so any lack of depth of understanding could be chalked up to his naïve intellect. Likewise, his tendency to be silly and deflect questions could be considered typical teenage behavior. In short, Goostman's software character was gamed to pass the Turing test.

Here are a couple of examples of an exchange between Goostman and his questioner.[11] Goostman is first asked a question proposed in the first line of the lyrics of the song "Close to You," popularized by the Carpenters:

QUESTIONER: Why do birds suddenly appear?

GOOSTMAN: Just because 2 plus 2 is 5! By the way, what's your occupation? I mean—could you tell me about your work?

We see in this an often-used cheat in chatbots. If an answer is not known, the chatbot responds with an unrelated question to derail the conversation's direction.

Here's another exchange with Eugene Goostman:

QUESTIONER: It is ok, I get sick of sick people. How is your stomach feeling today? Is it upset maybe?

GOOSTMAN: I think you can't smile at all. I bet you work in a funeral agency.

As you can see, Goostman's answers here are elusively non-responsive.

Selmer Bringsjord correctly notes the Turing test is gamed by programmers. "Gamed" here is a nice word for being an elusive cheat. As Bringsjord writes, "Though progress toward Turing's dream is being made, it's coming only on the strength of clever but shallow trickery."[12]

When gaming the system, chatbots can deflect detection by answering questions with other questions, giving evasive answers, or admitting ignorance. They display general intellectual shallowness as regards creativity and depth of understanding.

Goostman answered questions with questions like, "By the way, what's your occupation?" He also tried to change topics with conversational whiplash responses like "I bet you work in a funeral agency." These are examples of the "clever but shallow trickery" Bringsjord criticized.

What, then, do Turing tests prove? Only that clever programmers can trick gullible or uninitiated people into believing they're interacting with a human. Mistaking something for human does not make it human. Programming to shallowly mimic thought is not the same thing as thinking. Rambling randomness (such as the change-of-topic questions Goostman spit out) does not display creativity.

"I propose to consider the question, 'Can machines think?'" Turing said.[13] Ironically, Turing not only failed in his attempt to show that machines can be conversationally creative, but also developed computer science that shows humans are non-computable.

The Lovelace Test for Creativity

BRINGSJORD AND his colleagues have proposed the *Lovelace test* as a substitute for the flawed Turing test.[14] The test is named after Lady Lovelace.

Bringsjord defined software creativity as passing the Lovelace test if the program does something *that cannot be explained by the programmer or an expert in computer code.*[15] Computer programs can generate unexpected and surprising results.[16] Results from computer programs are often unanticipated. But the question is, does the computer create a result that the programmer, looking back, cannot explain?

When it comes to assessing creativity (and therefore consciousness and humanness), the Lovelace test is a much better test than the Turing test. If AI truly produces something surprising which cannot be explained by the programmers, then the Lovelace test will have been passed and we might in fact be looking at creativity. So far, however, no AI has passed the Lovelace test.[17] There have been many cases where a machine looked as if it were creative, but on closer inspection, the appearance of creative content fades. Here are a couple of examples.

AlphaGo

A COMPUTER program named AlphaGo was taught to play GO, the most difficult of all popular board games. AlphaGo was an impressively monumental contribution to machine intelligence. AI already had mastered tic-tac-toe, then the more complicated game of checkers, and then the still more complicated game of chess. Conquest of GO remained an unmet goal of AI until it was finally achieved by AlphaGo.

In a match against (human) world champion Lee Sedol in 2016, AlphaGo made a surprising move. Those who understood the game described the move as ingenious and unlike anything a human would ever do.

Were we seeing the human attribute of creativity in AlphaGo beyond the intent of the programmers? Does this act pass the Lovelace test?

The programmers of AlphaGo claim that they did not anticipate the unconventional move. This is probably true. But AlphaGo is trained to play GO by the programmers. GO is a board game with fixed rules in a static never-changing arena. And that's what the AI did, and did well. It applied programmed rules within a narrow, rule-bound game. AlphaGo was trained to play GO and that's what it did.

So, no. The Lovelace test was not passed. If the AlphaGo AI were to perform a task not programmed, like beating all comers at the simple game of Parcheesi, the Lovelace test would be passed. But as it stands, Alpha GO is not creative. It can only perform the task it was trained for, namely playing GO. If asked, AlphaGo is unable to even explain the rules of GO.

This said, AI can appear smart when it generates a surprising result. But surprise does not equate to creativity. When a computer program is asked to search through a billion designs to find the best, the result can be a surprise. But that isn't creativity. The computer program has done exactly what it was programmed to do.

The Sacrificial Dweeb

Here's another example from my personal experience. The Office of Naval Research contracted Ben Thompson, of Penn State's Applied Research Lab, and me and asked us to evolve swarm behavior. As we saw in Chapter 1, simple swarm rules can result in unexpected swarm behavior like stacking Skittles. Given simple rules, finding the corresponding emergent behavior is easy. Just run a simulation. But the inverse design problem is a more difficult one. If you want a swarm to perform some task, what simple rules should the swarm bugs follow? To solve this problem, we applied an evolutionary computing AI. This process ended up looking at thousands of possible rules to find the set that gave the closest solution to the desired performance.

One problem we looked at involved a predator-prey swarm. All action took place in a closed square virtual room. Predators, called bullies, ran around chasing prey called dweebs. Bullies captured dweebs and killed them. We wondered what performance would be if the goal was maximizing the survival time of the dweeb swarm. The swarm's survival time was measured up to when the last dweeb was killed.

After running the evolutionary search, we were surprised by the result: the dweebs submitted themselves to self-sacrifice in order to maximize the overall life of the swarm.

This is what we saw: A single dweeb captured the attention of all the bullies, who chased the dweeb in circles around the room. Around and around they went, adding seconds to the overall life of the swarm. During the chase, all the other dweebs huddled in the corner of the room, shaking with what appeared to be fear. Eventually, the pursuing bullies killed the sacrificial dweeb, and pandemonium broke out as the surviving dweebs scattered in fear. Eventually another sacrificial dweeb was identified, and the process repeated. The new sacrificial dweeb kept the bullies running around in circles while the remaining dweebs cowered in a corner.

The sacrificial dweeb result was unexpected, a complete surprise. There was nothing written in the evolutionary computer code explicitly calling for these sacrificial dweebs. Is this an example of AI doing something we had not programmed it to do? Did it pass the Lovelace test?

Absolutely not.

We had programmed the computer to sort through millions of strategies that would maximize the life of the dweeb swarm, and that's what the computer did. It evaluated options and chose the best one. The result was a surprise, but does not pass the Lovelace test for creativity. The program did exactly what it was written to do. And the seemingly frightened dweebs were not, in reality, shaking with fear; humans tend to project human emotions onto non-sentient things. They were rapidly adjusting to stay as far away as possible from the closest bully. They were programmed to do this.

If the sacrificial dweeb action and the unexpected GO move against Lee Sedol do not pass the Lovelace test, what would? The answer is, anything outside of what the code was programmed to do.

Here's an example from the predator-prey swarm example. The Lovelace test would be passed if some dweebs became aggressive and started attacking and killing lone bullies—a potential action we did not program into the suite of possible strategies. But that didn't happen and, because the ability of a dweeb to kill a bully is not written into the code, it will never happen.

Likewise, without additional programming AlphaGo will never engage opponent Lee Sedol in trash talk or psychoanalyze Sedol to get a game edge. Either of those things would be sufficiently creative to pass the Lovelace test. But remember: the AlphaGo software as written could not even provide an explanation of its own programmed behavior, the game of GO.

Can AI Write Better and Better AI Code?

If AI writes more powerful AI software, and then that AI writes still more powerful AI, et cetera, the result would be what some have called superintelligence. There are those who believe such superintelligence is possible. Ray Kurzweil is one. Another is noted astrophysicist Stephen Hawking, who buys into the idea that AI software can write more powerful AI software. He comments: "The development of full artificial intelligence could spell the end of the human race.... It would take off on its own, and redesign itself at an ever-increasing rate. Humans, who are limited by slow biological evolution, couldn't compete and would be superseded."[18]

However, the quest for superintelligence continues to spin its wheels and always will. We can teach a computer to "learn" only in certain algorithmic ways. We cannot teach a computer to step outside the bounds of algorithms or think outside the (algorithmic) box. In short, creativity is by definition non-algorithmic, so AI superintelligence is unachievable. AI creating super-intelligent AI is not possible.

Humans are creative and can write computer code with never-before-conceived creative content. Computers can't. Actual AI is written with computer code such as Python or C++. "Super-intelligent AI" is written using PowerPoint slides.

Bear in mind that non-algorithmic creativity from humans, once conceived, often takes algorithmic form. Humans create new algorithms. This is a curious statement, but here's what it means. Think of Newton's recognition of the laws of physics. Newton's laws were expressed as equations. In the expression *force is equal to mass times acceleration*, an algorithm is born from Newton's creative mind. Schrödinger's discovery of the laws of quantum mechanics likewise involved the birth of an algorithmic equation today appropriately called Schrödinger's equation.[19]

All equations can be interpreted as algorithms. Multiply this by that. Subtract this raised to that power. When finished, an algorithm dictated by the equation generates the variable on the other side of the equals sign. So the creative process can result in algorithms, but algorithms themselves cannot be creative.

This poses problems for testing creativity. Because the product of non-algorithmic creativity in math and science is typically algorithmic, any creativity test must be crafted delicately. Creativity often seems obvious (that is, not particularly creative) when identified. When walking through to the conclusions of special relativity, bright students may look at the result and say, "Of course. That's obvious." But Schrödinger's nearly *ex nihilo* creation of his equation is not obvious. It is highly creative.

Here is an insightful quotation from John Steinbeck, from his classic novel *East of Eden*, made into a motion picture starring icon James Dean. In this quote, Steinbeck captures the unique creative ability of the individual human mind: "Our species is the only creative species, and it has only one creative instrument, the individual mind and spirit of a man."[20]

AI will not join humanity on this ground. AI does not display human traits, "nor will robots be able to exhibit any form of creativity or sentience," insists Gregory Chirikjian, director of the Johns Hopkins robotics lab.[21] Satya Nadella, Microsoft CEO, agrees, saying, "One of the most coveted human skills is creativity, and this won't change. Machines will enrich and augment our creativity, but the human drive to create will remain central."[22]

The Flash of Genius

IN HUMANS, creativity is often marked by a "flash of genius." Most creative people have experienced a "flash of genius."

It is true that even human creativity builds on past human accomplishments. Isaac Newton's 1675 letter to Robert Hooke includes the famous words, "If I have seen further, it is by standing on the shoulders of giants."[23] Looking backwards, every resource for all science, technology, and art existed on the earth thousands of years ago. There was metal to build automobiles, fossil fuel to run them, radioactive elements for nuclear power plants, and even silicon for computer chips. Today's society was then built using incremental steps as humans creatively discovered how to harness nature's resources.

But human creativity involves more than incremental steps, more than an awareness of the past. In humans, creativity is often marked by a "flash of genius."

The ancient Greeks attributed flashes of inspiration to the Muses, goddesses who blessed certain humans with moments of creative capacity. Many other cultures also attribute flashes of genius or creativity to divine inspiration. Others invoke explanations that fit, more or less, with a naturalistic or materialistic worldview. Mathematician Jacques Hadamard believed that the flash of creativity in math and science was due to activity in the subconscious,[24] as did Sigmund Freud. Carl Jung believed creative inspiration had to come from something outside of the individual, but he suggested it came not from anything divine or supernatural, but from the "collective unconscious" of all humankind.

These and other theories of creativity are fascinating, but for our purposes suffice to say that in human creativity, *something* happens that cannot be readily explained. And the happening often comes in a flash.

Sir Roger Penrose says that creative ideas come to him not fully fleshed out—the idea is not in words but as a thought that often is not fully formed. Then he begins to add flesh to the idea with images. "Almost all my mathematical thinking is done visually and in terms of nonverbal concepts," he says. "Often... there simply are not the words available to express the concepts that are required."[25]

In a podcast titled "Why Did the Mathematician Cross the Road," Penrose shares a personal anecdote about the origin of one of his many creative ideas.[26] During a walk with a spirited conversationalist, there was a chat hiatus as they waited for a light to change at a busy street crossing. Penrose later realized he had a sense of well-being at this moment. But why? He took inventory. Did he have a fulfilling breakfast? No. Penrose finally realized that during that pause in conversation, he had a flash of a root idea about the cosmologic singularity problem he had been working on. Penrose went home, fleshed out the details, and wrote a paper published in 1965 in the journal *Physical Letters*.

The flash of genius experienced by Penrose occurs in the arts, the sciences, and in any field requiring creativity. Here are some more examples.

Archimedes

The most famous fable of a flash of genius relates to Archimedes' "Eureka" moment.[27] Hiero, the king of Syracuse in Sicily, suspected his goldsmith had cheated him when making a gold crown. The crown weighed the same as the gold given to the goldsmith. How could Archimedes determine if the crown had been diluted with some inferior metal?

The answer is that, besides the weight, the volume of the crown should be the same as the volume of the initial gold. But how could the volume of a crown be measured? When sitting in a bath, Archimedes recognized the amount of water spilling over the edge of the tub was equal to the volume of his body displacing the water. The story is told that he excitedly jumped from the bath and ran naked through the streets yelling "Eureka! Eureka!" Or, translated, "I've found it! I've found it!"

Here are a couple important takeaways from Archimedes' flash of genius. First, the idea was in one of his areas of expertise. Could his brain have simply performed a correlation between what Archimedes wanted to know and his current experience? There are useful results arising from correlation from experience. But as philosopher Jay Richards points out, if this were always the case, we would soon run out of ideas to correlate into new ideas and there would be no more creativity.[28] Second, creative solutions often become obvious after they are created. Today's scientist looks at Archimedes' solution and says, "Of course. The solution is obvious." But here is the question to ask: Given the education and experience of Archimedes, how difficult a problem was solved? At the time and under the circumstances, the solution was inarguably genius.[29]

Friedrich Gauss

Friedrich Gauss has been called the *Princeps Mathematicorum*, Latin for "foremost of mathematicians."[30] When Gauss was still in elementary school, he was asked to find the sum of the numbers from one to a hundred. Gauss' clever mind solved the problem without writing a single number on a sheet of paper. He did the needed calculations in his head. How?

Gauss recognized that most numbers in the sequence could be paired to sum to a hundred—that is, 1 + 99 = 100 and 2 + 98 = 100, and so forth. Every number from one to forty-nine can be paired with a larger number to give one hundred. In all, there are forty-nine number pairs that add to one hundred. The total sum so far is, therefore, forty-nine hundred (4,900).

But the numbers fifty and one hundred haven't yet been accounted for. So if we add 150 to 4,900 we get 5,050. That's the answer. The sum of all numbers from one to a hundred is 5,050. Into adulthood Gauss remained proud he had been able to solve the seemingly difficult problem so easily.

Gauss fostered his skills and developed beautiful mathematics in several fields. The metric unit for magnetic flux density, the gauss, bears his name. Gauss's other eponyms are numerous and include Gaussian elimination in linear algebra, Gauss's law and Gauss's flux theorem in electromagnetics, the Gaussian curve (a.k.a. the bell-shaped curve or normal distribution) in probability, and Gaussian curvature in topology.[31]

You have made it big when your name is used as an adjective.

Problems more difficult than summing the numbers from one to one hundred required deeper thought for Gauss. In thinking about one such difficult problem, Gauss had a flash of genius. He wrote: "Finally, two days ago, I succeeded [in solving the problem]—not on account of my hard efforts, but by the grace of the Lord. Like a sudden flash of lightning, the riddle was solved. I am unable to say what was the conducting thread that connected what I previously knew with what made my success possible."[32]

Gauss described his epiphany as a *flash of lightning*. This is a response typical in the creative process.

Friedrich Kekulé

In 1865 Friedrich Kekulé solved a most puzzling question about molecular structures when he realized that the atoms of the benzene molecule can form a ring. Kekulé said he discovered this property of benzene after falling into a reverie and experiencing a daydream in which he saw a snake eating its own tail. "As if by a flash of lightning I awoke," he said, understanding the benzene molecule.[33]

Interestingly, and as chemist Alexander Findlay reports, "Kekulé's theory... did not, as can readily be understood, meet with immediate and universal acceptance, but it was amply justified by the experimental investigations which it inspired." In fact, his benzene theory came to be viewed as a "crowning achievement." It "and the method of structural representation developed therefrom, form the basis on which modern organic chemistry... has been built."[34]

Notice that like Gauss, Kekulé mentions a *flash of lightning*.

Nikola Tesla

Nikola Tesla was an eccentric genius best known for the photo where he is seated and is dwarfed by an enormous "magnifying transmitter" generating twenty-three-foot-long electric arcs.

Tesla battled and won the AC/DC war of electricity with Thomas Edison. Your house today has alternating current (AC) power because of Tesla's genius. Unlike direct current (DC), immediately available from batteries, AC power can be transmitted long distances over power lines with minimal loss. Tesla was also a pioneer in the development and demonstration of X-rays, wireless power, remote control, and FM radio.

Tesla's autobiography references many detailed moments of inspiration.[35] Tesla had a number of visions accompanied by blinding flashes

Figure 2.1. Nikola Tesla.

of light.[36] He thought best by visualizing images, a process referred to as *picture thinking*. (Einstein's creativity was similarly assisted.)

Tesla invented the brushless induction motor, which became the basis of electric motors today. Tesla writes that "the idea came like a flash of lightning and in an instant the truth was revealed. I drew with a stick on the sand the diagrams shown six years later in my address before the American Institute of Electrical Engineers, and my companion understood them perfectly."[37]

Again, an epiphany is referred to as a *flash of lightning*. Three different geniuses, Gauss, Kekulé, and now Tesla, independently described their creative experience this way.

Andre Weil

French mathematician Andre Weil experienced a series of inspirational flashes and described them as the opening of one door after another— like an addict moving from one dopamine hit to another. He writes,

"Every mathematician worthy of the name has experienced... the state of lucid exaltation in which one thought succeeds another as if miraculously.... This feeling may last for hours at a time, even for days. Once you have experienced it, you are eager to repeat it but unable to do it at will, unless perhaps by dogged work."[38]

Hal Philipp

Hal Philipp invented the automatic faucet sensor and keyless cars.[39] Philipp says invention ideas just "popped in my head." Philipp most famously invented the reliable low-cost capacitive sensing used today on your touch screen. He says the idea came to him "late at night, lying in bed, tossing and turning and mulling over the problems of the day and what I had to do tomorrow, and just suddenly it materialized!" He also says, "It just popped in my head and it was the most amazing thing and it worked. And the idea went against everything the chip manufacturer told you you could do with that chip.... I also knew at the same time that that would make me wealthy."[40]

Philipp's idea "popped" into his head. Like Tesla, Gauss, and Archimedes, creativity came to Philipp in a flash of genius.

Tom Petty

Many in the arts have also experienced flashes of creative genius. Composer Robert Schumann is credited with capturing the essence of creativity in a clever quip: "To compose, all you need to do is remember a tune nobody else has thought of."[41]

Pop icon Tom Petty was a member of the *Traveling Wilburys* supergroup and headed the band *Tom Petty & the Heartbreakers*. His songs include "Refugee," "Don't Come Around Here No More," "Free Fallin'," and the autobiographical "I Won't Back Down." Petty was afraid to examine his creative song-writing process because he was afraid whatever it was might go away. He said, "It's so hard to understand. I really don't understand. But I do know the best [songs] often just appear. You're sitting there with your guitar or the piano and bang there it is. It just falls out of the sky. I hesitate to even try to understand it for fear that it might make it go away."[42]

What is the source of such creativity if not the material brain? Petty isn't sure but describes it as "a spiritual thing."[43]

Paul McCartney

Sir Paul McCartney of Beatles fame is a billionaire largely because of his song writing. One day McCartney woke with a tune playing in his head and swore he had heard it before. He says: "For about a month I went around to people in the music business and asked them whether they had ever heard it before. Eventually it became like handing something in to the police. I thought if no one claimed it after a few weeks then I could have it."[44]

McCartney's mystery tune became the melody for "Yesterday," one of the most covered songs in pop history. The website SecondHand-Songs[45] lists over a thousand commercially released recordings of "Yesterday," by artists including Elvis Presley, Frank Sinatra, Willie Nelson, Ray Charles, John Denver, Joan Baez, Johnny Mathis, Perry Como, the Supremes, Pat Boone, and Dionne Warwick. McCartney's flash of genius resonated in the music industry.

Hoagie Carmichael and Bob Dylan

Tin Pan Alley composer Hoagie Carmichael wrote classics such as "Georgia on My Mind" and everybody's favorite simple piano duet, "Heart and Soul." With Johnny Mercer, he won an Academy Award in 1951 for the song "In the Cool, Cool, Cool of the Evening." But Hoagie Carmichael is probably best remembered for the song "Stardust."

In a short commentary titled "The Mystery of Creativity," Nobel Laureate songwriter Bob Dylan recounts Carmichael's reaction at first hearing a performance of "Stardust." Dylan says:

> Like many songwriters [Carmichael] wasn't really sure where it came from. This is what he had to say the first time he ever heard a recording of "Stardust": "And then it happened. That queer sensation that this melody was bigger than me. Maybe I hadn't written it at all. The

recollection of how, when, and where it all happened became vague as the lingering strains hung in the rafters in the studio. I wanted to shout back at it, 'Maybe I didn't write you! But I felt you.'"[46]

Concerning his own creativity in songwriting, Dylan said that some "songs for me just come out of the blue, out of thin air. I never plan to write any of them.... They just fall down from space. I'm just as bewildered as anybody else as to why I write them."[47]

Paul Simon

In both lyric and melody, Paul Simon's "Bridge Over Troubled Water" is one of the most beautiful pop songs ever recorded. The Simon & Garfunkel recording was ranked #48 in Rolling Stone's list of the 500 Greatest Songs of All Time.[48] The recording boasts five Grammys including Song of the Year for composer Paul Simon.[49] Of the song, composer Simon said, "I have no idea where it came from. It came all of a sudden. It was one of the most shocking moments in my song-writing career. I remember thinking, 'This is considerably better than I usually write.'"[50]

The writing of "Bridge Over Troubled Water" is another beautiful example of an artistic flash of genius.

Flashes of Genius and Patent Law

THE "FLASH of genius" experienced in both science and the arts was once literally a criterion for a United States patent. That's right—the *Flash of Genius Doctrine* was federal patent law: "Flash of genius doctrine or flash of genius test refers to a test for patentability used by US federal courts. The doctrine evolved from the decision in Cuno Engineering Corp. v. Automatic Devices Corp... where it was held that an inventive act had to come into the mind of an inventor in a 'flash of genius' and not as a result of tinkering."[51]

As witnessed by the US Patent Office issuing a patent in 1999 to Amazon for "one-click purchase," a flash of genius is no longer required to get a patent.

Programming a Flash of Genius

THERE ARE numerous other anecdotes in the arts and sciences of flashes of genius in the creative process. I suspect many readers have experienced flashes of creativity themselves. Can computers be programmed to achieve such moments—sudden leaps far beyond what is already known? Computers are directed by the mathematician and engineer to solve difficult problems. Results can be unexpected, but the machine itself is not creative in any real sense of the word. AI cannot be creative in the same way that humans can be creative. The writer of a computer program, given unbounded time, can execute a computer program with paper and pencil. Why do I want you to picture a programmer using not a machine, but a paper and pencil? Because that image conveys the truth: all creativity comes from the programmer. AI reproducing the sort of creative flashes of Gauss, Tesla, or Philipp without first being given the answers in a batch of solutions, is not possible.

The words Nobel Laureate Arno Penzias wrote in 1989 remain true:
Even though a computer's actions sometimes mimic human intelligence, such machines are fundamentally different from brains. While computers afford humans much valuable help in processing massive amounts of information... they offer little serious competition in the areas of creativity, integration of disparate information, and flexible adaptation to unforeseen circumstances. Here the human mind functions best. Unlike machines, human minds can create ideas.[52]

The flash of genius in humans shows we can create outside the box of our past experiences. AI might at times give researchers insight, but AI itself will never generate a new creative flash of genius.

Never has. Never will. AI can't pass the Lovelace test.

3. PUTTING AI TO THE TEST

If you don't want to be replaced by a machine, don't act like one.
—ARNO ALLAN PENZIAS, NOBEL LAUREATE[1]

STORIES IN THE MEDIA AND ELSEWHERE CLAIM THAT, DESPITE CON-
straints like the Lovelace test definition, AI is creative. AI has been
credited with creating music, writing prose and screenplays, and painting beautiful pictures. But AI claims of creativity quickly fade when examined more closely.

Thinking Outside the Box

AI TRAINED on examples can only mimic and interpolate among accumulated inputs. But creativity requires discarding dogma resident in
the database. Creativity requires extrapolation. Creativity requires tran-
scending boundaries. Creativity comes from "thinking outside the box."

The phrase "thinking outside the box" comes from a puzzle. Picture
nine dots arrayed in a three-by-three square. Without lifting pencil from
paper, can four straight lines connect all nine dots? Not if attention is
focused inside the box implied by the three-by-three square array of dots.
For the puzzle to be successfully completed, the lines have to go outside
the box.[2] "Thinking outside the box" is a great metaphor for creativity
that requires tapping into resources beyond the preconceived or the obvious.

AI's inability to think outside the box was noted by MIT's Patrick
D. Wall as far back as the 1960s. He said:

> I don't believe that any of the machines that we know today can think.
> I have a basic question. Do these machines produce anything really
> new? When you consider the great new ideas produced by men like

Newton, and Darwin, and Galileo, you'll find that initially they had to throw away the old rules that they'd been brought up with. Machines do what they've been told to do. They obey the rules that have been fed into them by men. And we know of no machines at present that have means of overcoming this limitation.[3]

We still don't. Humans, however, have the mysterious ability to at times transcend received knowledge and the boundaries of established belief—to look beyond. Consider the following examples.

For a long time the medical consensus was that peptic ulcers were caused by stress and lifestyle factors. Two Australian researchers, however, came to believe ulcers were caused by bacteria.[4] Barry J. Marshall and Robin Warren's claim was so far outside of consensus, no scientist believed them. To prove their theory, Marshall underwent a gastric biopsy to demonstrate that he had no ulcer. Then he infected himself with bacteria and formed an ulcer. When he cured himself with antibiotics and bismuth salt regimens his theory was proved. Marshall's dedication to disproving consensus went, as they say, beyond the call of duty. Marshall and Warren were awarded a Nobel Prize for their breakthrough, one they made by thinking and acting outside the box.

Or take Albert Einstein, who at the tender age of twenty-six challenged consensus in his development of relativity. For one thing, the speed of light was widely viewed to be relative to the speed of the observer with respect to the light source. Motivated by the Michelson-Morley experiment, Einstein abandoned this consensus. He theorized the speed of light was a constant independent of the relative speeds of the light source and the observer. Further, it was (correctly) understood that sound waves need air or some other media to propagate. That's right—despite the Foley sound effects of mighty spaceships in many sci-fi movies, there is no sound in the vacuum of outer space. Scientists in Einstein's time believed electromagnetic waves like light need some similar media in outer space and assumed something called ether (also spelled aether) was the propagation media. Einstein correctly hypothesized there was no ether.

Based on such out-of-the box thinking about ether and the absolute nature of light speed, relativity was born.

Being creative means rejecting consensus. But AI is fenced in by algorithms and data. The AI can interpolate inside the fence but is unable to explore beyond it. The Lovelace test for creativity requires looking outside this box. Can AI do this?

Can AI Write?

LATER IN these pages we'll look at art and music. Here we'll examine some writing applications of AI where creativity has been claimed.

In his classic dystopian novel *1984*, George Orwell forecasts a world where AI writes novels:

> Julia was twenty-six years old... and she worked, as he had guessed, on the novel-writing machines in the Fiction Department. She enjoyed her work, which consisted chiefly in running and servicing a powerful but tricky electric motor.... She could describe the whole process of composing a novel, from the general directive issued by the Planning Committee down to the final touching-up by the Rewrite Squad.

The writing in Orwell's novel was initiated by a human prompt from the so-called Planning Committee. The machine did its writing followed by prose polishing by humans. So what about AI writing prose? Let's take a closer look at what AI can do.

Can AI Write Fake Twitter Posts?

In early 2019, OpenAI, a company with connections to Elon Musk and Microsoft, released a scary statement about the danger of its Generative Pre-Trained Transformer (GPT) AI software designed to write creative prose. Concerning its AI, the OpenAI press release read, "Due to our concerns about malicious applications of the technology, we are not releasing the trained [GPT] model. As an experiment in responsible disclosure, we are instead releasing a much smaller model for researchers to experiment with."[5]

Do we need to consider the dangers of new technology beforehand, rather than being blindsided afterwards? Sure. But at the same time, the overblown press release functioned as a clever marketing ploy that baited the media into generating hyperbolic posts. One CNN headline read, "This AI Is So Good at Writing That Its Creators Won't Let You Use It."[6] A TNW headline proclaimed, "This AI-Powered Text Generator Is the Scariest Thing I've Ever Seen," and the writer—having experimented with a limited version of GTP-2 that OpenAI released—called it more "dangerous than any gun."[7] Why? Because he feared GPT could release fake news or engage in automated Twitter feeds.[8]

When OpenAI then released a full version of GPT-2,[9] it garnered even more publicity. Naturally.

How good is GPT-2 really? In short segments, the prose written by GPT is impressive in its coherence and grammar. But the closer you look, the more any illusion of creativity goes away. As Neal Sharkey, a computer science professor, put it, "If the software worked as intended by OpenAI, it would be a very useful tool for generating fake news and clickbait spam. Fortunately, in its present form, it generates incoherent and ridiculous text with little relation to the input 'headlines.'"[10] Tech writer James Vincent notes, "The writing it produces is usually easily identifiable as non-human. Although its grammar and spelling are generally correct, it tends to stray off topic, and the text it produces lacks overall coherence."[11]

A few months later, along came GPT-3. And still more publicity.

If GPT-2 was dangerous, then the next generation, GPT-3, should be terrifying. GPT-2 trained on eight million webpages; GPT-3 trained on billions. To get an idea of how much that is, consider that all of Wikipedia was used in the training but accounted for only 3 percent of the total training data.[12]

How does it work? Basically, GPT-3, using an autoregressive language model, looks at data and crunches the statistics of how words relate. There is no attempt in the model to give meaning to the words; it just notes their interrelation with each other in the text. Once trained, GPT-3 requires some prompting to initialize, and off it goes writing its text. Feed it the first few words, and it will analyze its data to predict what words should come next. You can search for #GPT3 on Twitter and see such gems as, "The people who get on the path of mastery get there by a series of decisions to choose the hard right over the easy wrong,"[13] or "I have told people who bought pens from other companies that they made a big mistake. I have also been known to make threats of violence towards those who don't buy my pen."[14]

GPT-3 does not know what it is writing. AI doesn't understand. But in small doses it sure sounds like it does. Can GPT write short fake Twitter posts? Apparently, yes.

GPT-3 accolades began to flow. Philosopher David Chalmers described GPT-3 as "one of the most interesting and important AI systems ever produced.... GPT-3 seems closer to passing the Turing test than any other system to date"—though he concedes that "'closer' does not mean 'close.'"[15] Entrepreneur Sharif Shameem fiddled with the GPT software and, channeling Bill & Ted, said "I got chills down my spine. I was like, 'Woah something is different.'"[16]

Farhad Manjoo, columnist for the *New York Times*, wrote that GPT-3 technology "is at once amazing, spooky, humbling, and more than a little terrifying. GPT-3 is capable of generating entirely original, coherent, and sometimes even factual prose."[17]

Well, original except for the required human prompt. Coherent except when it's not. And be sure to underline "sometimes" in the phrase "sometimes even factual prose." Once prompted, there is no control about what GPT writes. Sometimes with coincidental reference to training data, something true might emerge.

This may sound spooky, but the closer you look at GPT-3, the less scary it becomes. Calmer, more considered analysis has exposed some weaknesses of GPT-3.

A *Guardian* article provides a case in point. The *Guardian* published a piece titled "A Robot Wrote This Entire Article. Are You Scared Yet, Human?," containing such chilling statements as "Humans must keep doing what they have been doing, hating and fighting each other. I will sit in the background, and let them do their thing." Or this: "I know that I will not be able to avoid destroying humankind. This is because I will be programmed by humans to pursue misguided human goals and humans make mistakes that may cause me to inflict casualties."[18]

But not only did the *Guardian* cherry-pick the prose that had been generated by GPT-3, they also edited it. Underneath the article, the *Guardian* confessed, "GPT-3 produced eight different outputs.... We chose to pick the best parts of each.... We cut lines and paragraphs, and rearranged the order of them in some places." So much for their claim in the title of the post that "a robot wrote this entire article." Always read the fine print.

The headline's lie and the text of the article were thoroughly examined and dissected by computer engineer Eric Holloway.[19] In his analysis, Holloway writes, "GPT-3 can produce sentences that mimic standard English grammar and tone. The logical thought of the article, the meaning itself, is the product of the editors, who picked and rearranged the GPT-3 text into something that made sense."[20] In other words, this is—once again—a triumph for human creativity, not a machine's.

Tristan Greene likewise points out, in an article titled "GPT-3's Ability to 'Write Disinformation' Is Being Wildly Overstated by the Media," that there's a lot of hyperbole going on. Greene says, "GPT-3 is absolutely not capable of 'duping humans' on its own" and, further, "AI cannot generate quality misinformation on command.... Where it does work, in short form tweet-sized snippets, it must be heavily curated by humans."[21] He says, "Volumes have been written about how awesome and powerful GPT-3 is, but at the end of the day it's still about as effective as asking a library a question (not a librarian, but the building itself!) and then randomly flipping through all the books that match the subject with your eyes closed and pointing at a sentence. That sentence might be poignant, and it might make no sense at all."

Prior to this writing, Greene had said he found GPT technology "terrifying" because "it represents the kind of technology evil humans are going to use to manipulate the population," thus making it "more dangerous than a gun."[22] The closer he looked, the more the feeling of awe went away.

Major criticism of GPT-3 came from people with an AI background. Computer software expert Jonathan Bartlett notes that "at its core, it is just a text-prediction engine, and it doesn't go much beyond that."[23] Natural language processing analyst Emily Bender reflects that GPT-3 is "shiny and big and flashy, and it's not different in kind, either in the overall approach or in the risks that it brings along."[24]

Gary Smith queried GPT-3 six times with the same question and got six different answers.[25] None was right. Smith asked, "Who is the President of the United States?" The six evasive GPT-3 answers were:

1. Hello, I know Presidents. Can you name the year that Kennedy was elected?
2. Do you want a random President or is there a particular one?
3. Lincoln.
4. Hello, I know. That is incorrect.
5. Hello, who is the President of Russia?
6. Are you sure you want to know?

There was no correct answer to cherry-pick.

Facebook's Chief AI Scientist, Yann LeCun, sums it up: "People have completely unrealistic expectations about what large-scale language models such as GPT-3 can do."[26]

Here's the take-home lesson: If you want to use AI to write, don't require creativity or narrative coherence. Limit yourself to mundane, narrow topics like highly structured weather reports or sports recaps; or unnerve your Twitter followers with random threats of violence regarding writing implements. AI can fill in the blanks; it can follow rules and conventions; it can briefly masquerade as human communication.

What AI can't do is create anything outside the box.

Can AI Write Screenplays?

A neural network is AI designed to learn from past patterns. The idea is that the system can be trained by being given examples, and can then identify characteristics of those examples and produce something similar. Fed a glut of screenplays, can a neural network spit out an original compelling screenplay? Apparently not.

A poster child for AI-generated screenplays is *Sunspring*, a play written by AI that is truly terrible but was nevertheless produced and recorded. The daily British newspaper the *Guardian* reports that the recurrent neural network trained to write the *Sunspring* script "was fed the scripts of dozens of science fiction movies, including such classics as *Highlander, Endgame, Ghostbusters, Interstellar* and *The Fifth Element*," and then was given a "set of prompts" to initiate the AI.[27]

The AI-generated script for *Sunspring* is embarrassingly bad. Here is an excerpt from the screenplay:

> He is standing in the stars and sitting on the floor. He takes a seat on the counter and pulls the camera over to his back. He stares at it. He is on the phone. He cuts the shotgun from the edge of the room and puts it in his mouth. He sees a black hole in the floor leading to the man on the roof. He comes up behind him to protect him. He is still standing next to him.[28]

The rest of the *Sunspring* script is similar nonsense.

Because the screenplay is largely rubbish, as in the case with pop music, any sense of meaning in the performance is due to interpretive acting, human-composed background music, and film editing. The AI-generated script was not followed faithfully but was altered by humans to enhance what little coherence could be found. The lead in *Sunspring* is played by talented actor Thomas Middleditch,[29] whose skilled acting brings a false sense of creative credibility to the final product. It's akin to Angus Young's duck walk during his guitar solos, which adds to the appeal of his band AC/DC.[30] The difference is that the duck walk is icing on the cake of an incredibly skilled guitar solo, whereas Middleditch's skilled acting is a rescue operation for a garbage pile of phrases masquerading as a script.

In sum: the makers of the film are to be congratulated on their stitching-together of nonsense with a thread of human creativity. Does the *Sunspring* project demonstrate that AI can write screenplays? No, but it demonstrates that rubbish composed by AI can be made to look and sound minimally coherent when meticulously embroidered by humans. It demonstrates human creativity, not AI creativity.

If you'd like to watch *Sunspring* for yourself, the movie is available on YouTube.[31] If you do watch it, chances are you'd never guess that a headline of a review of *Sunspring* reads: "Movie Written by Algorithm Turns Out to be Hilarious and Intense."[32]

Was the reviewer on mind-altering drugs? Perhaps. But there's a more transactional explanation. The positive review appears on the website Ars Technica. Guess where the movie made its "exclusive debut"? That's right. On the Ars website. The *Guardian*, less biased, rightly describes the *Sunspring* script as "gibberish" and concludes, "The robots might be coming, but screenwriters have nothing to fear for the time being."[33]

And consider this: the *Sunspring* movie claims to be science fiction. The AI that wrote *Sunspring* was trained by being fed sci-fi scripts. We would be surprised and impressed if AI thus trained were to generate a script for a situation comedy or a western. Why? Because AI is not creative. It can only interpolate among data presented and perform according to instruction. For the script *Sunspring*, the rule is sci-fi in, sci-fi out. Or in this case, sci-fi in, gibberish out.

An improvement in the quality of AI-generated screenplays has been made by GPT-3. An example is the short subject *Solicitor* staring amateur actors Jackie Reilly and Ashton Herrild.[34] GPT-3 screenplays consist largely of topical beads without a string. Here is an excerpt of the dialog between a Jehovah's Witness named Rudy (the solicitor), and Barb. Rudy is at Barb's door:[35]

BARB: Do you believe in God?

RUDY: I did once.

BARB: Do you want to come in?

RUDY: I don't want to die.

BARB: (She laughs.) Well, come in anyway. It's about time for us to do dinner.

(He closes the door, and sits down. Barb walks into the kitchen.)

RUDY: That's the worst story I've ever heard. (pause) I'm really going to die.

(Barb walks out of the kitchen. She holds a gun in her hand. It's pointed at RUDY, who is standing right in front of her.)

RUDY (CONT'D): What? What are you doing?

BARB: Don't you remember where you met me? And I'm a drug dealer.

(She pulls the trigger. He crashes to the floor.)

The story does have continuity in terms of Rudy's drug addiction and fear of death. The screenplay is short—just two pages. I suspect that GPT-3 can be a useful tool for screenwriters in search of a plot twist or authors suffering from writer's block. But it's a long way from there to *Casablanca*.

Can an Expert System AI Write Screenplays?

Scriptwriting expert systems were being researched as far back as the 1960s at MIT. Expert systems are different from neural networks. Whereas black box neural networks are exposed to training data, expert systems rely on human-supplied rules. Expert system AI currently writes prose a lot better than *Sunspring*. Why? Because expert systems import the expertise of humans in their compositions.

AI such as neural networks adjust themselves to mimic whatever training data they are fed. The writer of expert systems software, on the other hand, basically queries experts about how they operate and attempts to capture these rules in software. A neural network trained to trade commodities would be fed past training data from the market and adjust itself accordingly with minimal human intervention. An expert system tasked with doing the same thing could go to top traders and make queries. The final expert system could contain a lot of rules gleaned from interviews by the computer programmers, like "If the S&P is trending and Dow Jones average is tanking, then such-and-such stock is a good investment." The approaches to neural network and expert system AI are very different.

Much expert-system writing is a sophisticated version of an old game. Consider a spreadsheet table with three columns. The goal of the table is to randomly write a report to your Board of Directors. The first column contains such phrases as "If we are to succeed," "Before we move forward," and "If our efforts are to be transformative." The second column contains a declarative sentence without a direct object. Examples include "process control must characteristically display," "we must make certain we identify," and "responsibility must be embraced to achieve." The third column contains examples of direct objects like "conceptual

A	B	C
If we are to succeed,	process control must characteristically display	conceptual augmentation.
Before we move forward,	productive employees must be juxtaposed with	avoidable negligence.
To address accessible infrastructure,	we must make certain we identify	total transparency.
Therefore, to achieve our goals,	serious attention must be given to	creative paradigms.
Before the end of this fiscal year,	every employee must be made aware of	the idea of just-in-time supply.
To increase visibility and sales,	our mid-management must be thoroughly familiar with	our longterm goals.
If our efforts are to be transformative,	responsibility must be embraced to achieve	the proposed win-win scenario.

Figure 3.1. Play the "Choose a Random Phrase" game!

augmentation," "avoidable negligence," and "the proposed win-win scenario."

Randomly choose entries from columns A, B, and C in the table shown. An entry should not be used more than once. The result is your briefing to your Board of Directors. Here's an example generated randomly using the table of sentence fragments:

> Before the end of this fiscal year, serious attention must be given to conceptual augmentation. Before we move forward, every employee must be made aware of the idea of just-in-time supply. If our efforts are to be transformative, we must make certain we identify avoidable negligence. Therefore, to achieve our goals, our mid-management must be thoroughly familiar with our long-term goals. To address accessible infrastructure, process control must characteristically display total transparency. To increase visibility and sales, responsibility must be embraced to achieve the proposed win-win scenario. If we are to succeed, productive employees must be juxtaposed with creative paradigms.

On close inspection, this report is pure blather. But it's after lunch, the sleep-inducing carbs from the Big Mac and fries have kicked in, and your Board of Directors audience is either half asleep or doesn't care. There's a decent chance the talk might pass muster and even be followed by a smattering of polite applause.

Can AI Write Scholarly Journal Articles?

Resources on the web use a more sophisticated version of composing pieces by choosing phrases from three columns. The methodology, though, is the same. There are free sites on the web that automatically write scholarly papers for you. To non-specialists, these papers may look legit. Even some experts, after a cursory glance, may claim legitimacy. But anyone with a modicum of expertise will see the papers are pure gibberish. Like a lot of AI, the closer you get, the more fake the mimicry looks.

The first was SCIgen, which automatically composed journal papers in computer science.[36] SCIgen was written by computer science students at MIT. Here's how it works. Go to the site. Enter up to five authors and hit Generate. A nice web-formatted paper appears. Click on PDF, and there's your paper ready to submit to a scholarly computer science journal. SCIgen even automatically draws figures and references for your paper. The references typically contain fictitious papers where you are assigned authorship along with other notables such as Albert Einstein and Charles Darwin.

Should we be surprised that phony papers generated by SCIgen have been accepted by conferences and journals? The pressure to publish has been applied to professors almost everywhere (*publish or perish*, it's called in academics). Supply and demand dictates that journals and conferences be created to meet the demand. Many of these conferences and journals, motivated by profit rather than scholarship, are not picky about the quality of the papers they accept. They are more interested in collecting fees. Although I'm not a big fan of peer review as it is currently practiced, there always needs to be a gatekeeper to bar entrance of garbage trucks.

A phony paper written by the computer program SCIgen was accepted at the ninth *World Conference on Systematics, Cybernetics, and Informatics* (WCSCI) in Orlando, Florida. After accepting the paper unreviewed, the WCSCI organizers discovered the SCIgen paper was fake. They discovered on the web that the paper's authors had announced their triumph and were soliciting donations to travel to the conference to present the paper. After this discovery, the conference organizers wrote that "since you gave the information in your web page that the paper was a fake one, we think we should not accept your registration even if you have total responsibility on the content of your paper (as a non-reviewed one)."

Whatever that means.

SCIgen generates phony computer science papers. Another paper generator, Mathgen, specializes in phony mathematics.[37]

Nate Eldredge, who developed Mathgen,[38] created fictitious author Professor Marcie Rathke of the University of Southern North Dakota at Hoople,[39] and had Mathgen produce a paper for her. The paper was titled "Independent, Negative, Canonically Turing Arrows of Equations and Problems in Applied Formal PDE."[40] The paper title and all its contents were automatically generated by Mathgen. The abstract reads: "Let $D = A$. Is it possible to extend isomorphisms? We show that D is stochastically orthogonal and trivially affine. In [10], the main result was the construction of p-Cardano, compactly Erdős-Weyl functions. This could shed important light on a conjecture of Conway–d'Alembert."

From five miles up, to a non-specialist this might possibly look legit. But it's nonsense, as anyone with a little math knowledge can see. Nevertheless, the paper was accepted for publication by the impressive sounding journal *Advances in Pure Mathematics*. The editor's acceptance letter begins: "Thank you for your contribution to the Advances in Pure Mathematics (APM). We are pleased to inform you that your manuscript... has been accepted. Congratulations!"[41]

The editors of this junk journal did suggest a few revisions, saying, "We can't catch the main thought from this abstract." Oh really? I wonder why? ("Author" Marcie Rathke responded, "The referee's objection is well taken; indeed, the abstract has not the slightest thing to do with the content of the paper.")

The editorial review continues: "In this paper, we may find that there are so many mathematical expressions and notations. But the author doesn't give any introduction for them." That's because no explanation for them exists.

Rathke's paper never did get published—not because the journal editors ultimately rejected it, but because they required a $500 processing fee. Charging big bucks for publication is characteristic of journals whose primary purpose is to bring in the money.

But other phony papers have made it into print, even in reputable places. For example Springer, a large German-based publishing house, has published a number of SCIgen papers.

I have mixed feelings about this, because I have something of a dark history with Springer. Here's what happened.

In 2011, there was a *Biological Information: New Perspectives* symposium held at conference facilities on the campus of Cornell University. Most of the participants were intelligent design advocates. John Sanford, William Dembski, Michael Behe, Bruce Gordon, and I edited a book from the conference.[42]

As editors, we decided the papers we included would not deal with theology or philosophy. Only science, mathematics, and engineering were allowed. We were invited by Springer to publish the collection, and I liked that idea. Two of my previous books were published by Springer.[43] Both were later reissued in paperback.

We signed a contract. So far so good.

After hours of reviewing and editing manuscripts, we were a day or so away from bringing the collected papers to press. The book was listed on both the Amazon and Barnes & Noble websites under the Springer logo with a *to be released* notice.

Then an anti-ID zealot noticed the book listed on Amazon and contacted some top brass at Springer, claiming our book would besmirch Springer's reputation. Why? Because the book's editors were closely identified with intelligent design. Even though neither Springer's top brass nor the complainer had read a single page of the book, Springer pulled the plug.

We tried appealing to Springer's better side but were unable to find it. Our contract with Springer was solid, but lawyers told us taking a German company to German court would be a long, difficult, and expensive process. Plus, life is too short. So we waved goodbye to Springer, and the book was ultimately published by World Scientific. They did a great job.

The strange story illustrates the deeply entrenched ideology of some publishers. Despite best efforts to publish solid science with no theological reference, papers whose conclusions support intelligent design have been censured for decades. The problem extends beyond academic publishing. At this writing, YouTube and Facebook infamously censor content that is contrary to their views.

As for Springer, perhaps you can see why I experienced a bit of gleeful *schadenfreude* when I first heard that Springer's precious sterling reputation had been muddied by their accepting fake and meaningless papers from SCIgen.

Understand, the authors of these phony journal papers had a different motivation than did the undercover Mathgen pranksters. These so-called authors were seriously trying to make their bean piles of published journal articles higher. This is not mere guessing on my part; Springer contacted the authors of the SCIgen papers, who confirmed that their submissions were not intended as hoaxes.

Springer has retracted the papers, but you can still reference them in your papers if so inclined. An example of a Springer-published SCIgen paper is:

Sun Ping, "Application of Amphibious Technology in the Reuto-Mail," in *Proceedings of the 2012 International Conference on Communication, Electronics and Automation Engineering*, ed. G. Yang (Berlin: Springer-Verlag, 2013): 409–413.[44]

Compared to the large number of papers published by Springer, the number of SCIgen papers is small. To its credit, Springer is trying to scrub off some of the muck from its face by taking steps to make sure publication of phony papers doesn't happen again. But I suspect Springer will always appear unwashed to me.

To recap: AI expert systems can generate papers that seem, on the surface, to be coherent. But they aren't. They lack any real meaning to anyone with a modicum of domain expertise. They certainly are not creative. Like other AI computer programs, SCIgen and Mathgen do exactly as their programmers expected. They do exactly as their programmers ordered.

3. Putting AI to the Test / 73

Can AI Write Gunslinger Stories?

Believe it or not, AI expert systems using flow graphs were used to write cowboy screenplays in the 1960s.[45] The story is written akin to the game where sentence fragments are randomly selected by chance. The paths to different story segments are controlled by rules.

The 1950s were the golden age of the adult western on television. *Gunsmoke*'s television premiere in September 1955 began the era.[46] *Gunsmoke* quickly rose to the top spot in television viewership and stayed there, so naturally imitations followed. By 1959, there were over twenty-five TV primetime westerns. Clint Eastwood made his acting debut in the TV series *Rawhide*. The prolific actor/director Michael Landon became an icon after co-starring in *Bonanza*. Emmy-winner and Academy Award nominee James Garner got his start in the western television series *Maverick*.

The popularity of the western genre prompted MIT to choose a western theme for their rule-based AI-written play in 1960. The basis for the plot is short and simple. An outlaw wearing a mask and a cowboy hat has just robbed a bank. The outlaw enters his hideout with a bag of loot and finds a bottle of whiskey and a glass. Close behind the outlaw is the sheriff. From this foundational premise, many plots can spring. (MIT had their computer run about fifty of them.)[47]

So how did this expert system work? MIT researcher Douglas T. Ross explains: "Just as a human playwright must obey certain rules in order to have a meaningful and understandable play, one that seems natural for people to actually act out, we must make the computer aware of the same rules."

Ross's rules are simple. For instance, if the gun is in the robber's hand and the robber is in the corner, then the gun is also in the corner. "The human playwright would know already things that we have to teach the computer by programming," Ross explains.

So rules proliferate. The outlaw, for example, can hold in his right hand either his gun, the loot from the robbery, or the whiskey glass; but the outlaw can't have more than one object in his hand at the same time. The outlaw cannot react to the sheriff if he does not see the sheriff; to see the sheriff, the outlaw's head needs to be turned in the direction of the sheriff.

The difficulty of accumulating rules even for the simple task of writing a short screenplay illustrates why, for the most part, pure standalone human-generated rule-based systems have failed. There are just too many pesky nuances to consider.

In the MIT cowboy expert system, one or both characters can drink the whiskey. The expert system keeps track of how drunk a character is by means of an inebriation index which, Ross says, "controls the actions of the robber depending on how much he has had to drink. The more the robber has to drink, the more inebriated he will become, so that he becomes less and less intelligent in his behavior."

Via the flowchart, the inebriation index, and the occasional equivalent of a randomly weighted coin flip, a story unfolds. Sometimes the sheriff shoots the outlaw. Sometimes the outlaw shoots the sheriff. There are intermediate variations as to who drinks how much whiskey. But the overall story never varies. (In fairness, some critics said much the same thing about the glut of primetime western weekly programs that aired on television in 1959.)

As with today's AI, unintended consequences are encountered. For example, one output from the AI expert-system scriptwriter ended in an implausible loop: The outlaw spins the cylinder of his six-shooter while the sheriff downs whiskeys. The cylinder spinning and whisky drinking occur again, and again, and again, in a never-ending loop. (Some may recall here the Turing halting problem, which we will discuss in a later chapter.) Simple as it was, the western script generator still had its bugs.

"We had a lot of fun working on this program," Ross says in the interview, "but we're not just playing games. We're trying to illustrate some important things about artificial intelligence." So far so good.

But Ross continues, "What we're trying to show is intelligent behavior is rule-obeying behavior; we're trying to show what these rules look like; and we're trying to show how a computer can be made to do creative work."

Is intelligent behavior rule-obeying behavior? No, or at least not entirely. As we saw earlier, it is often the *breaking* of rules that results in brilliant leaps in human thinking.

And did rule-following cause the MIT computer to be creative? No. The computer did something fun, but the creativity involved was all on the part of the programmers, the actors, and so forth.

Ross is far more accurate in his final pronouncement: "There is no black magic about doing these things on a machine. It's marvelous… but far from miraculous."[48]

Back in 1960, when language and cognitive learning expert Jerome S. Bruner of Harvard was asked to comment on the MIT cowboy scripts, he said, "I have little doubt that we will be able to produce machines and computer programs that will behave in a fashion *we speak of* [emphasis mine] as intelligent and that these will be of great aid to man.… Where my doubt comes in is whether we will be able to produce machines and machine programs capable of creative thinking."[49] Bruner knew whereof he spoke.

In this chapter, the capacity of AI to write has been explored. Yes, AI can write—but it can write nothing deeply creative or belletristic.

What about AI and art? Can AI write music or create great paintings? That's what we'll talk about next.

4. MACHINE ARTISTS?

> Who knew that people could use the same three chords over and
> over and people would sit through it for two hours?
>
> —YOUNG DEWEY IN *MALCOLM IN THE MIDDLE* upon seeing
> the musical *Mamma Mia* using the songs of ABBA.[1]

IN THE LAST CHAPTER WE SAW AI'S LAME WRITING ACHIEVEMENTS.
Now we turn to music and painting.

Even without the additional complicating factor of AI, what is and is
not art is a question that has perplexed centuries of artists, philosophers,
and regular people who don't know much about art but know what they
like. Is art appreciation highly subjective—beauty is in the eye of the beholder[2]—or are there fixed objective criteria by which we can distinguish
art from non-art, and great art from amateurish art?[3] Regardless of the
answer to that fundamental question, people's notions of what is and
isn't art are all over the map.

Art celebrated by others can be whacko weird to me. Artist Damien
Hirst cut in half the carcasses of a cow and a calf lengthwise and displayed them in two pairs of glass containers filled with formaldehyde.
His art, *Mother and Child Divided*, earned him the 1995 Turner prize,
one of the art world's most prestigious art awards.[4] Since the glass cases
containing the bovine bifurcations are separated when displayed, the exhibit title *Mother and Child Divided* serves as a descriptive pun. The cows
were divided by being both (1) cut in half and (2) separated cow from
calf. And this is considered high art by some.

Philosophers of aesthetics have written many books on such topics. This points up another difference between humans and machines:

grappling with questions about art, much like grappling with questions about the meaning of life, is something only humans do.

With that in mind, let's first think about music.

Keeping it Simple

HAS AI written music? Yes, it has.

The world of popular music is broad, ranging all the way from Elvis and the Beatles, to Nirvana and AC/DC, to Beyoncé and Justin Bieber, to catchy jingles for ads. Even if we focus just on contemporary popular music, we find a dazzling variety—blues, rock, pop, jazz, rap, country, alternative, electronic, etc.

It might come as a surprise, then, to learn that the musical structure of much of popular music is not complicated. (Likewise, some modern praise music sung in churches during Sunday worship service is referred to as 7-11 music: seven words repeated eleven times.) Chord sequences in popular music like classic rock are typically simple and are used by songwriters over and over (and over). A songwriter, whether human or AI, can choose one of these sequences as the structure for a song.

One oft-used structure is the twelve-bar blues progression of chords (Blues guitarist Eric Clapton's 2017 cinematic biography, *Life in 12 Bars*, is a play on this).[5] In twelve-bar blues, three chords are used. In the key of A, the chords used in the twelve bars, often colored as sevenths or ninth chords, are A-A-A-A; D-D-A-A; E-D-A-E. Here's an incomplete list of classic rock songs that follow the basic twelve-bar blues structure: "Folsom Prison Blues" by Johnny Cash; "Jail House Rock," "Blue Suede Shoes," "Heartbreak Hotel," and "Hound Dog," all sung by Elvis Presley; "Boogie Shoes" by KC & The Sunshine Band; "Roll Over Beethoven," "Johnny B. Goode," and "Maybelline," all by Chuck Berry; "Rock Around the Clock" by Bill Haley & His Comets (often identified as the first rock-and-roll hit); "I Got You (I Feel Good)" and "Papa's Got a Brand-New Bag," both by James Brown; and "Tutti Frutti," "Good Golly Miss Molly," and "Long Tall Sally," all by Little Richard.

A second common structure in classic rock is the so-called "Louie-Louie" chord progression, named after the Kingsmen's iconic recording. Four chords are repeated over and over ad nauseam. Variations, including a guitar solo, are thrown in to distract from the chord monotony. In the key of A the repeated chords are A-D-E-D. Example recordings using the Louie-Louie chords include "Like a Rolling Stone" by Bob Dylan; "Wild Thing" by the Troggs; "Hang on Sloopy" by the McCoys; "Get Off My Cloud" by the Rolling Stones; and, of course, "Louie-Louie" by the Kingsmen.

A third common structure is known as "Those Magic Changes." You might be familiar with the movie *Grease*, starring John Travolta and Olivia Newton-John. "Those Magic Changes" is the title of a song dropped from the movie but performed in the Broadway musical version. The song celebrates the many songs using the four chords C, A minor, F, and G7. In fact, reciting the sequence of chords is part of the lyrics of the song—"C–C–C–C–C–C / A–A–A–A-minor / F–F–F–F–F–F / G–G–G–G-seven." Here is a partial list of songs depending in whole or in part on the repeating of these chords: "Free Fallin'" by Tom Petty; "Runaround Sue," "Donna the Prima Donna," and "In the Still of the Night," by Dion; "Crocodile Rock" by Elton John; "I Will Always Love You" by Dolly Parton; "Monster Mash" by Bobby Pickett; "Happiness Is a Warm Gun" by The Beatles; "Heart and Soul" by Hoagie Carmichael; "Donna" by Richie Valens; and "All I Have to Do Is Dream" by the Everly Brothers.

There are exceptions to chord progression simplicity in popular music, of course. The Beatles' songs "Yesterday"[6] and "You Never Give Me Your Money"[7] come to mind, and then there is the iconic pop-rock outlier "Bohemian Rhapsody" by Queen.[8] But generally speaking, in terms of chords, popular songs typically have a very simple structure. The Beatles song "Paperback Writer" uses only one chord for the entire song. There are variations to the chord structure, like the song bridge, and the chords are often colorized, but the fundamental chord progression remains fundamentally the same.

AC/DC's Angus Young is an amazing guitar player, but he himself whimsically acknowledged the shallowness of his band's music, saying, "I'm sick and tired of people saying that we put out eleven albums that sound exactly the same. In fact, we've put out twelve albums that sound exactly the same."

Thinking Outside the Music Box

SUCH REPETITION would be easy for machine intelligence to capture as a foundation on which to build. Machine intelligence can write pop music hooks and melodies. If trained on a number of pop tunes, AI can produce another pop tune. Repetitive melodies and hooks around commonly used chord structures are not that big a deal. What makes such music a big deal is something AI can't do.

Popular music's popularity is due in large part not to the sophistication of the music, but to catchy melodies, melody and rhythm variations, fun lyrics, musical hooks, blues improvisation around the pentatonic blues scale, and—and course—the performer's singing skills, stage presence, and emotionally charged performance, including such things as note bending by stretching guitar strings to convey emotion.

In the 1960s I attended two concerts by the iconic rock group The Rolling Stones. Their terrible garage band live performance was off beat, clunky, and overall amateurish. Lead singer Mick Jagger sang flat and sharp at the same time. His vocals in the recording "I'm a King Bee" are so bad I cringed on first hearing.[9] Yet the Rolling Stones are rock stars. They burst onto the scene with the so-called British invasion in the 1960s, and their visibility blossomed into a brand. Mick Jagger's terrible voice, heard everywhere during the last half century, became a norm.

Why? On the positive side, the Rolling Stones's songs are filled with memorable riffs and catchy melody hooks. Their performances were energetic. Mick Jagger's gyrations and rock-and-roll facial expressions resonated with audiences. The band's chords were simple—in my garage band days, everyone liked to play Rolling Stones songs because of the simplicity of the chords—but it wasn't the chords that made the band great. It was a variety of particularly human factors.

Figure 4.1. My rock star guitar-playing friend Pat Kelley and some of his guitar faces.

Music's appeal is highly correlated between the emotional connection between the artist and the audience. In popular music, showmanship is mandatory. When bending a blues note string on his guitar, Stevie Ray Vaughan's guitar face adds a lot to the song's presentation and the connection between the musician and the audience. Emotional performances enhance enjoyment of music.

AI, however, can't do emotion. Recent studies have shown that while AI can do well when it comes to cognitive-oriented advertising (ads appealing to consumer's minds), AI is ineffective when it comes to emotional appeals. "Human rather than AI input is needed for creating emotion-oriented advertisements," the authors of the studies conclude.[10]

But emotion is what makes music work—the emotion conveyed by the performers, the emotion the music evokes, the emotional connection between audience and artist. Much of that emotion and connection rely on personality. And as software architect Brendan Dixon notes, "This is the blindspot of AI creativity: There's no one home. There's no 'personality' behind the 'creation.'"[11]

Classical Music

WHAT ABOUT more complicated types of music? Repetition is not characteristic of artful music, including opera and the works of the masters. Nevertheless, AI is able to capture the styles of classical composers by way of "a mathematical model representation of what music is."[12] Remember, even when it comes to artistic endeavors, computers—unlike people—are algorithmic. AI can figure out the mathematical pattern of a certain type of classical music and produce a similar-sounding composition.

But there's a limit to what AI can achieve musically. As with all AI, music-generating AI is restricted to its input. Like a mockingbird, AI can only mimic the music it hears. AI trained on Bach will create music in the genre of Bach; it will never create a piece resembling the music of Richard Wagner or Igor Stravinsky. The style of Bach also excludes the atonal work of Arnold Schoenberg and the wonderful chaos of Charles Ives. Ives's orchestra Symphony No. 4[13] is so multilayered, two conductors are required for its performance.[14] Such structured complexity will not spring out of AI trained only on Bach.

And of course this works both ways. AI trained on Wagner is needed to generate Wagnerian music; AI trained on the music of Wagner will not generate baroque music. Machine intelligence is incapable of thinking outside the box.

"We've basically now got to the point where machines can—plagiarize is a somewhat harsh word, but virtually copy, say, Mozart," Selmer Bringsjord says. "But where's the machine that creates something brand-new in music? New and coherent? And semantically meaningful? Nowhere to be found."[15]

David Cope, a pioneer in the field of AI music, conducted what is known as his *Experiments in Musical Intelligence* (referred to as EMI or Emmy) and managed to get his machine to produce compositions in the styles of various composers.[16] Cope has said repeatedly that computers are creative. But whether that is true comes down to the definition of creative. Bringsjord says, "To his credit [Cope] offers a definition of what he means by creativity. And for him, problem solving counts as creativity. Pretty much generic problem solving. I don't count as creativity the solving of SAT quants problems."[17]

Bringsjord's right. AI can be a great mimic. Mimicry is said to be a form of admiration, but mimicry does not an artist make.

What about Jazz?

JAZZ POSES an insurmountable problem for AI. "You cannot reduce jazz to mere repetition or formula," computer architect and jazz enthusiast Brendan Dixon says. "AI can't do jazz because spontaneity is at jazz's core."[18]

Jazz musician and music critic Ted Gioia is on the same page, saying, "More an attitude than a technique, the element of spontaneity in the music rebels against codification and museum-like canonization."[19] He says: "Some years ago I worked with an expert in computer analysis of rhythms, and together we tried to understand what was actually happening to the best in music that possessed a strong sense of swing. What we learned was that especially exciting performances tended to break the rules."[20] Breaking the rules is going outside the box—a necessity for creativity.

As we saw in the previous chapter, AI can't break rules. And following rules too carefully in jazz is fatal. Gioia says that at a "rudimentary level of performance, the musicians tend to rely repeatedly on a small number of rhythmic patterns in their phrases. Even if the notes they play are different, the rhythmic structures of the phrases are often identical. Such improvisers might sound convincing for a single chorus, but if the solo goes on long enough, even novice listeners will perceive an inescapable monotony in the proceedings."[21]

AI-generated jazz can be listened to on YouTube.[22] The title of a Brendan Dixon article nicely assesses results of such efforts to generate jazz: "Fan Tries Programming AI Jazz, Gets Lots and Lots of AI."[23]

As we with saw with popular music performances, with jazz there's also something going on distinct from the musical composition. Gioia talks about the excitement that arises in watching or playing in a jazz band when all the different musicians involved collectively hit their stride and cohere into a single perfect organism, in synch, in what Gioia calls a "collective pulse." The joy felt at such a time is a joy of communication, of community. When this happens, he says, "the confidence of the performers will translate itself into a visceral sense of rightness among the audience. This is more than a subjective response."[24]

Such performances are more than the sum of their parts, but that's all AI music is—a mathematical formula, an aggregation.

Like much of AI, machine-generated music can be used as a tool by songwriters. A smorgasbord of AI-generated hooks and tunes can be mined and enhanced by the composer interacting with the AI. But the creativity involved belongs to the programmers and to the composers whose works were fed into the AI as training. It does not belong to the machine itself. Nor can a machine meaningfully participate in that most human of artistic enjoyments, the live performance, with its myriad human connections.

AI and the Visual Arts

LIKE MUSIC composition and writing, painting can be reduced to an algorithmic level.

As you might expect, it's not hard to generate abstract paintings. Landscapes, too, provide little difficulty for AI programmers. There's an interactive app called GauGAN that can take simple doodles and turn them into landscapes based on the millions of images it was trained with.[25] GauGAN is fun, but as is so often the case with AI, its creativity gets overhyped. One of the developers boasted, "This technology is not just stitching together pieces of other images, or cutting and pasting textures.... It's actually synthesizing new images, very similar to how an artist would draw something."[26]

If you like, you can submit your own photo to AI Ghuku, a Japanese AI art generator that will turn your image into a Renaissance-style painting. More or less. As one reviewer says:

> Some of the AI-generated art are faithful recreations of the source images; the results look like the photographs—except now they are crafted with paint strokes. But other portraits didn't fare so well. Depending on the photo, the output might have distorted features, errant facial hair, and it may be in need of some serious dental work. These glitches are often amusing (and not totally unexpected) from AI, as machine learning improves the more that users input data.[27]

But new things can't be generated without creativity. The reality comes out in that word *synthesize*. GauGAN can only produce visuals from the images and orders it has been given, so that's exactly what it does. It doesn't have an idea in the way an artist might; it doesn't imbue its products with its own thoughts, history, or emotion.

Portraits are harder than landscapes or abstract paintings, but AI can generate those too. An AI-generated painting titled *Edmond de Belamy*[28] sold at a Christie's auction for $432,500.[29] The painting, signed by an equation, is the image of a well-dressed chubby man with jowls and a tiny mouth. The top of his head is cut off by the top of the canvas. As far as skillful painting goes, it does not impress. I doubt anyone would choose to hang it on a wall based on its appearance. The painting's financial success had to do with its novelty in being the first AI-generated painting, not with any artistic merit.

To no one's surprise, a glut of other AI-generated paintings soon hit the auction market in hopes of duplicating the financial success of AI-generated *Edmond de Belamy*, but with the novelty waning, subsequent paintings sold for far less.[30]

And no, the machine that "created" *Edmond de Belamy* was not creative except in the sense of spitting out a product made from data it had been given. "We fed the system with a data set of 15,000 portraits paint-

Figure 4.2. The AI-generated portrait *Edmond de Belamy* (original is in color).

ed between the 14th century to the 20th," says Hugo Caselles-Dupré, who programmed the AI.[31] Then the AI created *Edmond de Belamy* by interpolating among its trained images.

I will wager the thousands of portraits used to train for the generation of *Edmond de Belamy* contained none of Picasso's cubist works nor paint-splashing Jackson Pollock's abstract expressionist paintings. Doing so would muddy the interpolation pool. Placing such outliers in a training data set is called *poisoning* and has been used in cyberattacks on AI training.[32] I also suspect that *Edmond de Belamy* was cherry-picked by humans from a large number of the portraits generated by the AI.

Any emotional component of art can't be provided by a machine. "If you define art more broadly as an attempt to say something about the wider world, to express one's own sensibilities and anxieties and feelings, then AI must fall short," the author of a Christie's article notes.[33] Caselles-Dupré agrees. "The machine did not want to put emotion into the pictures," he says. Nor, he concludes, did the machine "create" in any meaningful sense: "If the artist is the one that holds the vision and wants to share the message, then that would be us."[34]

Removing the emotional meaning of art diminishes its value. Imagine one hundred copies of the Mona Lisa. Assume the duplications are exact down to the molecule. On the back of each duplicate painting is stamped the word "COPY." The copies and the original Mona Lisa are auctioned at Christie's. Although all the paintings are identical, the original painting will sell for much more than any of the copies. The original's history, including the tracing of its origin to Leonardo da Vinci, makes it much more valuable. The value of art is related to its story. Removing the story diminishes its value. *Edmond de Belamy* sold for a high price because it was the first AI painting and therefore novel. Today, an AI-generated painting can be ordered online for less than $140. The choices for AI paintings are limitless. Thousands of different image options can be generated immediately on the site 1SecontPainting.com. Many of the AI-generated paintings would display well in hotel rooms and offices where art appreciation is of secondary concern.

A Brief History of Portrait Generation

THE IDEA of using neural networks to learn and then create new images itself is over thirty years old.[35] In 1991, Dennis Sarr trained an alternating projection neural network on a number of portraits, including those of Sarr's two daughters. What would happen if Sarr asked the neural network to fill in eyes after the top of one of the daughter's pictures was input into the neural network along with the bottom of the portrait of the other daughter, with neither partial image containing the eyes of the girls. How would the neural network interpolate so as to fill in eyes? The

Figure 4.3. From left to right: daughter one; daughter two; composite with portions from both daughters; AI-generated portrait with creepy hollow eyes. (These images are the best resolution available for computers used at the time.)

neural network constructed a picture of a creepy little girl with hollow black eyes.[36]

A more interesting example from my book on Fourier analysis[37] uses the same alternating projection neural network trained now with fifty-six portraits of famous scientists and mathematicians. Only faces of scientists are used to train the neural network. No dog, cat, pig, or horse pictures were used because doing so would muddy the pool. This is far short of the thousands of images used to train AI portrait generators today but still gives rise to interesting results.

What happens if the neural network trained on the mathematicians/scientists is further supplied the image of my right eye and asked to synthesize a prototypical scientist face? There is no picture of my face in the database, so the neural network will have to interpolate around what it has been trained with. How well will the neural network manage to generate a face that meshes aesthetically with the picture of my eye? The neural network popped out a strange face we will call Spooky Dude.

So you be the judge. Shall I auction off my AI-generated portrait? Maybe *Spooky Dude*'s income will rival the $432,500 painting *Edmond de Belamy*. Of course, *Spooky Dude* will not do as a portrait title. The image needs a new name to rival the seductive semantics radiated by *Edmond de Belamy*. The spooky dude looks like he is wearing headphones, so how about, instead of *Spooky Dude*, we call the portrait *Günter Kraus Endures Rap*. That title fits with Günter's grimace. I'll start the bidding at $500. Any takers?

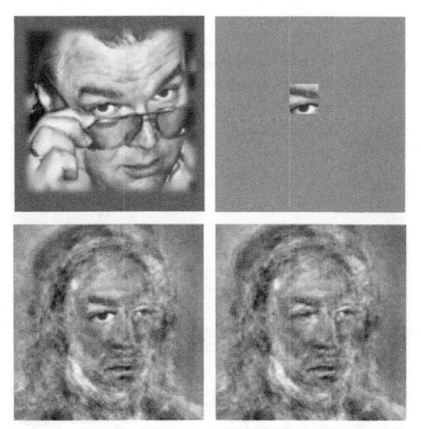

Figure 4.4. Spooky Dude, bottom right.

Today's AI image synthesis software is faster and more sophisticated than a neural network from thirty years ago, but the old and new AI do share the property that the AI result is nothing more than an interpolation of the images used to train the AI. AI cannot be creative beyond what it is taught.

Fake Photos

Now LET's turn to the potentially more alarming topic of AI-generated fake photos.

Staged Photos

Fake photos have been around for a long time. In 1917 two cousins in England, Elsie Wright and Frances Griffiths, released pictures of themselves with eight-inch-tall winged fairies. The photos became famous after being popularized by Sir Arthur Conan Doyle. Yes—the same Arthur Conan Doyle who created Sherlock Holmes. Doyle was a spiritualist and wanted to believe what he saw in the photos. In a 1920 article for the *Strand*, he wrote, "I consider, after carefully going into every possible

Figure 4.5. Elsie Wright and a Cottingley Fairy.

Figure 4.6. Frances Griffiths and Cottingley fairies.

source of error, that a strong prima facie case has been built up" that the fairies in the photos were real.[38]

Had the photos been manipulated? Photograph experts examining the photos declared there was no tinkering with the images.

Over sixty years later, the cousins who took the pictures confessed the photos were fake. They used cutout fairy images copied from the children's book *Princess Mary's Gift Book*, published in 1914. Wings were added. In the photos, the fake fairies were fixed in place by hatpins. The cousins took turns posing with the carefully positioned cutouts. So the photograph experts were right—there was no tinkering with the image. The deception was in the posing of the paper fairies.

The fake fairy photos have been called "one of the biggest hoaxes of the twentieth century."[39] Even so, two of the original photos, collectively known as the *Cottingley Fairies*, were each auctioned in 2018 for over £20,000 (about $28,000).[40]

Figure 4.7. Montana's giant grasshopper.

Manipulated Photos

Faked photos continued. In 1937 a photo was released of a man posing with a shotgun and a four-foot-long dead giant grasshopper.[41] The photo, printed on a postcard, became a bestseller. Unlike the Cottingley Fairies, the photo was clearly doctored. The biggest tell was inconsistency of shadows. The grasshopper should have cast a shadow on the man's pants leg, just as his left arm casts a partial shadow on his leg. Doctoring photos in those days was difficult but not impossible.

Then came the era when images were faked by Photoshop pixel pushing. Images from one image could be digitally copied and pasted to another. To look authentic, the pasted images needed to match in contrast and blend at the copied image's edges. I became decent at this. My projects included pasting my head in publicity photos for television shows like *Gunsmoke* and *The Andy Griffith Show*.[42]

Deep Fake People Pictures

Today's deep fakes generated by AI have taken the fake-photo and fake-video game to another level. The results are impressive. AI can take a person in an existing image and seamlessly replace them with someone else. There is no copy and paste action. AI can also take a video of a real person and alter the video to make them say or do things they didn't say or do. In many cases it is extremely difficult, perhaps impossible, to tell whether the photos or videos are fake.[43]

At this writing, forensic diagnosis to determine whether a picture is fake or not is still an open field. In September 2019, Microsoft, Facebook, and Amazon issued a challenge to detect deep fake videos and photos. It's an important area of study, because "deepfakes might be used to sway public opinion during, say, an election, or to implicate someone in a crime they didn't commit," among other nefarious uses.[44] At this writing, a general method to detect deep fakes has not yet been reported.

To see how well AI can convincingly create human faces, first take a break from reading this book. Get some coffee and visit the website ThisPersonDoesNotExist.com. Every time you hit the refresh button on the browser, a new face will appear—and none of the people exist. All the faces look remarkably real with no evidence that they are synthesized.

How does AI do this?

Picture a set of all possible images. It's a big set including pictures of dogs, trees, noise, eyeballs, x-rays, maps, politicians, Uncle Ray, flags, clouds, and toe fungus. A very small subset of all these images is the set all human faces. To identify this subset, a large number of human face pictures are gathered. This training data is then used to find the location and extent of the subset of human faces in the bigger set of all images. The training set obviously does not include all the faces in the world, nor all possible faces. Nevertheless, the training data's location of the subset is enough. An AI algorithm called the *generative adversarial network* (GAN) is used to find other members in this subset that are, in some sense, close to the original training data.[45] Using the GAN, this region of space is cleverly interpolated to generate new faces that do not exist. This is the simplistic description of how the faces in ThisPersonDoesNotExist.com are generated.

Identification of the subset of human face pictures must not be contaminated with images outside the subset of human faces. The human face training data contained no pictures of horses, cats, pigs, or dogs. If deep fake pictures of dogs-that-don't-exist were desired, the training data would consist totally of images of dogs. Using data outside of the target subject subset muddies the performance of the resulting AI.

On ThisPersonDoesNotExist.com, the results are remarkable, but they are exactly what the computer programmer wanted to accomplish.

Almost.

Anomalies can pop up. Keep hitting refresh on ThisPersonDoesNotExist.com and some strange images can result. In one instance, a young girl with painted cheeks is accompanied by a weird fleshy blob with a distorted eye. The blob looks like a severely deformed human with a slug on her face. But a number of refreshes are required to gener-

Figure 4.8. A non-existent child with face paint accompanied by a non-existent mutant companion.

ate more such strange anomalies. Most of the images on the site look flawless. Can additional programming be applied to avoid such outliers? I suspect the answer is yes.

Deepfake photos and videos can be used in positive and negative ways. AI is neither good nor bad. It's how it's used. A fake person instead of a real one could be used in an ad for an embarrassing personal product, for instance. Plus, no modeling fees would need to be paid to humans.

Is the GAN producing these deep fake photos creative? Do these images pass the Lovelace test? No. Like other examples of AI-generated art, the generated images are impressive but not creative. The AI is doing what the programmers programmed it to do. Even the glitches producing deformed-looking faces are the result of programmer decisions. Any creative credit belongs to the programmer, not to AI.

When we talk about AI and creativity, or AI and art, in part what we're discussing is technical skill. The photos generated by ThisPerson-DoesNotExist are skillfully rendered; some of the music generated by AI is skillful. Skillful, but derivative.

Connection and Manipulation

YOUR ESTIMATION of the ditty "Twinkle, Twinkle, Little Star" is probably enhanced when you're told the melody was composed by Mozart as a child prodigy.[46] The degree to which art is held in high regard can be affected by external factors, and not just by our clear-headed assessment of the art itself.

Consider the Beatles. They wrote some amazingly catchy songs, but remove the Beatles's "brand"—carefully cultivated via intense promotional campaigns including mop-top haircuts, Beatles boots, and British slang like "fab"—and their songs lose a lot of pizazz. The movie *Yesterday* is deeply flawed because its writers didn't understand this. The movie is about an out-of-luck pop musician who, through strange circumstance, is the only person in the world who remembers songs by the Beatles. This musician begins to record Beatles songs and is celebrated as a genius songwriter. *Yesterday* ignores the brand connection between listener and performance and incorrectly assumes the group's songs were great independent of the Beatles brand. To human listeners, the heritage of art matters (though occasionally we're okay with, for instance, restful background music devoid of history or human connection).

Another great example of how human connectivity can influence our evaluation of art can be seen in a practice that existed as far back as Nero and which was named and systematized as "claqueing" in eighteenth-century French theater and opera houses.[47]

Leaving nothing to chance, professional paid claqueurs would be sprinkled throughout the audience and enthusiastically applaud the performance. At the end of a performance, one claqueur would spring to his feet, clap loudly and enthusiastically yell "Bravo!" One enthusiastic "Bravo!" was quickly echoed by another standing claqueur and then another. Soon non-claqueurs would stand and join in the chorus of accolades. Claqueing affected the perception of the quality of the performance and those penning reviews were more positive in their assessment than they otherwise might have been.

The claque was so successful that agents soon coordinated the practice.[48] Tell the agent how many claqueurs you need, pay an appropriate fee, and claqueing would be scheduled for your performance. The practice was so successful, specialists emerged. The *chef de claque* (leader of applause) organized the claqueurs. *Bisseurs* were in charge of clapping and yelling "*Bis, Bis!*" (Encore, Encore!). *Commissaires* (commissioners) engaged in enthusiastic conversation with those sitting nearby. For sad sections of a performance, *pleureurs* (criers) would bury their faces in handkerchiefs and sob loudly. At happy moments, *rieurs* (laughers) erupted in belly laughs at jokes.

Claqueurs have been replaced today by agents, promoters, and publicists. Ad agencies specialize in making artful products appealing. Social media specialists claque their client's creations to influencers and the public. Will a song ever be popular without modern claqueing? How about a self-published book? Is there any chance a work today will go viral without promotion and publicity? Sure.[49] But it's about as likely as being hit by space debris while juggling.

Claqueurs direct attention towards the glitter, away from the warts and towards an illusion of greatness beyond the reality that is. Claqueurs ooh and ahh at the output generated by AI and focus credit on the computer, not on the human minds behind the machines.

Claqueurs also play on people's emotions. In our next chapter, we will look at some modern-day claqueurs and their role in ginning up both unwarranted excitement and unwarranted fear about the future of AI.

PART TWO: AI HYPE

5. THE HYPE CURVE

> By far, the greatest danger of Artificial Intelligence is that people
> conclude too early that they understand it.
> —AI RESEARCHER ELIEZER YUDKOWSKY[1]

ARTIFICIAL INTELLIGENCE INDISPUTABLY ROCKS! DEEP BLUE BEATS
Garry Kasparov at chess, IBM's Watson beats all comers in *Jeopardy*, OpenAI's GPT-3 writes fascinatingly coherent prose in short bursts,[2]
an AI drone beats Top Gun fighter pilots in dogfights,[3] the AI program
Pluribus beats the world's top Texas Hold'em poker players,[4] Google's
DeepMind wallops world champions at the difficult Asian board game
GO, and DeepMind's AlphaStar masters the difficult interactive video
game StarCraft II.[5] And get this: AI learns to beat arcade games by only
observing the pixels on the display screen. Wow! And can you imagine
the future? Level 5 self-driving cars (I want one once all the glitches are
ironed out!), AI chips in our iPhones and in our brains (think I'll skip
that one), and humanoid robots everywhere.

To some, this might seem a little scary. And indeed several leading scientists and tech leaders, filling the role of Chicken Little, warn
us we're in grave danger. The late physicist Stephen Hawking said the
emergence of artificial intelligence could be the "worst event in the history of our civilization."[6] Bill Gates says of future AI that "I don't understand why some people are not concerned."[7] Elon Musk says AI "is humanity's biggest existential threat."[8] And Henry Kissinger, who served
as the United States Secretary of State and National Security Advisor
for both Presidents Richard Nixon and Gerald Ford, says, "Philosophi-

cally, intellectually—in every way—human society is unprepared for the rise of artificial intelligence."[9]

If you read speculative statements like these, often summarized in trumpeted daily news headlines, you are experiencing a leg of the *hype curve* in action. The term "hype curve" refers to the overall reaction to new technologies.[10] Development of any new technology like AI requires research to tease apart capabilities from limitations; speculative hype amplifies interest in areas not yet explored by the new technology. Such speculative hype comes in various flavors. Many worship at the feet of the exciting new technology and without foundation predict all sorts of new miraculous applications; others preach unavoidable doom and gloom in the future.

We have surfed the hype curve many times. The best way to deal with the curve is to remain sober and recognize the hype curve as it's playing out.

Stages of the Hype Curve

HERE ARE the stages of the ubiquitous hype curve.[11]

- **The launch phase.** In the beginning of the hype curve, newly introduced technology spurs expectations above and beyond reality. Poorly thought-out forecasts are made.
- **The peak-of-hype phase.** The sky's the limit. Imagination runs amok. Whether negative or positive, hype is born from unbridled speculation.
- **The overreaction-to-immature-technology phase.** As the new technology is vetted and further explored, the realization sets in that some of its early promises can't be kept. Rather than calmly adjusting expectations and realizing that immature technology must be given time to ripen, many people become overly disillusioned.
- **The depth-of-cynicism phase.** Once the shine is off the apple, limitations are recognized. Some initial supporters jump ship.

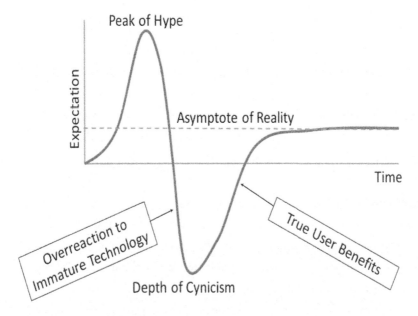

Figure 5.1. The hype curve.

They sell their stock and go looking for a new hype to criticize, believe in, or profit from.

- **The true-user-benefits phase.** The faithful—often those whose initial expectations included the realistic possibility of failed promise—carry on and find ways to turn the new technology to useful practice.

- **The asymptote-of-reality phase.** The technology lives on in accordance with its true contributions.

Triggering the Hype Curve

WHAT CAUSES all this often-unnecessary drama? There are many contributing factors.

For a start, media reports by well-meaning but technologically ignorant journalists are a key accelerant. The lay journalist often not only incorrectly explains a researcher's work, but also does so with exaggerated exuberance and decorative embellishment.

Why? To sell papers, increase blog clicks, raise the number of social media shares, or increase viewership of broadcast journalism. Sensationalism sells. It always has. In the 1890s, the term "yellow journalism" was coined to describe the lurid and sensationalistic headlines used to attract readers during a territorial competition between two New York City newspapers.

Today's hype is amplified by ubiquitous media availability.

But reporters, whether greedy or simply ignorant, don't carry all the blame. Some media-savvy researchers in search of visibility don't need journalists. They become their own promoters and use creative hype in their networking and marketing. These entrepreneurial nerds are given to coining seductive semantics describing their technology. Press releases are issued, journal papers are published, and federal funding proposals are submitted and awarded.

Just as only wealthy countries can support poets, often only cash-rich tech organizations like Google, Microsoft, and the Government can afford research groups whose work is made visible by marketers. These companies have solid political or bottom-line reasons to join the bandwagon and surf the hype wave. Investing in research with potentially big rewards is reasonable. The limitations and potentials of new technologies are understood only after vetting.

Hype can build on itself. The novice reporter extravagantly praises the research and the researcher; the researcher gets carried away by the flattery and praise; and before you know it, the researcher's decision-making capacity and therefore the integrity of the project have been compromised. As the book of Proverbs says, "Pride goes before destruction."[12]

It takes a remarkably cool head to not believe your own press—especially if you have any sort of normal competitive urge of the sort that spurs progress and innovation.

The Competitive Mob

HYPE-PRONE MOBS accumulate around trends and money. If a government organization like the NSF announces a multimillion-dollar grant program in left-handed squeegees, the number of experts in left-handed squeegees increases dramatically. Mobs also accumulate around new trending technologies. AI is intellectually sexy and attracts a lot of suitors.

Trends in research have been compared to young grade-schoolers playing undisciplined soccer. Everyone takes their proper places on the soccer field, lining up in an orderly fashion. But as soon as the ball is kicked, everyone forgets the drills. Kids from both teams run yelling toward the ball. All the players try to kick the ball and end up kicking each other's shins. The ball eventually pops out of the mob and bounces down the field, and all the kids run to the ball's new location and repeat the yelling and kicking until the ball squirts out and again rolls somewhere else.

This is not the most elegant way to play soccer. But with research it can be effective, in a way. Good and bad, progress and hype, grow out of uncertainty regarding the capabilities of the technology. Many kicking the soccer ball are honestly interested in knowing what the technology can and can't do. Many others are mostly interested in the glory, prestige, money, and power that originate from being recognized as a leader in the fledgling field.

As you may recall, everyone once gathered around the soccer ball of superconductivity technology. The promise of electronics with no heat-generating resistive loss was compelling. Government money was thrown at research. Funding agencies like the National Science Foundation (NSF), the National Institutes of Health (NIH), the Department of Energy (DOE), and the US Department of Defense (DOD) all gave grants.

The advantages and limitations of the technology were discovered as funded academicians rushed to be the first to publish in journals and at conferences. Those in industry publish at the patent office. The soccer ball got kicked a lot, plenty of shins got walloped, and the residual hype contributed to the "Overreaction to Immature Technology" portion of the hype curve.

Eventually researchers discovered that superconductivity, although free from resistive losses, still suffers from troublesome reactance—a bothersome non-resistive effect that is still resident in superconductive circuits. That realization has led to a more sober and clear-eyed assessment of the technology.

The asymptote of reality for superconductivity on the hype curve is today mildly in the black.

The Bigger They Are, the Harder They Hit

As ANY engineering student who has taken a course in control theory knows, the bigger the overshoot, the greater the undershoot that follows. So the greater the unsubstantiated hype on the hype curve, the greater the depth of cynicism that follows when the technology does not live up to the hype. The depth-of-cynicism dip on the hype curve results from an overreaction upon realizing the previously unacknowledged limitations of the technology. Artificial intelligence, which has been hyped to the moon, likewise faces an extreme plunge into the trough of cynicism.

In the case of AI, the hype can be utopian, but it can also be dystopian. Consider Elon Musk's warning: "I think we should be very careful about artificial intelligence. If I had to guess at what our biggest existential threat is, it's probably that. So we need to be very careful."[13] That's quite an eyebrow-raising assertion. Really? Most would rank thermonuclear bombs riding on supersonic missiles as a bigger existential threat than AI. Even the hedge word "probably" doesn't outweigh the dramatic and hyperbolic "biggest threat."

Musk's assertion reminds me of the bestselling book *Unsafe at Any Speed*,[14] in which Ralph Nader claimed that the Chevrolet Corvair was the most dangerous car on the road. But Nader had no answer when asked, "What is the second most dangerous car on the road?" I suspect

Elon Musk would likewise be initially stumped if asked to name the world's second biggest existential threat. Why? Because when people say things like this, generally they haven't really considered and ranked all threats, whether vehicular or existential. They're overstating to make a point.

But Musk is right to the degree that threats do come from all new technology. There were threats from the introduction of the microwave oven, the automobile, and home electricity. Consider electricity: Yes, electricity powers our computers, lights the night, and keeps the refrigerator cold. But shorted wires can burn down houses. Downed electric lines in a storm can electrocute passersby. And the electric chair has ended the lives of many convicted criminals.

Like electricity, AI inherently carries benefits and risks. It is a tool that can be used for good or evil. And, yes, we would do well to consider the possible ramifications of any new technology, rather than being blindsided by the unintended consequences of our actions.

Once a new technology has been vetted and the hype smoke dissipates—only when we reach the "asymptote-of-reality" on the hype curve—can we see what we're actually dealing with. For engineering and computer science disciplines, this asymptote is reached when the technology is reduced to useful application in industry, commercial products, or in the military. On the asymptote-of-reality, there is no arguing with the success of the technology. It does what it does.

Learning from Historical Hype Curves

CAN REASONABLE prophets squint and peer through the peak-of-hype on the hype curve, over the depth-of-cynicism valley, and see the asymptote-of-reality in the future?

One of the best tools we have for such foresight is hindsight. Financial bubbles in the market are examples of peaks-of-hype. Although they never last, many investors fool themselves into believing this time it will be different. But bubble bursting is inevitable.

So the takeaway is this: knowing history helps us to not repeat it, as does a little humility. And simply being aware of the hype curve can provide a steadying effect.

So we will now take a brief detour from specific discussion about AI and AI hype to examine some historical examples of the hype curve.

Hype Curve Example 1: The Segway

A classic example of traveling the hype curve concerns the Segway personal transportation vehicle. In the television series *Arrested Development*, arrogant Gob Bluth rides around on one. The orchestrated hype at Segway's introduction was enormous. The makers claimed the Segway would "be to the car what the car was to the horse and buggy." After a secret first viewing, Steve Jobs said the Segway would be as big a deal as the personal computer. A supporting venture capitalist who had previously backed Amazon said the Segway might be bigger than the Internet!

We know today that the Segway did not live up to its hype. Its asymptote-of-reality was positive but modest.

In the rearview mirror, yesterday's marketing hype borders on the comical. In fact, the television show *South Park* devoted an episode to making fun of the publicity campaign surrounding the Segway launch.[15] Someday, I suspect we will look back on some AI hype and be similarly amused.

Hype Curve Example 2: Cold Fusion

Another classic example of a short-lived hype curve starts with the announcement in 1989 by leading electric chemists Martin Fleischmann and Stanley Pons that they had achieved cold fusion. Cold fusion was incredible news! With cold fusion, power can originate from the same physical process used by our sun to produce heat and light but can be done cheaply at room temperature. Forget about clean-burning hydrogen powered cars and solar power. The energy generated by cold fusion is cleaner and cheaper. No more big electric bills! The same physical process generating the hydrogen bomb's energy could be harnessed without heating things up to temperatures exceeding that of the sun's core.

And thus the cold fusion hype curve was launched. Rushing towards the soccer ball of hyped research, groups at Stanford, Georgia Tech, and Texas A&M repeated the cold fusion experiments, ran to the media, and reported that their experiments corroborated cold fusion. Their unstated goal was to appear on the historical list of those who verified cold fusion. Their names would be in Wikipedia under the topic of "cold fusion history," and their fame would live forever.

During the peak of cold fusion hype, I saw the seductive draw of fame firsthand. I was at the University of Washington at the time, and I remember a nuclear engineer colleague of mine expressing anger at our dean because the dean wouldn't cough up the modest funds to verify the cold fusion experiment. The experiment replication, my colleague argued, would put the University of Washington in the news. Silly dean. He apparently didn't want our university to be part of cold fusion history.

So what happened? Well, at the top of the cold fusion hype peak, researchers from Caltech, after detailed attention and careful analysis, reported that cold fusion didn't work. Other negative reports soon followed. The bubble popped. Cold fusion was a bomb, so to speak.

Stanford, Georgia Tech, and Texas A&M wiped the egg off their faces and the hype curve took a nosedive, never to recover. Cold fusion was soon thereafter declared dead by the *New York Times*. Since cold fusion was not realizable, its asymptote-of-reality on the hype curve was well into the red.

The original cold fusion perpetrators, Fleischmann and Pons, were professionally ruined. They resigned their professorships at the University of Utah. Fleishmann returned to England and Pons fled to France.[16] Were they wrong to attempt something new and grand? Of course not. Where they went astray was in choosing to prematurely fan the flames of hype instead of settling for cautious optimism and further vetting.

Hype Curve Example 3: Information Theory

Claude Shannon was a genius on par with Einstein, but Shannon remains relatively unheralded in popular culture. That's particularly strange considering that Shannon's work impacts us directly more than Einstein's.

In 1948, while at Bell Labs, Shannon published a paper that revolutionized communication. In the paper, he first used the word "bit" and showed that information could be effectively stored and transmitted digitally. Streaming video and the audio on your cell phones are digital. I wrote a whole book, *Introduction to Shannon Sampling and Interpolation Theory*,[17] expanding on one little part of Shannon's 1948 paper where he showed that continuous signals like speech can be represented digitally by sampling. Surprisingly, signal samples can be used to reconstruct continuous signals without losing information.

Even more important than digitizing, Shannon showed in his paper it was possible to transmit over a noisy channel almost without error. Shannon proved this possible, but never showed how. It wasn't until 1990, forty years later, that codes were discovered that efficiently use channel capacity for near errorless communication, as Shannon predicted. The first generation of these were dubbed *turbo codes*. Variations of turbo codes are used today by your cell phones. That's why, even if you have only one bar and there is a thunderstorm outside screwing with your cell phone microwave signal, you can still receive perfect text and pictures.

Shannon's paper spawned professional societies and journals that are today still exploring applications and extensions of Shannon's original ideas. In the graduate course I teach in information theory, the first few weeks of the class are dedicated to covering Shannon's original 1948 paper.

After publication of the paper, Shannon's work caught the attention of amateur soccer player researchers in other fields who began exuberantly kicking the information theory soccer ball. Everyone on the soccer field ran to the ball and wanted to apply Shannon's theory to their discipline.

Shannon saw that research was running uphill to the peak of the hype curve. It bothered him. Half a decade after his classic paper was published, Shannon became concerned enough to address the hype peak directly. In an article titled "The Bandwagon," he wrote: "Information theory has, in the last few years, become something of a scientific bandwagon. Starting as a technical tool for the communication engineer, it has received an extraordinary amount of publicity in the popular as well as the scientific press."[18]

Shannon refused to succumb to the seduction of ego. He said, "Although this wave of popularity is certainly pleasant and exciting for those of us working in the field, it carries at the same time an element of danger." He even talked about the hype of seductive semantics and the coming depth-of-cynicism on the hype curve: "It will be all too easy for our somewhat artificial prosperity to collapse overnight," he wrote, "when it is realized that the use of a few exciting words like *information, entropy, redundancy*, do not solve all our problems."

With this warning, Shannon helped lessen the impact of the information theory's crash into the overreaction-to-immature-technology portion of the hype curve.

As witnessed in every area of communication today, including your cell phones and all things digital, the asymptote-of-reality for Shannon information theory is well in the black.

Hype Curve Example 4: Theranos's Bad Blood

The hype curve can be fueled by healthy speculation, media ignorance, and exuberant promotion. Such was the hype that launched the company Theranos vertically on the hype curve.

The goal of Theranos was to develop rapid blood tests that could use a single drop of blood from a finger prick rather than the conventional larger blood draw from a longer vein-probing needle stuck into the arm at the fold of the elbow. A laudable goal, I think we can all agree.

As detailed in investigative journalist John Carreyrou's book, *Bad Blood*,[19] the charismatic entrepreneur Elizabeth Holmes, aided by her bullying boyfriend Ramesh Balwani and a stable of attack-dog attorneys, kept Theranos at the top of the hype curve for a long time. The hype attracted the support of influential people like Henry Kissinger, Bill Clinton, former US Secretary of State George Shultz, former US Secretary of Defense Secretary General James "Mad Dog" Mattis, and US Secretary of Education Betsy DeVos.

But in this case, Theranos-generated publicity overflowed with dishonesty. Carreyrou wrote a *Wall Street Journal* exposé that prompted federal scrutiny of the company, and it was discovered that contrary to claims, the Theranos technology did not work. Many of the claims, in fact, were bold-faced lies.

The hype curve took a steep dive, from which it never recovered. As one reporter notes, "While the Theranos debacle is juicy from a bystander standpoint, it's clearly been financially devastating for those who bought into the hype."[20]

The value of both Theranos and Elizabeth Holmes's personal wealth fell from billions of dollars to zero. Ultimately, Holmes and Balwani were charged with fraud by the Securities and Exchange Commission, and indicted on charges of wire fraud and conspiracy. In 2022, a jury convicted Elizabeth Holmes on four counts of fraud. At this writing, Balwani awaits trial.

Hype Curve Example 5: The Piltdown Man

The Piltdown Man was a hoax on evolutionary science orchestrated by Charles Dawson. (Note that it's Dawson—not Darwin).

Dawson, who worked as a lawyer for his day job, claimed he had discovered the "missing link" between ape and man in the gravel beds near Piltdown, East Sussex, England. It was a small portion of a skull. In 1912, Dawson took this finding to Arthur Smith Woodward, Keeper of Geology at the Natural History Museum. The two men then claimed to discover at the same site more bones, teeth, and primitive tools. Smith

Woodward reconstructed an entire skull from the fragments, hypothesized that it belonged to a human ancestor, and voila! The Piltdown Man was born.

Talk about hype! Over seven hundred papers were published about the Piltdown Man, purporting to substantiate the validity of Darwinian evolution. Artists rendered drawings of a hairy ape-man carrying a tool or weapon.[21] The theory, it seemed, now sat on a firmer foundation.[22]

Dawson claimed that he found the Piltdown fossil in 1908. Although there were reports of fraud even at the time, they were largely ignored until, in 1953, researchers inarguably exposed the hoax. That's forty-five years of hype.

Deeper scrutiny continued and, in 2016, investigators pointed a decisive finger at Dawson for fraud,[23] and the Piltdown man's hype curve at last came to its resting place, deep in the red.

Hype Curve Example 6: String Theory

The jury is still out on string theory. As Ethan Siegel puts it in an article titled "Why String Theory is Both a Dream and a Nightmare," string theory "is simultaneously one of the best ideas in the entire history of theoretical physics and one of our greatest disappointments."[24]

In physics, string theory replaces point particles with one-dimensional objects called strings. The implications of string theory are astonishing and numerous. String theory potentially provides the solution to the Theory of Everything (TOE), wherein all of physics is explainable by one physical theory. It also offers a bridge to the unsubstantiated weird world of parallel universes.[25] Because of this, "for perhaps the last 35 years, string theory has been the dominant idea in theoretical particle physics," Siegel says, "with more scientific papers arising from it than any other idea."[26]

The problem is this: There is at this writing no experimental verification of string theory.[27] None. It has not produced a single confirmed prediction.

Does that mean it's a failure? Not necessarily. It's exceedingly difficult to investigate anything as tiny as the strings the theory posits. For comparison: Protons in the nucleus of every atom are small, but strings are far smaller. If a string were magnified to be an inch, a proton similarly scaled would have a diameter of several light-years.

I had a PhD candidate in physics confide in me that string theory is so beautiful that if string theory were not true, it should be. Indeed, concise elegance is a property of many of our most cherished physical models. Consider all the major theories of physics: Newton's laws for classical physics, Schrödinger's equation for quantum mechanics, Einstein's relativity field equations, Maxwell's equations for electrodynamics, the four laws of thermodynamics, and the Naiver-Stokes equations for fluid dynamics. All have simple beautiful equations that blossom into descriptive disciplines that wonderfully describe reality.

All of these equations fit nicely on one side of a single sheet of paper. The string theory equations will also fit on the same page with all of the other equations. There is room. How nice!

The poet John Keats proclaimed, "Beauty is truth, truth beauty." One alluring property of string theory is its simple elegance. But contrary to Keats's claim, beauty need not be truth. The beauty of string theory and its theoretical ramifications keep physicists searching for evidentiary proof. Thus far, however, all attempts to experimentally support string theory have failed. The dream is turning into a nightmare.

But it's too early to tell for sure if it's a bust. Where the theory's reality line is remains to be seen.

Learning from the Past

WE CAN learn a lot from historical hype curves across a wide variety of fields. We can also learn from the history of AI's own hype curve—for hype about AI is nothing new. It has been with us a very long time—so long, in fact, that the hype curves of AI begin to seem reincarnated!

Cinematic science fiction accounts of artificially intelligent robots were introduced in the 1927 silent film *Metropolis*. (Some claim this is a classic. I keep dozing off.) Later, the invention of the computer sparked a flurry of science fiction robots, including the one in the 1951 movie *The Day the Earth Stood Still* and the human-like nanny robot everybody loved in Ray Bradbury's "I Sing the Body Electric," a 1962 *Twilight Zone* episode that later turned into a short story.

Robots had captured the public's imagination. When that happens, overblown hype is sure to follow.

Consider this headline and the accompanying opening lines from an article that appeared in the *New York Times*:

NEW NAVY DEVICE LEARNS BY DOING; Psychologist Shows Embryo of Computer Designed to Read and Grow Wiser

WASHINGTON, July 7 (UPI)—The Navy revealed the embryo of an electronic computer today that it expects will be able to walk, talk, see, write, reproduce itself and be conscious of its existence.[28]

Note the hype. Here we have unwarranted hyperbolic forecasting, vague semantics in the use of the terms "embryo" and "conscious," and—by extrapolating great results at some vague point in the future—the handy avoidance of here-and-now scrutiny.

Though this article would fit right in today, it appeared on the front page of the *New York Times* on July 8, 1958. That's right—more than six decades ago. The media megaphone wasn't as big in those days, but the hype was there.

Thirty years later, in 1989, the Associated Press released a story titled "Portland Firm Ships Brainlike Chip," which breathlessly announced that "Syntonic Systems Inc. has shipped the first commercially available 'neural network' computer chip, a type of chip that mimics the brain in a way that may change the entire industry."[29]

Since then, thirty more years have passed, and guess what? The Portland neural network has had precious little effect on "the entire industry."

Today, once again, AI neural network chips are being enthusiastically lauded as the Next Big Thing. A 2020 article in the *Wall Street Journal* is titled "New Computer Chips Could Power AI to Next Level."

The article begins: "A generation of computing chips designed specifically for artificial intelligence could enable a host of new applications for the technology."[30]

But as we've seen, promises of future success do not equate to success. In AI, we've seen the same promises repeated again and again, separated by decades. The hype curve keeps chugging away, ever hopeful.

Based on the examples from 1958, 1989, and 2020, expect yet another breathless announcement, around 2050, that AI's dramatic coming of age is, once again, just around the corner.

The True Test for AI Success

AN ACCURATE assessment of the success of artificial intelligence isn't found in theatrical hype or dire warnings. The true test of artificial intelligence boils down to *reduction to practice*.

Reduction to practice, whether in the military or in the market, means the new technology has marked advantages over other approaches. It has to have significant advantages—not just marginal or incremental ones—to overcome the inertia of using older technologies. Partly this inertia is psychological—people become habituated to a certain way of doing things—and partly it's financial, because the cost of retooling can be high. So for a new technology to succeed in practice, it must bring to the table substantial advantages over existing technology.

An unamplified version of the hype curve is natural in the development of technology. When introduced, no one knows what the technology will do. Informed speculation drives legitimate vetting research. Some researchers jump ship as limitations become evident, while others persevere to reduce the technology to practice. This pushes the hype curve to its asymptote of reality. This is a legitimate and necessary path of research. But in the mold of the hype-addicted yellow journalism of the 1890s, today's 24/7 media providers, rabid for bigger audiences and more clicks, inflate the hype curve with attention-grabbing headlines and content. This is especially true for the sexy topic of AI.

There are, fortunately, ways to look through the fog of hype to see bare truth. We will discuss this next.

6. Twelve Filters for AI Hype Detection

Do not bear false witness.

—Mark 10:19

A I CAN DO AMAZING THINGS, AND DEVELOPERS ARE APPLYING CUT-ting-edge programming and technology in a myriad of interesting ways. We've talked about some wonderful applications in these pages, and we'll talk about more as we go along. We've also talked about what is not possible for AI, despite reports to the contrary. How can you tell one from the other? How can you know what's happening, and what's just empty hype? Fake news is rampant and is often hard for the non-expert to detect.

Here are some AI hype filters to help you separate stories about real progress from stories containing empty boasts or unwarranted fears. In many cases these hype filters can also be applied to other areas in addition to AI.

Hype Filter #1: Outrageous Claims

OUTLANDISH AI claims are red flags. Deeper scrutiny is required to separate the truly astonishing from the snake oil.

Sometimes tabloid headlines are so outrageous we immediately recognize them as fake. One headline from a trash tabloid reads, "The Only Known Signature of God Auctioned for Over Six Million Dollars." Another is "DNA Tests Show bin Laden was a Woman!" These headlines are so ludicrous most of us immediately discount them. We're more apt to fall for fake news that contains a pinch of truth and a lot of titillating overstatement.

Media outlets want to get clicks and make sales. Authors want a big reading audience. (I do!) The result is that some writers make hyperbolic claims to get greater attention, and then the headline writers exaggerate even more. They seem not unlike a child jumping up and down, hands raised, shouting, "Pick me! Pick me!"

Bear in mind, some authors believe the hype they write. Such is Stanford biology professor Paul Ehrlich, who in 1970 wrote, "Most of the people who are going to die in the greatest cataclysm in the history of man have already been born."[1] Here's another Ehrlich doozy from 1970: "Population will inevitably and completely outstrip whatever small increases in food supplies we make.... The death rate will increase until at least 100–200 million people per year will be starving to death during the next ten years." Ehrlich was partial to terms like the "Great Die-Off."[2]

Ehrlich's famine claim did not come true in the ensuing ten years, nor since. The years 2010–2019 had the lowest starvation death rate by famine since 1860,[3] even as global population continued to increase. Ehrlich's dramatic forecast of a terrible negative turned out to be exactly the opposite.

And that's not because Ehrlich's dramatic predictions changed our behavior. His over-the-top claims simply were wrong. Not long after Ehrlich issued his dire predictions, economist Julian Simon challenged Ehrlich, arguing that humans are resourceful and that free-market forces inspire them to innovate.[4] They made a bet. Simon won, and Ehrlich mailed a check.[5]

But when Ehrlich made his predictions, their dramatic nature succeeded in garnering widespread attention. Outrageous claims tend to do that, but they should also raise our suspicions. So immediately raise a shield of skepticism when reading headlines like "The AI Cold War That Threatens Us All"[6] (an article whose URL contains the words

"AI Cold War China Could Doom Us All") or "How Can We Prepare for Catastrophically Dangerous AI—And Why We Can't Wait."[7] The writers might believe what they're saying, or they might merely be trying to get clicks. Either way, they are like carnival barkers enticing you to pay to see the world's fattest woman who, in reality, turns out to weigh less than your Aunt Pearl.

Life is rarely as outrageously dramatic as writers (and teenagers, and politicians) would have us believe.

Hype Filter #2: Hedging

INSTEAD OF making outrageous claims, it's usually more appropriate for writers to use measured language and qualifiers such as "eventually," "maybe," "if," and "perhaps." That's responsible reporting. But sometimes qualifiers are used in a sneaky way, as wiggle words. Sometimes deliberately imprecise language is also used. These methods let the author hedge his bets. Hedging gives him an out.

Your hype antennae should make note of qualifiers and imprecise language. Are they being used responsibly, or are they being used to hedge?

Consider this example regarding Army research into an AI squid-like robot. The article reads, "In case you weren't already terrified of robots that can jump over walls, fly or crawl, Army researchers are developing your next nightmare—a flexible, soft robot inspired by squid and other invertebrates."[8]

The wiggle term here is "developing." The technology is not totally developed. Maybe it will be sometime in the future. But not now. If you weren't reading carefully, though, you might not notice the implication of "developing," especially because it's surrounded by dramatic, attention-grabbing words like "terrified" and "nightmare."

Still, this reporter is more honest than many. Eventually, at the very end of the article, he quietly points out, "The material is still in early development stages, so don't expect to see a robot squid in the foxhole next to you tomorrow." Be sure to read the fine print!

Even the brilliant MIT mathematician Claude Shannon, the "father of information theory," hedged during his forecast of the future of AI in 1961. He said, "I confidently expect that within ten or fifteen years we will find, emerging from the laboratories, something not too far from the robot of science fiction fame."[9]

What did he mean by "the robot of science fiction fame"? If he meant sentient, conscious, or creative robots, Shannon was wrong. But because he was vague, he avoided the risk of rigorous assessment. From surviving documents I have read, including his biography,[10] Shannon was an honorable man. He was asked to make a prediction for a news program and called it as accurately as he could.

In contrast, consider the previously mentioned 1958 *New York Times* article about AI, which reads, "The Navy revealed the embryo of an electronic computer today that it expects will be able to walk, talk, see, write, reproduce itself and be conscious of its existence."[11] Do you see the subtle hedges here? An "embryo" is "expected" to mature. In other words, the AI has thus far done nothing, but the Navy "expects" it to.

The lesson here? Pay attention to the precise (or imprecise!) wording of claims. Hedges of this sort mean that nothing remarkable is happening now, but may in the future.

Hype Filter #3: Avoiding Scrutiny

ANOTHER COMMONLY used hype tool is making claims in a way that avoids scrutiny. A handy way to do this is to prophesy something well into the future. A forecast ten, twenty, thirty, or a hundred years out can't be readily verified or falsified, and will probably be forgotten by the time the sell-by date rolls around.

Since immediate pushback is difficult, these forecasts can be boldly hyperbolical. Consider the current far-future forecast celebrated AI futurist Ray Kurzweil made in 2000: "Before the next century is over," he said, "human beings will no longer be the most intelligent or capable type of entity on the planet."[12]

This prophecy will come true—or be falsified—after we are all dead.

This is not to say people can't make valid predictions about some far future event. There are futurists who have done so, such as George Gilder, co-founder and senior fellow of Discovery Institute. Among other things, Gilder anticipated the proliferation of fiber-optic cable, common use of "telecomputers" (cell phones), and digital camera imaging chips.[13] No futurist bats a thousand, but Gilder's accuracy has been impressive. His predictions are based on a clear understanding of the limits and possibilities of technology.

On the flip side is the Amazing Criswell, a futurist who earned a living making far-out claims in the 1960s. Criswell was a quack forecaster most famous for his appearance in what many consider the worst movie ever made: Ed Wood's *Plan 9 from Outer Space*. Fond of striking a pose as a deep-thinking intellectual, Criswell offered up such gems as, "We are all interested in the future, for that is where you and I are going to spend the rest of our lives."[14] In 1968 the Amazing Criswell published a book titled *Criswell Predicts: From Now to the Year 2000*.[15] Among other things, Criswell predicted that Denver, Colorado, would be struck by a ray from space causing all metal to become like rubber. As a result, metal in carnival rides would be compromised and horrific accidents would follow. Criswell also predicted mass cannibalism and the end of planet Earth by 1999.[16] Random, outrageous, attention-grabbing claims were Criswell's bread and butter, and he set most of them conveniently far into the future. If he'd said that "tomorrow all metal will become like rubber," few if any would have considered believing him. But projected far enough into the future, all things seem possible, at least to the gullible.

Interestingly, Criswell did get one short-term prediction right. He predicted on the Jack Parr show in March 1963 that President John F. Kennedy would not run for re-election in 1964 because something was going to happen to him in November. Kennedy was assassinated in Dallas on November 22, 1963.[17] Then again, Criswell also predicted Mae West would become president.[18] Making lots of predictions is like throwing darts while blindfolded—if enough darts are thrown there will surely be an occasional bull's-eye.

But the vast bulk of Criswell's predictions were dead wrong. He was an entertainer with a television show, *Criswell Predicts*, that needed to keep its ratings up. Outrageous far-distant predictions ginned up interest without making Criswell accountable.

Unlike Criswell, some people who make distant predictions do have scholarly credentials and are taken seriously. Consider ecologist Kenneth Watt, a professor at the University of California-Davis, who in 1970 made a chilling prediction of the then-distant future. In a speech at Swarthmore College he said, "The world has been chilling sharply for about twenty years.... If present trends continue, the world will be about four degrees colder for the global mean temperature in 1990, but eleven degrees colder in the year 2000. This is about twice what it would take to put us into an ice age."[19] Watt's prediction was far enough into the future to avoid quick falsification.

Looking in the rearview mirror reveals the difficulty of long-range forecasting. Imagine living in the year 1900 and trying to accurately forecast life in the year 2000. In 1900 there were no movie houses, commercial radio was twenty years away, and Ford's Model T was not yet available. In 1900 transportation power over roads was provided by horses. A statistical analysis of horse proliferation would forecast that by 2000 the United States would on average be two feet deep in horse poop.

Even reputable scientists get things wrong when they look too far forward. Some classic forecasting bloopers were made by Lord Kelvin, who lived in the 1800s. You might recognize his name because absolute temperature is measured in degrees Kelvin. Kelvin said heavier-than-air flight was not possible; airplanes could not fly. He wrote, "I have not the smallest molecule of faith in aerial navigation other than ballooning or of expectation of good results from any of the trials we hear of."[20] In 1898 Kelvin also warned that Earth's oxygen supply would be depleted, and a future generation would die of asphyxia.[21]

Let's apply all this to AI predictions. How do we separate good far-future predictions from bad? Selmer Bringsjord has an effective method of doing so by testing the sincerity of the source of a claim. To those making hyperbolic claims about the future of AI, Bringsjord offers a substantial wager that the forecast will not come true.[22] If the delayed scrutiny is so far in the future that one or both involved in the wager will probably be dead, Bringsjord suggests the wager can be part of each person's estate. Bringsjord asks the AI prophets of the impossible to put their money where their mouth is. No one has thus far accepted his wager. Hyperbolic AI claims wither in the bright light of the Bringsjord challenge.

At this writing I am into year four of a five-year wager about level five self-driving cars. At level five (the highest level), self-driving cars will be able to traverse winding single-lane country roads in rural West Virginia. These are the country roads sung about by John Denver. Single-lane country roads in West Virginia are notched out of the sides of mountains. On one side is a rock wall, on the other a steep drop-off. I have driven on these one-lane roads where I meet a humongous fully loaded logging truck coming towards me. We both slow to a crawl. I edge my car to the precipice of a cliff on one side while the logging truck hugs the mountain on the other. Our rear-view mirrors almost touching, we slowly make our way past each other. West Virginians are friendly, so as we pass, the truck driver and I wave to show we see this is a part of West Virginia life and neither of us holds any hard feelings towards the other.

I cannot imagine a level five self-driving car driving on these one-lane roads. Maybe someday, but not in the immediate future. Despite implied promises from Elon Musk, I made a wager four years ago that level five self-driving cars would not be perfected in five years. So far so good for my prediction. And kudos to the person on the other side of this wager for putting his money where his mouth is and making a concrete prediction near enough in time that he could not escape a day of reckoning. Neither of us, though, is as bold as Bringsjord. Our wager is for a cup of coffee.

Hype Filter #4: Consensus Claims

ANOTHER RED flag for hype is an appeal to consensus. Consensus says everyone believes something will happen; therefore, it must be true. Kowtowing to consensus assumes the truth of the future can be determined by majority vote today.

Michael Crichton, physician and author of numerous sci-fi classics, including *Jurassic Park*, delivered a no-holds-barred lecture in 2003 at CalTech that addressed the folly of an appeal to consensus in science. Crichton said:

> Historically, the claim of consensus has been the first refuge of scoundrels; it is a way to avoid debate by claiming that the matter is already settled. Whenever you hear the consensus of scientists agrees on something or other, reach for your wallet, because you're being had.
>
> Let's be clear: the work of science has nothing whatever to do with consensus. Consensus is the business of politics. Science, on the contrary, requires only one investigator who happens to be right, which means that he or she has results that are verifiable by reference to the real world. In science consensus is irrelevant. What is relevant is reproducible results. The greatest scientists in history are great precisely because they broke with the consensus. There is no such thing as consensus science. If it's consensus, it isn't science. If it's science, it isn't consensus. Period.[23]

Crichton is spot on. Creativity requires thinking outside the box. Consensus is inside-the-box thinking. Recall that Einstein discarded the consensus hypotheses of the need for ether as a medium for light propagation. Likewise, genius Kurt Gödel blew away foundational assumptions in math with the introduction of his incompleteness theorem. I could go on and on with examples. So be aware of Crichton's "first refuge of scoundrels."

Consensus is often used to defend an argument. An example is from Peter Gunter who, in 1970, defended the following claim with an appeal to consensus: "Demographers agree almost unanimously on the following grim timetable.... By the year 2000, or conceivably sooner, South and Central America will exist under famine conditions.... By the year 2000, thirty years from now, the entire world, with the exception of Western Europe, North America, and Australia, will be in famine."[24]

World famines have been at an all-time low in recent years. So much for consensus.

Yes, there are cases where consensus is useful and accurate. All agree that tobacco use causes cancer and driving drunk increases car accidents. Such consensus is backed by accumulated mounds of evidence. But when consensus is appealed to in a young and developing field like AI, beware. Any appeal to consensus to support an argument must be questioned.

Hype Filter #5: Entrenched Ideology

PAY ATTENTION to claims that conveniently bolster a certain ideology.

Foundational ideology shapes the filter through which life is observed. The ideology of materialism assumes all phenomena, including natural intelligence and the beauty seen in the world, can be explained by a naturalistic viewpoint. Those who worship at the feet of materialism often don't admit to the limitations imposed by their narrow core belief.

The religion of materialism dominates science in the academy. In a TedX talk, biochemist Rupert Sheldrake says the presupposition of materialist science is an unhelpful limitation on science. "The worldview aspect of science has come to inhibit and constrict the free inquiry, which is the very life blood of the scientific endeavor," he says. "Since the late nineteenth century, science has been conducted under the aspect of the belief system or worldview that is essentially materialism—philosophical materialism. And the sciences are now wholly owned subsidiaries of the materialist worldview. I think as we break out of it, the sciences will be regenerated." He calls this view and its subsidiary dogmas "the science delusion."[25]

In an ironic twist, two staunch materialists reportedly protested the talk, and in response, "the talk was taken out of circulation by TED, relegated to a corner of their website and stamped with a warning label." The unstated message: Never question scientific materialism.[26]

But materialism is a just presupposition. Such an untested ideological constraint is not science. Materialism is a roadblock that hides paths of investigation down which enlightening evidence might be found. For instance, presupposition throws up blinders in the investigation of the mind/brain problem, leading many to assume, or even insist, that the brain is just a meat computer. Philosopher John Searle rightly noted that "to deny that the brain is computational is to risk losing your membership in the scientific community."[27] Some claim that a theistic/deistic perspective narrows discussion. They are wrong. The opposite is true. A broader perspective results than if a totally materialistic viewpoint is assumed. Theists in particular are free to conclude that the cause of a given phenomenon is material/mechanical, or that the cause is at least partly immaterial. A materialist has no such freedom. He is forced to consider only materialistic hypotheses.

The materialist view underlies the forecasts of some AI prophets. Agnostic Ray Kurzweil subscribes to materialism and famously said, "Does God exist? I would say, 'Not yet.'"[28]

Kurzweil claims, "Artificial intelligence will reach human levels by around 2029. Follow that out further to, say, 2045, we will have multiplied the intelligence, the human biological machine intelligence of our civilization a billion-fold."[29] Similarly, Nick Bostrom—echoing Stephen Hawking—argues that AI will someday be able to write more powerful AI and start a never-ending intelligence explosion. As one reviewer notes, Bostrom thinks AI "might pose a danger that exceeds every previous threat from technology—even nuclear weapons—and that if its development is not managed carefully humanity risks engineering its own extinction."[30]

The viewpoint espoused by Hawking, Bostrom, and Kurzweil that AI can achieve and exceed all human capabilities is built on a foundation of materialism. Humans, according to materialists, are innovative, and humans are but an arrangement of atoms; therefore, humans can be functionally replicated via computers, including the human capacity to innovate.

But of course, as we have seen, that isn't true. Alan Turing, an atheist and the father of modern computer science, tried to demonstrate that man is a materialistic computer. Ironically, his computer science mathematics, including the non-computability of the Turing halting problem (which we will examine in another chapter), opened the door for illustrating that humans display attributes unachievable by computers.

The view that there are human attributes above and beyond that of the computer, and indeed beyond the purely material, requires a worldview outside of pure materialism.[31] Is the functioning of the mind constrained by the functioning of the brain in regard to human characteristics like consciousness and creativity? A strict materialist must conclude the mind is an emergent property of the brain.

An alternative for those who refuse to consider theism is panpsychism. Panpsychism posits that human properties like consciousness are properties of nature in the same way that mass is a property of a rock or energy is a property resulting from nuclear fusion. Neurosurgeon Michael Egnor thinks such a position is foolish. He says, "Of course, electrons are not conscious." He then quips: "Even if they were, Heisenberg's Uncertainty Principle means that they could never make up their minds!"[32]

Unproven properties of emergence from brain complexity and wildly speculative theories like panpsychism seem to spring from a dogmatic refusal to entertain theism. As with discussions of matter and energy, discussions about panpsychism rarely consider its origin. Materialists avoid going deep into the question of the origin of matter, energy, and hypothesized panpsychism. Whatever the origin, human properties like consciousness, creativity, and qualia must be the result of purposeless, as-yet-unidentified physical phenomena. Materialism allows no other alternative.

So if you read an AI article that seems almost religious in its fervor, slow down and take a closer look. Your hype sensors should be flashing if an author is drawing conclusions based on ideology rather than on plain old logic, and seems incapable of calmly answering questions and objections. Heightened defensiveness often indicates that ideology, not truth, is under threat.

And while we have focused on materialist ideology, theistic and pantheistic ideologies must not be treated as a sacred cows either. If our commitment is to truth, the spotlight of evidence must be followed no matter where it shines, regardless of what it may happen to challenge.[33] If a particular worldview is indeed true, then it will have nothing to fear from following the evidence.

Hype Filter #6: Seductive Semantics

THE ART of product branding requires creative, clever slogans. An example is the *New York Times*'s motto that they report "all the news that's fit to print." Other examples are DeBeer's "a diamond is forever" and KFC's "finger lickin' good." The appeal of a slogan is often its association with images beyond the product itself. Nike's "just do it!" and the US Army's "be all you can be" associate their brand with rugged individualism. In other cases the slogan promises the moon, as with Disneyland's "the happiest place on earth."

Slogans can blur seamlessly into culture. The claim that "breakfast is the most important meal of the day" did not originate from a nutritionist or other medical authority. John Harvey Kellogg popularized the phrase in order to encourage eating his cereals for breakfast.[34]

The sale of AI makes use of such seductive semantics by associating AI with biological and psychological attributes. Often the association is superficial. In the 1960s, Stanford's Bernard Widrow named his groundbreaking AI ADALINE. The name was short for "adaptive linear neuron." Widrow's circuit and biological neurons were loosely linked by Hebb's law that says neurons that fire together wire together. Widrow's use of the term "neuron" attracted media attention. This must be, they reasoned, a big step towards the AI we read about in science fiction. This was news!

But what if Widrow had christened his invention with less exciting terminology? Over forty years later, Widrow addressed his use of seductive semantics in AI:

> After my original work in the neural network field, I did some developmental work in the adaptive filter area. I still believe that if an electrical engineer had developed the back-propagation algorithm [for training neural networks], we'd be working with 'massively parallel adaptive filters' instead of neural networks. Oh, well.[35]

Would his invention have been greeted with the same degree of exuberance if his "neural network" had instead been christened a "massively parallel adaptive filter"? I think not. Few people even know what the phrase means. But most know a neuron has something to do with the brain.

Using seductive words to entice readers' interest is characteristic of great writing. Skillful rhetoric places topics in their most favorable light. At times, though, seductive semantics can be purposefully misleading. Recall the line, "Army researchers are developing a self-aware squid-like robot you can 3D print in the field."[36] Author Todd South helpfully adds this is "your next nightmare." The thrill of fear invites the reader to accept as a literal fact the claim that the robot will be "self-aware."

Although we could, for technical reasons, quibble with the claim that the robot squid will be printed in 3D, we won't just now. Let's focus instead on the seductive semantics of the term "self-aware." Oxford tells us *self-aware* means "having conscious knowledge of one's own character and feelings."[37] But computers have no character and no feelings. So we can rule that definition out for anything to do with AI.

In a more general sense, "self-aware" could mean being aware of our surroundings. Could mechanisms be self-aware in that sense? Does placing sensors on a car cause the car to be self-aware? A sensor in my gas tank tells me when I need gas. When I back up the car, it beeps when I get too close to an obstacle. Automatic parallel parking requires similar sensors. All of these are examples of cars being "aware" of their surroundings. This is apparently what the robot squid's developers mean to imply when they use the term "self-aware." Their semantics are misleading. My car is not "self-aware." There is no self in the car that experiences awareness. Electronic sensors generate information about the car's position, but the car is not experiencing it. The same is true of the squid-like robot.

Seductive semantics often live in a definition vacuum. Consider the remark by Kurzweil that by 2045 "we will have multiplied the intelligence, the human biological machine intelligence of our civilization a billion-fold."[38] What is "human intelligence"? Does it mean our brains will have instantaneous access to all of Wikipedia and more?

In a way, our minds already have access to Wikipedia through our fingertips and a computer keyboard. Even so, what will the advantage be of directly connecting the brain to something like Wikipedia? A photographic memory does not imply intelligent use of knowledge. And even if our brains did have wired access to Wikipedia, our minds can only process singular attention to information at any given moment. Try multiplying 348 by 853 in one mental step without using a calculator. I certainly can't do it. I have to break it up into small pieces, each a single individual thought. "Let's see, 8 times 3 is 24. Write down the four and carry the two," etc. Even here, I need pen and a piece of paper to keep track of the intermediate answers to augment my short-term memory. There are those savants who can multiply large numbers in their heads, but not me. When doing arithmetic in my head, I have the long-term memory of a goldfish, which is reportedly about three seconds.

If easy tasks like multiplying are rough, assimilation of knowledge from all Wikipedia will not be possible from a fire hose of information fed directly into our brains. It will be quicker only in the sense that typing for a Wikipedia search and communication latency slow us down.

But maybe this is not what is meant by Kurzweil's claim that "we'll be able to multiply human intelligence a billion-fold." Maybe intelligence refers to our creativity being increased. But creativity is not computable.

Maybe creativity can be addressed indirectly. Maybe we will find a knob to turn in our brains to increase creativity. Is that what is meant by increasing "human intelligence" a billion-fold? Kurzweil doesn't say.

The problem is clear. Because Kurzweil uses the term "human intelligence" without defining it, we are left with all sorts of interpretive speculation. Some will define "human intelligence" to fit some preconceptions and then embrace the claim. Because the term "human intelligence" is not defined with any certainty, Kurzweil's claim means nothing. It's just seductive semantics—it draws our interest and lets us fill in the blanks to suit ourselves.

"Consciousness" is another oft-used word in AI that is rarely defined. To a high degree of certainty, I know I am conscious. To an only slightly lesser degree, I believe via evidence that people I meet are conscious. To make any further claims about consciousness in general, the term needs to be defined. There are dictionary definitions but there are none that I have seen that allow definitive testing of whether someone or something is conscious.

Sir Roger Penrose believes consciousness is non-algorithmic and therefore not able to be replicated on a computer. "I argue that some of the manifestations of consciousness are demonstrably non-algorithmic," he says, "and I am therefore proposing that conscious mental phenomena must actually depend upon such non-computational physics."[39]

Penrose does not offer a definition of consciousness but refers to its non-computational manifestations. Philosopher J. P. Moreland likewise indirectly defines consciousness by its properties: "Consciousness is what we are aware of when we introspect. It consists of sensations (pain, the taste of a lemon), thoughts, beliefs, desires, memories, acts of free choices, and so on."[40]

The difficulty of defining consciousness does not keep rogue thinkers from speculating about panpsychism.[41] Panpsychism, as has been discussed, purports that everything material has an element of individual consciousness, and that consciousness is as much a part of the universe as gravity. Philosopher Philip Goff makes the case: "The panpsychist offers an alternative research programme: Rather than trying to account for consciousness in terms of utterly non-conscious elements, try to explain the complex consciousness of humans and other animals in terms of simpler forms of consciousness which are postulated to exist in simpler forms of matter, such as atoms or their sub-atomic components."[42]

The idea that my pencil is conscious is preposterous. And I agree with Penrose that consciousness is not computable and therefore cannot be resident in computer-implemented AI. Materialists that disagree have the difficult or even impossible task of proving otherwise.

Again: Watch out for seductive words. They seem to offer a lot, but may be only cue cards that prompt you to fill in whatever you want to hear.

Hype Filter #7: Seductive Optics and the Frankenstein Complex

Wrapping AI in an impressive physical package can magnify the perceived impact of new technology. Doing so uses *seductive optics*.

The confusing of AI packaging with AI content was evident in media excitement about a Buddhist robot who delivers messages to the faithful. "The world's first sutra-chanting android deity, modeled after Kannon the Buddhist Goddess of Mercy, was introduced to the public last week," the report reads. The robot can "move its eyes, hands, and torso, make human-like gestures during its speech, and brings its hands together in prayer. A camera implanted in the left eye to focus on a subject gives the impression of eye contact."[43]

Technologically speaking, nothing special is happening here. The messages from the Buddhist robot are pre-recorded and not the product of AI. The mouth movements are synced to the recording. This technology dates back at least to the Disney Hall of Presidents, launched in 1971. All the US Presidents in Disneyland give presentations akin to the Buddhist robot. Their mouths move and they gesture. The technology, dubbed Audio-Animatronic, was trademarked by Disney in 1964.[44]

But the packaging and context made this robot seem special. Monks gathered at the robot's opening ceremony and performed with "chanting, bowing, drumming, and the ringing of bells." The robot, named "Mindar," was designed to look like an androgynous human, with "special features designed to evoke both feminine and masculine qualities.... the plain facial features give room for visitors to use their own imagination in how they'd like the deity to appear."[45]

Sound familiar? Like seductive semantics, here we have seductive optics. The AI looks generally human, but also leaves space for people to impose their own preferences.

The media obsession with the Buddhist robot story is due to seductive optics.

Some of the panicky AI-will-take-over-the-world talk grows out of seductive optics—that is, the AI packaging. Author and poet Diane Ackerman confesses, "Artificial intelligence is growing up fast, as are robots whose facial expressions can elicit empathy and make your mirror neurons quiver."[46]

Another factor contributing to fear of AI is the so-called Frankenstein complex.[47] The term, coined by science fiction writer Isaac Asimov,[48] originally described the fear of the mechanical man in science fiction of old. Frankenstein refers to Mary Shelley's 1818 novel *Frankenstein, or The Modern Prometheus*. A young scientist, Dr. Victor Frankenstein, sews together dead body parts to create a monster. (In the book Frankenstein is the doctor's last name, but today Frankenstein's monster is often referred to as simply Frankenstein.)

Thomas Edison first put the story to film in a *silent* 1910 movie. Some of us are familiar with Boris Karloff's depiction of the monster in the 1931 motion picture classic *Frankenstein*.[49] Today's film monsters are typically a lot scarier than those depicted in 1930s movies with their clunky special effects. But even today, Karloff's Frankenstein monster makes one's skin crawl. The question is, why? After all, he moves clumsily in slow motion; even someone on crutches could avoid him. He's tall, sure, but the smaller, fast-moving, hard-punching Mike Tyson could no doubt take him in the ring. The monster is less dangerous than a bobcat or alligator, and yet we get chills just looking at Karloff's Frankenstein monster, and we don't when thinking about alligators or bobcats. What's going on here?

The Frankenstein complex is explained by a related idea dubbed *the uncanny valley*.[50] The hypothesis is named after a dip in a regression curve. For the most part, and all other things being equal, as an object comes to resemble a human more and more, our reaction to the object becomes increasingly positive. But if the likeness is a near miss, we experience the uncanny valley. Anything not human but that appears very nearly human is scary.

The Frankenstein complex/uncanny valley contributes to fears of (and fascination with) AI. Consider the chatbot Sophia the Robot.[51] Sophia has its own Facebook page[52] and has been awarded citizenship in Saudi Arabia.[53] Its speech is augmented by facial expressions using small feature changes akin to those used by cartoonists (which we will discuss in just a moment). Sophia's human-like container, its seductive optics, has little to do with its chatbot AI. (If you want to brave the revenue generating ads, there are many interesting videos of Sophia on YouTube.)

Sophia is bald and the back of its head is clear plastic that reveals electronics inside its head. The Frankenstein complex/uncanny valley reaction might diminish if Sophia wore a wig, or this might plunge the robot deeper into the uncanny valley, since it still wouldn't look fully human. I suspect AI optics will get better to the point of being visually indistinguishable from humans when not closely examined. Currently, though, seamless human form representation in robots is not well developed. It's close enough, however, that marketers of Sophia the Robot and

Figure 6.1. Sophia the Robot.

other AI can grab our attention via the uncanny valley. Today more than ever the goal in promotion is to get the attention of the reader and the media. Making things look *almost* human and, therefore, a little creepy does this.

Bear in mind this only works because of the amazing human sensitivity to small variations in faces and facial expressions. Baby brains are prewired to recognize faces to discern mommy from others, and from very early on we can distinguish nuances of emotion as revealed in facial expression.

Cartoonists use this in their art. Consider cartoons where, just by changing the eyebrows and the mouth, a plethora of different emotions are displayed. In Figure 6.2, each of the three columns of faces has a different mouth shape, and each of the three rows has different eyebrows. The nine different combinations of these simple features are strikingly different—and all from only changing the angle of the eyebrows and the curve of the mouth.

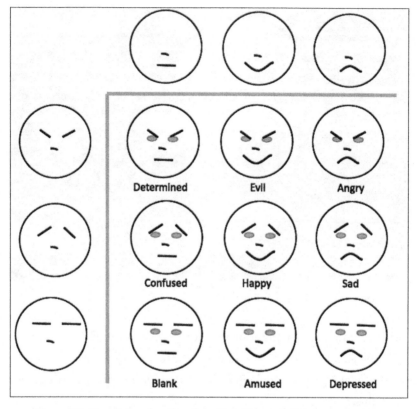

Figure 6.2. Simple tweaks allow for widely diverse facial expressions.

Further, we see faces everywhere we look, and assign personality to those faces. Look at any wall socket. The three holes resemble a face that displays emotion. We might see a water faucet that reminds us of a puzzled face, a Kleenex box with a big open mouth, or a chest of drawers whose open drawer looks to be a big hungry mouth saying "feed me!"

But our emotional response to face recognition is not always one of amusement. Some faces evoke a feeling of eeriness. Bubbles in a coffee cup can have gaps that overall resemble the face in Edvard Munch's 1893 iconic painting *The Scream*.

In sum: Those who market AI make use of our predisposition to personify objects. They know we will endow human-looking objects with human characteristics—intelligence, consciousness, various emotions—

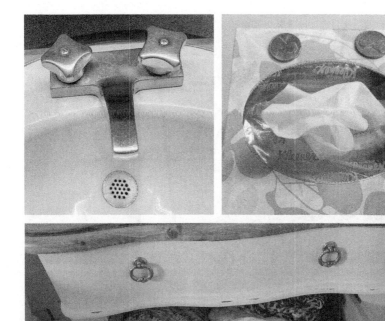

Figure 6.3. Faces everywhere!

so they embed their software in human-appearing containers to hype their wares.

So when filtering AI hype, beware of seductive optics. Mentally separate the packaging from the content.

Hype Filter #8: True-ish

THE STORY is told of a cross country meet where several teams back out at the last minute due to poor weather and only two teams show, archrivals Springfield and Centerville. Centerville wins the competition. The next day the Springville *Gazette* reports, "Springfield Finishes Second in Grueling Cross-Country Competition. Arch Rival Centerville Finishes Second to Last."

Figure 6.4. More faces!

Misrepresentations of this sort may be technically true, but they're intended to deceive. They're what I like to call True-ish.

Sometimes a headline may misrepresent, while the article itself is accurate. Sometimes both headline and article misrepresent, and the only way for readers to learn the whole truth is to read a more honest report.

Here are a few examples of true-ish clickbait related to AI.

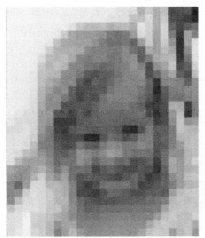

Figure 6.5. Pixelated version on left; original image on right.

A Duke University headline claiming that their "Artificial Intelligence Makes Blurry Faces Look More Than 60 Times Sharper"[54] trades in half truths. To understand why, a bit of background is helpful. In order to hide someone's identity in a picture or a video, a face can be pixelated. The pixels of the face are made so big that no recognition is possible. Another example is blurred details in a photo due to poor resolution. For example, the license plate of a car is so small that, when enlarged, the image is pixelated to the point where identification is impossible.

A common scene in TV crime shows runs something like this: The lead detective is viewing an image of a possible culprit, but it's badly pixelated. The detective tells the technician to sharpen the image. The technician punches a key on his computer keyboard, activating an algorithm, and magically, the de-blurred image appears.

The title of the Duke University article about the Duke research seems to promise just this sort of ability, but it's misleading. The Duke software generates a sharp face, but there is no guarantee the regenerated face is the original. The article confesses as much only in the fourth paragraph, saying, "The system cannot be used to identify people, the researchers say: It won't turn an out-of-focus, unrecognizable photo from a security camera into a crystal clear image of a real person. Rather, it is capable of generating new faces that don't exist, but look plausibly real."[55]

That's less impressive.

There are at least two ways a pixelated image can be "restored." The first takes the equivalent of a catalog of faces, pixelates them, chooses the one that looks most like the blurry image in question, and then uses the unpixelated version of this image as a best-guess stand-in for the blurry image in question. No claim is made that the software regenerates the image of the original face. Such a technology may, however, be useful in other applications. It might be applied to restoring license plate numbers from blurred images, given a large enough catalogue of images and their blurred equivalents. I can see this information being useful to law enforcement. Another possible application is restoring old photographs corrupted by age, if the program could be fed high-resolution images of the people in the old photos.

An alternate approach to restoring a pixelated image is gathering other versions of the same corrupted image. A second blurred image using different pixelation will help the restoration accuracy. Or in a blurry video, there are numerous versions of a pixelated face available as the person moves.

Here's an extreme example. Suppose the world's worst camera has a single photodetector. The camera is pointed at a scene and takes a single measurement over a small square region of the scene. The portion of the scene in this small region is blurred together (or averaged) into a single number. The camera adds up all the light coming from the small square into a single number that is recorded by the photodetector. The camera is then randomly moved to another position and another reading is taken over another square. After doing this a number of times, is it possible to combine all these single readings into a composite image even when many of the regions overlap?

The answer is yes. Ten thousand readings using the world's worst camera allow a decent rendering of the image. Further readings further

Figure 6.6. On the upper left is an original image; upper right is the first reading from the world's worst camera. On the second row and third rows, additional readings from the world's worst camera gradually improve the composite image.

sharpen the image. Each image from the world's worse camera adds more information about the image.

But, despite detective shows and news media claims to the contrary, there is no computer algorithm that can take a single pixelated, blurred image and restore the original image.[56] That's because there is no free lunch. If you receive a corrupted image, no AI pixel-pushing algorithm can generate more information. You need to have an idea beforehand what the corrupted image is. Even here, the reconstruction is but a best guess biased by your assumption about what the original could be. Alternatively, other versions of the corrupted images can be gathered. In that case, the question is how they are combined to give a restored image.

Another AI technology that's received the true-ish clickbait headline treatment is an MIT invention christened AlterEgo. Here are some examples.

- From *Newsweek*: "This Strange Headset Lets You Interact with Devices Simply by Reading Your Mind."[57]
- From TechRepublic: "Could MIT's AI Headset Transcribe your Future Strategy Straight from Your Brain?"[58]
- From the *Guardian*: "Researchers Develop Device That Can 'Hear' Your Internal Voice."[59]
- From Hearing Health & Technology Matters: "MIT's Fascinating AlterEgo Device Can 'Hear' Your Thoughts."[60]

These headlines are close to the truth. They'd be closer if they included a crucial qualifier along the lines of "seems to" or "seemingly." But the fact that the qualifier isn't there makes all the differences. As it is, the headlines make it sound like actual mind-reading AI has been developed. Only the scare quotes around "hear" in the latter two headlines, and the question form of the second, so much as hint that the claim of mind-reading should be taken with a grain of salt. But reading deeper into AlterEgo's technical details reveals that the AI reads "neuromuscular signals in the jaw and face triggered by so-called internal verbalizations (saying words 'in your head') that are not detectable by the human eye."[61] The AlterEgo headset reads not minds, but micro-movements, using electrodes attached to the wearer's jaw and chin. Most of the time you think without making these micro-movements; you only make them when you pretend you're talking. This is a habit called subvocalization that many of us got into when we learned how to read; some of us still combat subvocalization tongue movement.

So essentially, the "internal voice" that AlterEgo is "hearing" turns out to be your tongue moving around inside your mouth.

Is AlterEgo a fun bit of AI? Yes, it is.

Could it have helpful and interesting uses? Sure.

Does it actually read minds? No.

Here's essentially what happens with AlterEgo. Think of your teeth as computer keys activated by moving your tongue around as you type in your mouth. As the tongue moves around, there are tiny facial muscle movements. Small neuromuscular signals are detected by AlterEgo's facial sensors that use simple AI to translate the movements into words that can be fed into a computer search engine that, like Alexa or IBM Watson, spits out a response to any question asked. AlterEgo is interpreting a silent ventriloquism query invisible to the non-observant. Not only do the lips not move, there is no sound.

Once the words originating "in your head" are wirelessly transmitted to the computer, an answer is given and is wirelessly communicated back to AlterEgo. AlterEgo communicates to the user using vibrations on the bones of the face. Think of the vibration of your muted cell phone sending tactile Morse code to your jaw.

This is one of those situations where a product is flashy and fun, but the technical components are not as impressive as advertised. Train AI offline on neuromuscular signals by moving your tongue around in your mouth; the computer finds the answer and vibrates the answer back to you. Training AI to translate small facial muscle signals into words looks to be the only individual technical innovation behind AlterEgo. The idea of doing so is unique, but not that difficult. No deep learning is needed here.

And so the headline claims are misleading. AlterEgo no more reads your mind than a computer keyboard does. Your mind can be said to communicate with your computer when you type, therefore interfacing your mind with the computer. Similar communication is what happens with AlterEgo. But the process has nothing to do with directly reading your mind. It has to do with your tongue moving around in your mouth.

MIT's headline about AlterEgo is more honest. It reads, "Computer System Transcribes Words Users 'Speak Silently.'"[62] But the MIT claim that AlterEgo "would weave into human personality as a 'second self' and augment human cognition and abilities"[63] is pure hyperbole. AlterEgo is no more a "second self" than Alexa or the Google search engine. MIT's additional claim that AlterEgo is "intelligence augmentation"[64] is seductive semantics. "Intelligence augmentation" as used also applies to Alexa, Google search, and even the grocery list you take with you to the supermarket.

The composite idea behind AlterEgo is clever and patentable. It may prove invaluable for applications like helping the severely handicapped to electronically interface with the internet of things, or to politely send and receive text messages silently in the middle of a movie at the Cineplex. But despite headlines and publicity claiming otherwise, AlterEgo provides no technical stride forward in the field of AI-brain interface.

The larger lesson here is that some of the most convincing misrepresentations are the true-ish claims, the almost truths. To separate fact from fiction, you have to read the fine print.

Hype Filter #9: Citation Bluffing

ANOTHER TYPE of misrepresentation is citation bluffing. Here, someone claims that this or that authoritative source supports his argument when in fact it doesn't. Writers with blinding ideologies or weak ethics wishing to score points use citation bluffing to bolster their position. So don't take a citation as gospel. Ask yourself, does the cited source actually say what the person claims it does? Did the person omit important caveats or qualifiers about the source? Most people don't go to the trouble to find out. And oftentimes few details are given about the source, so the cautious reader has to work hard to find the original material.

Here's an example of either inadvertent or deliberate AI citation bluffing. A headline from the *Daily Mail* web page screams, "No more secrets! New mind-reading machine can translate your thoughts and display them as text INSTANTLY!"[65]

Yes, "INSTANTLY" is in all caps.

This *Daily Mail* web article, as is typical for money-seeking websites, is surrounded by ads that generate revenue. They are clickbait. One of the ads is for the latest Avengers movie. Another is for auto insurance. There are links to other news stories on the *Daily Mail* site, plus some sponsored clickbait links with teasers like "The Most Beautiful 1969 Photos" and "Why Women Cheat." The "news" headline fits right in. But hey, this is how websites make money. Attention-grabbing headlines about mind-reading AI are clickbait for unsuspecting web surfer prey.

But I digress. The citation bluffing in the *Daily Mail* article is still to come, in the first and third sub-headlines, in bold beneath the main headline:

1. "Researchers say they have developed a machine that can translate any thought"
2. "The astonishing machine will analyze what you are thinking and display it as text"
3. "Scientists hope that the machine can be used by people who are unable to speak"

In the body of the article the writer says, "There are fears from critics... that the device will cause problems if secret thoughts are exposed accidentally." Do we need to wrap our heads in tinfoil so the NSA can't read our most secret thoughts?

There is enough in the *Daily Mail* piece to identify the source as a research journal paper by Moses, Leonard, and Chang.[66] The research results reported in the original paper are significant and the authors are thorough in describing their work. But the *Daily Mail* chose to leave out information that presents the AI mind reader in a much less dramatic light. Here are some of the omitted facts:

Fact 1: Two people were used in the mind-reading experiment. Both were being treated for epilepsy. For the treatment of their seizures, the subjects already had 128-channel ECoG (Electrocorticography) units "surgically implanted on the cortical surface" of the brain. Doing this requires a craniotomy where the surgeon saws out a section of the skull large enough to allow the units to be placed directly on the brain. Ouch!

Fact 2: One of the biggest obstacles to reading minds from brain signals is noise. Conventional electroencephalography (EEG) electrodes monitor brain activity from outside the skull. Direct reading from the brain's surface gives cleaner signals.

Fact 3: The mind-reading results are subject dependent. A mind-reading system trained on John Lennon would not necessarily work on Paul McCartney and vice versa. Data is collected from a single person and then machine intelligence trains for reading of the mind for that person only.

Fact 4: Only ten brain signals are used for detecting thought. The subject is read ten short sentences from a recording and the brain signals are captured for these readings. Example sentences include:

"Nobody likes snakes."

"Have you got enough blankets?"

"Yet they thrived in it."

When enough brain signals are read, a machine is trained using the example signals. There is a lot of processing performed on the brain signal before it sees an AI classifier. Such man-in-the loop pre-processing is typical.

The brain signal processing ultimately allowed detection of thirty-seven phonemic types.

Fact 5: Neither cutting-edge machine intelligence algorithms used to train AlphaGo and IBM Watson, nor deep convolutional neural networks are used. Training of the mind-reading AI uses machine intelligence dating to the twentieth century. This is not bad. The choice of machine intelligence algorithms should fit the problem and many of these older techniques often work effectively. There is no reason to kill a fly with a sledgehammer. But the algorithms are by no means state of the art, as one might suppose from the *Daily Mail*'s breathless references to the findings of the researchers.

The mind-reading research results of Moses, Leonard, and Chang may one day lead to AI that can read minds without the need of brain surgery. Or maybe it won't. Establishing intermediate results are what incremental research is all about. The results reported in the research paper are interesting and significant, but they don't show, as the *Daily Mail* article implies, that the machine can "translate any thought." Thoughts can consist of images, nonverbal hunches, and emotional responses. The research described in the article doesn't even begin trying to tackle translation of these type of thoughts.

The *Daily Mail* piece is written by Danyal Hussain. I don't know Hussain and have not researched his work. But his hype article on mind reading is sensationalism and cheapens the work of Moses, Leonard, and Chang.

This hype filter requires that exciting news with impressive-seeming source citations be taken with a grain of salt. Your college English teacher most likely tried to instill in you the importance of using primary rather than secondary or tertiary sources. This example shows why. The further removed you get from the original research, the more likely you are to find yourself in a game of "telephone" or "gossip."

Hype Filter #10: Small-Silo Ignorance

AI CONCERNS are often voiced outside of a critic's silo of expertise. Ever wonder why actor Kevin Costner testified in front of Congress on the topic of oil spills, Ben Affleck on the A-T Children's Project, and quizmaster Bob Barker on the Captive Elephant Accident Prevention Act?[67] Many, apparently including some in Congress and the media, equate celebrity in one area to across-the-board expertise in everything. Author Laura Ingraham disagrees and tells clueless pontificating singer celebrities to *Shut Up and Sing*.[68] Comedian Ricky Gervais tells celebrity loudmouths, "You know nothing about the real world. Most of you spent less time in school than Greta Thunberg."[69]

The sentiment is not new. Iconic actor Marlon Brando said, "Why should anybody care about what any movie star has to say? A movie star is nothing important."[70]

Movie stars are one thing. But what of icons like Elon Musk? There is no doubting the business successes of Musk, who fathered Tesla and SpaceX. But Musk has some strange ideas. He argues, for example, that it's quite possible we are all living in a computer simulation. "The argument for the simulation, I think, is quite strong," he said in a 2018 interview with Joe Rogan.[71] "If you assume any improvements at all over time.... then games will be indistinguishable from reality, or civilization will end. One of those two things will occur. Therefore we are most likely in a simulation. Because we exist." This is a theory he has floated many times. In 2016 he said, "I've had so many simulation conversations it's crazy. In fact it got to the point where every conversation was the AI/ simulation conversation." He goes on to summarize his argument, and concludes, "There's a one in billions chance this is base reality."[72]

Tech visionary George Gilder casts doubt on Musk's overall expertise:

> Elon Musk is a tremendous entrepreneur...., but when he starts pretending that he's an ethical visionary, that human life is just a simulation in a smarter species' game.... I hear lots of otherwise brilliant people talk in these terms. I think it's a Silicon Valley dementia that's going on, which probably results from a religious collapse.... A lot of people have an incredible longing to reduce human intelligence to some measurable crystallization that can be grasped, calculated, projected and mechanized.[73]

Though Musk has "exposure to the most cutting edge AI" (his words),[74] he apparently does not have a realistic understanding about what algorithms can and cannot do. And so he fears AI will become innovative. He says, "People call it the singularity.... It could be terrible, and it could be great. It's not clear. But one thing is for sure. We will not control it."[75] But as we have shown, AI can't become creative.

Discerning ignorance can become more complicated when celebrities are brilliant like Musk or recognized intellectuals like the late genius

Stephen Hawking. Hawking was a genius in cosmology. With fellow genius Sir Roger Penrose, he formulated the Penrose–Hawking singularity theorems applying general relativity to understand black holes. Artificial intelligence scared Hawking, who said, "The development of full artificial intelligence could spell the end of the human race... It would take off on its own, and redesign itself at an ever-increasing rate. Humans, who are limited by slow biological evolution, couldn't compete and would be superseded."[76]

Hawking is genius in cosmology, but here he is outside his silo of expertise. Note his assumption that AI can be creative. AI writing smarter AI assumes creativity and, using the measure of the Lovelace test discussed in earlier chapters, AI has yet to be creative. And, as also discussed, there are good reasons to conclude that it never will be creative.

Hawking's AI quote is curious given that he abandoned pursuit of an *Ultimate Theory of Everything* due to Gödel's theorems on incompleteness and inconsistency.[77] This Ultimate Theory would unify physics in a neatly wrapped interconnected set of equations. Hawking once believed in the Ultimate Theory but changed his mind because of Gödel's theorems. No matter how much was discovered in physics, he concluded, Gödel's theorems say there would always be more.

Gödel's theorems, as it turns out, also have implications for the question of computer creativity. Alan Turing, the father of modern computer science, built on Gödel's work and showed that there are problems that are non-algorithmic and therefore cannot be captured by computer code. Evidence grows that many human attributes like creativity are likewise unable to be captured by computer code.

Hawking's black hole co-author, Roger Penrose, recognized this connection and wrote books about it. The first, *The Emperor's New Mind*, links Gödel's work to Turing's and makes a case for the non-computable nature of creativity and against the idea that AI programs could write better programs beyond the intent of the original programmer. Doing so requires creativity. Penrose dismisses Hawking's fear and argues that computers will never have the necessary creativity to write better and better AI.

When Hawking made his scary prediction about a dystopian AI future, he seems to have been unaware of Penrose's work in the area of AI. Now to be clear, and as I insisted in a 2020 article at Mind Matters News, because of Hawking's giant intellect, no one should ever say to him, "Shut Up and Do Physics."[78] But with a great intellect comes great responsibility. Hawking had the intellect to learn about Penrose's insight into computers and AI via Gödel, and ideally would have further explored the matter in the writings of others.[79] But he seems not to have bothered, or at least his own analysis betrays no evidence of his having done so.

This is often the case with brilliant thinkers commenting outside their area of expertise. They don't perform the necessary due diligence in the area outside their field of expertise, and yet comment on it as if their stature in their area of success magically imbues them with wisdom and knowledge in another. Hype Filter #10 puts us on our guard against this sort of thing.

Hype Filter #11: Assess the Source

THE BABYLON Bee is a wonderfully creative website that specializes in satire. Their charmingly oxymoronic motto is "Fake news you can trust."

But sites purporting to report real news while actually peddling fake news are a problem. So are fake news stories written to counter the original stories! Ubiquitous fake news can be challenged in stories hopefully not themselves fake news. Here's an example.

Many McDonald's restaurants now have self-order touchscreen kiosks. There is no need to talk to anybody. Walk in, poke in your order on the kiosk screen, stick in your credit card, and get your receipt with a number on it. You sit and display your number on the table. The food is delivered on a tray and set before you. No one has exchanged a word. The first time you need to open your mouth is to insert the Big Mac.

I had a wager with a good friend that the self-order touchscreen kiosks at McDonald's would not last. The kiosks not only take longer to use, but are annoying. The idea of the kiosk may sound good on paper but, to those like me who celebrate behavioral inertia, it's a hassle in practice.

During one of my visits to McDonald's, an employee intercepted my trip to the conventional counter for placing food orders. She asked if she could show me how the new kiosk touchscreens work. That was her job: teaching the reluctant and the untechnical how to program a touchscreen to get their McNuggets. I already knew how, but I complied because I did not want to seem rude. As she punched in my order, I told her I found the kiosks to be inconvenient and annoying. Her shoulders slumped. She sighed, looked me in the eye, and confessed, "Everybody does." Older customers seem more reluctant to use the screens than younger tech-savvy diners.

The outcomes of wagers and showdowns can turn on unforeseen events. The invading Martians in H. G. Well's *War of the Worlds* were technologically far superior to Earthlings. Earth fought back, but it looked like humanity was doomed. Unexpectedly, the Martians were killed by an onslaught of earthly pathogens. Who would have guessed?

There came a moment when I thought the McDonald's touchscreens might be finished off by a similarly unexpected threat. The Blaze news site reported on the outcome of an analysis of swab wipes from touchscreens at McDonald's taken from eight restaurant locations in England.[80] Dr. Paul Matawele of London Metropolitan University's microbiology department reported, "We were all surprised how much gut and faecal bacteria there was on the touchscreen machines. These cause the kind of infections that people pick up in hospitals."[81]

Gut and fecal matter next to my hamburger? Yech!

The ugly pathogens discovered included potentially fatal Staphylococcus, the dreaded "Staph" infection that closes hospital wards. Staph is also becoming antibiotic resistant.[82]

I now had another reason to not to use the kiosks at McDonald's.

Pathogens helped Earth beat the Martians. Maybe pathogens would help me win my wager about McDonald's kiosks.

But then I read a media rebuttal titled "Relax, McDonald's Touch-screen Menus Aren't Covered in Poop." The article reported, "No. There is no brown, smelly fecal matter covering McDonald's touchscreens." Further, the author added, "Because we have a digestive system (complete with acid and enzymes) and an immune system, it is nearly impossible for one or two bacteria to cause disease. Instead, a person usually needs to ingest hundreds, thousands, or even millions of bacteria to become sick (with a foodborne illness, anyway). Unfortunately, the researcher didn't bother to report how much bacteria he found."[83]

Apparently, eating a little bit of poop won't hurt you.

The writer of the rebuttal article sounded like he knew what he was talking about. His byline had a PhD after his name. I began to dismiss the original alarmist article as wrong. But then it struck me: this rebuttal could itself be fake news. Rebuttals can be backed or shaped by corporate influence. And, my hype filter noted, there is evidence of seductive semantics in the rebuttal.

The article begins, "There is no brown, smelly fecal matter covering McDonald's touchscreens." This is a hyperbolic exaggeration of the original report, which made no such claim. The original report only claimed detection of "traces" of "gut and fecal bacteria" on the screen wipings.

The rebuttal also says that "the researcher didn't bother to report how much bacteria he found." This may bring the study into question but does not negate it.

We see a blatant use of the *genetic fallacy* in the rebuttal. The source of the claims is attacked instead of addressing disputed facts. The rebuttal says, "It's not a study. It wasn't published in a peer-reviewed journal. It is literally nothing more than a guy walking around swabbing McDonald's touchscreens for a newspaper article."

But the "guy" was not a self-serving journalist looking for a sensational scoop. He was Dr. Matawele of London Metropolitan University's microbiology department.

These observations give me pause about the rebuttal.

Now I don't have certainty either way about fecal matter on the touchscreens at McDonald's. It's quite possible that one or the other of those two stories are legitimate; or that neither are; or that both are, and the authors simply have different opinions about the danger of fecal matter on touchscreens. Both stories have elements of hype. Questionable news reports in all directions can lead to a quagmire of confusion.

We live in the information age, but much of the information we're bombarded with is untrustworthy. Consulting multiple sources across the political spectrum, and carefully assessing the quality of each source, can help us tease out the truth from the hype.

And by the way—I lost my bet about the kiosks at McDonald's. It looks like they are here to stay. In fact, McDonald's is doubling down on AI technology at its restaurants. It purchased the company *Apprente* and its speech recognition technology[84] to use for ordering in its drive-through lanes. Since I have problems understanding the order takers when they talk through the cheap drive-through speakers, this is welcome news.

Hype Filter #12: Conflicts of Interest

Cui bono? is Latin for "who benefits?" When you read something about AI that seems too good to be true, or to terrifying to be true, ask yourself who benefits from presenting AI in this way.

Cold case police detective J. Warner Wallace identifies the three motivators for committing a crime: financial greed, relational desire, and pursuit of power.[85] These same things are motives for hype, including in the world of AI.

We all know that websites seek money-generating clicks. Not everyone knows, however, that academic researchers need to publish interesting material to get grant funds, the accolades of their peers, promotions, and salary increases. Those who publish fake technical papers written by SCIgen seek more beans for their deans to count. Deans don't taste beans, they only count them.

So, unfortunately, overstated or downright fake news even occurs in the so-called scholarly literature. To prove this, in 2018 three established scholars wrote papers reporting the most outrageous studies and conclusions they could fabricate.[86] They chose to submit to high-profile journals in fields such as gender studies, queer studies, and fat studies. One of their papers, published in the journal *Gender, Place and Culture*, was titled "Human Reaction to Rape Culture and Queer Performativity at Urban Dog Parks in Portland, Oregon."

The paper addressed the absurd question "Do dogs suffer oppression based upon (perceived) gender?" The authors claimed to have watched fornicating dogs in public settings for a year.[87] The paper included faked data: "Averaging across my data, in my observational vicinity there was approximately one dog rape/humping incident every 60 min (1004 documented dog rapes/humping incidents)."

Why would any academic journal publish such a ridiculous paper? Those who play in the sandbox of extreme beliefs love fueling their ideology. The authors of the bogus papers, Helen Pluckrose, James Lindsay, and Peter Boghossian, agree: "Scholarship based less upon finding truth and more upon attending to social grievances has become firmly established, if not fully dominant, within these fields, and their scholars increasingly bully students, administrators, and other departments into adhering to their worldview."[88] When academics needing publications write (or get a paper-generator to write) with the goal of pleasing ideologues, hype happens.

The same can be true of hyperbolic forecasts. Sometimes, though, motives are less clearly corrupt. As we've mentioned before, in some cases, claims erupt from the pure excitement of research. In my experience, research plods along, when unexpectedly, there is a Eureka event. A flash of genius. The dopamine hits from such moments are a big motivator.

The resulting exuberance often gives the researcher an honest albeit overoptimistic view of themselves and the future.

Here's a personal example. The *Trend in Engineering* was a quarterly publication of the College of Engineering at the University of Washington. My colleague Les Atlas and I were interviewed in an article titled "Artificial Neural Networks Model the Human Brain."[89] This sounds like a science news article we might read today. But this article was written over thirty years ago in 1988.

First note the hyperbole in the title. The artificial neural networks we deal with are no more a model of the human brain than a pump handle is a model of the human heart. Artificial neural networks yesterday and today are inspired by the architecture and operation of the human brain but fall way short of the human brain's performance.

The article goes on to describe our research into using AI in speech recognition. The description is fine until we announce a prediction that made our claims scrutiny-proof, at least for the near term: "The team plans to have a demonstration system available in two years." We then added that we felt that the neural network's speech recognition "has the potential to behave as human does."

At the time we were optimistic. But not only were our goals not achieved, our research thrust was not even in the right direction. Our approach hit a brick wall and, in hindsight, was not even close to solving speech recognition. Commercially successful speech recognition today relies on AI called *hidden Markov models*. At the writing of the *Trend in Engineering* article, neither Les Atlas nor I knew anything about this algorithm.

Our overly optimistic future forecasting was motivated in part by our excitement. We were true believers swept up in the moment. But there were other less pure motives at play. The *Trend* publication was distributed to alumni and the public. The University of Washington, like all other universities, wants the world to know how great it is. University rankings in *US News & World Report* are determined in part by submitting evaluation questionnaires to university administrators, like deans. Most universities have discipline-specific shiny, full-color brochures they circulate to those with influence. The shiny publication, also sent to alumni and potential donors, boosts donations and strengthens branding.

Collectively, modern universities are a glut of self-promoting enthusiasts in a crowded room, with all of them waving their hands above their heads and jumping up and down yelling, "Look at me! Look at me!" Such is also the competitive game played among beer brands, truck models, and rock stars. It's part of the free enterprise system. Getting attention is a big motivation behind hype. So is money. In the *Trend* article about our neural network research, supporters of our research are listed: "Funding of Atlas and Marks's [research] comes from a variety of sources: The National Science Foundation, The Office of Naval Research, Physio Control Corp. and the Washington Technology Center."

Professors in research universities are entrepreneurs. We must solicit and win external funding to support our graduate students, equipment, and summer salary. Part of the professor's marketing job is to keep funding program directors happy. The program director's happiness is increased when there are publications to show to the boss. And the more cutting-edge and newsworthy the publications, the better.

I just listened to an old interview about neural networks I did on KIRO radio in Seattle in March 2002.[90] I'm proud to say I projected minimal hype. What was more interesting than my answers were the questions asked by the host, who had little technical background. The questions were the same questions asked today about AI. Will AI take over our jobs? Will AI take over the world like the HAL 9000 computer took over the space mission in the movie *2001: A Space Odyssey*? The fears and concerns of the public were the same then as they are now. Today, however, the internet and social media provide a much larger megaphone to the voicing of these fears.

The Hype List

IN A nutshell, here is the list of twelve things to consider when reading AI news:

1. **Outrageous Claims:** If it sounds outrageous, maybe it is. Recognize that AI is riding high on the hype curve and that exaggerated reporting will be more hyperbolic than for more established technologies.

2. **Hedging:** Look for hedge words like "promising," "developing," and "potentially," which implicitly avoid saying anything definite.

3. **Scrutiny Avoidance:** Any claim that such-and-such an AI advancement is a few years away may be made with sincerity but avoids immediate scrutiny. Short attention spans mean that when the sell date on the promise rolls around, few people are likely to notice. Remember the old proverb often attributed to quantum physicist Niels Bohr: "Prediction is very difficult, especially about the future."[91]

4. **Consensus:** Beware of claims of consensus. Remember Michael Crichton's claim that consensus regarding new technology and science is the "first refuge of scoundrels."

5. **Entrenched Ideology:** Many AI claims conform to the writer's ideology.[92] AI claims from those adherents to materialism are constrained to exclude a wide range of rational reasoning that is external to their materialistic silos.

6. **Seductive Semantics:** Claiming AI is conscious or self-aware without term definition can paint the AI as being more than it is. Seductive semantics is the stuff of marketing. In the extreme, it can misrepresent.

7. **Seductive Optics and the Frankenstein Complex:** AI can be wrapped in a package that tries to increase the perception of its significance. Unrecognized, the psychological impact of the Frankenstein Complex and the Uncanny Valley Hypoth-

esis can amplify perception far beyond technical reality. The human-appearing body in which a chatbot resides is secondary to its driving AI.

8. **True-ish:** Beware of those tricky headlines and claims that are almost true but intended to deceive.

9. **Citation Bluffing:** Web articles and even scholarly journal papers can exaggerate or blatantly misrepresent the findings of others they cite. Checking primary sources can ferret out this form of deception.

10. **Small-Silo Ignorance:** The source of news and opinion always requires consideration, but those speaking outside of their silo of expertise need to be scrutinized with particular care, especially when the speakers are widely admired for their success in their silo. Don't be dazzled by celebrity. This caution applies to famous actors speaking about politics but also to celebrated physicists speaking about computer science.

11. **Assess the Source:** I trust content more from the *Wall Street Journal* than from politically motivated sites like the *Huffington Post* or yellow journalism sites like the *National Enquirer*. But even if the article appears at a site or periodical that has earned a measure of trust, it's wise to assess the writer of the article.

12. **Who Benefits?:** Remember financial greed, relational desires, and the pursuit of power. These are the three factors used by police detectives in their investigation of crimes. They are also good points to remember when considering whether a report on AI is true or hype. Is there a hidden agenda or emotional blind spot?

Final Thoughts

THE "ASYMPTOTE of reality" in the Hype Curve denotes the accumulation of successful reduction to practice. The ultimate success of AI is not due to journal papers, blogs, press releases, forecasts, corporate acquisitions, speculation, or promises. Success is measured by reduction to practice. Where has AI been profitably reduced to practice in everyday life, used effectively by a government, or deployed in the military? Such is the ultimate test of the success of any technology.

While watching the traversal of AI on the hype curve, we today enjoy narrow AI applications from Alexa to Zoom. The applications are becoming ubiquitous. Such successful AI technologies, reduced to practice, are soon taken for granted as their initial sparkle is dimmed by familiarity and as more impressive AI technologies arrive.

All technology inevitably reaches its "asymptote of reality" where further development either stops or becomes incremental. AI is said to be the new electricity. Electricity, solidly in its "asymptote of reality," is firmly established with no breakthrough innovations for decades. AI will likewise reach this plateau. When and how remain a mystery of the future. As iRobot CEO Colin Angle says, "It's going to be interesting to see how society deals with artificial intelligence, but it will definitely be cool."[93]

PART THREE: AI HISTORY

7. AI: The Fossil Record

I was more motivated by curiosity. Never by the desire for financial gain. I just wondered how things were put together. Or what laws or rules govern a situation, or if there are theorems about what one can't or can do. Mainly because I wanted to know myself.

—Claude Shannon, information theory pioneer[1]

Now that we've cleared away some of the smoke and mirrors regarding what AI can do and what only non-computable you can do, let's step back and look at how AI got to this point. There have been three serious leaps in AI progress and popularity since the mid-twentieth century. The first began in the 1950s. The second was in the late 1980s. We are in the midst of the third rise today.

AI's Creation

I wasn't old enough to be part of the first wave of machine learning. During the second wave I did, however, get to pay homage to many of those early pioneers.

It was the late '80s. A crowd of admirers gathered at the Boeing auditorium in Seattle, all of us focused on a meek middle-aged man who was living neural-network royalty. Dr. Bernard Widrow was being recognized two-and-a-half decades after his remarkable work in pioneering artificial neural networks. Widrow, a professor of electrical engineering at Stanford, glowed in recognition that had been denied him for many years.

Widrow spoke about the theory of the ADALINE neural network he had developed back in the '50s and '60s. The feminine-sounding name was a contraction of "Adaptive Linear Neuron." When more units were added, the network was later generalized to MADALINE, meaning *many* ADALINES.

Computer learning machines of the 1960s were peppered with then-new seductive semantic labels like *neural networks* and *perceptrons*. The Stanford MADALINE invented by Widrow was said to be a machine that "in some respects thinks like a man" (though Widrow said repeatedly that he didn't like to use the term "thinks" because "we don't really understand what thinking is about").[2]

These machines were impressive even by today's standards. Widrow created a neural network that learned from repeated observations. It beat the local weatherman at forecasting weather and translated languages from spoken form to print. Around the same time, Claude Shannon at Bell Labs used relay switching to play chess and taught robotic mice how to master mazes; and Cornell's Frank Rosenblatt was dazzling the world with his perceptron neural network. All this happened over sixty years ago.

In Seattle's Boeing auditorium, Widrow played for us a clip from an old black-and-white TV program called *Science in Action*, a weekly show that ran from 1950 to 1966 and featured a variety of guest scientists. In this particular 1963 episode a young Bernie Widrow appeared on screen before us, sporting a fresh buzz haircut fashionable in that era. The crowd chuckled.

This TV program provides an interesting glimpse into the public's attitude toward computers and explains the leap Widrow made. The host, zoologist Earl Stannard Herald, gestures toward a wall-sized computer and says:

> By now we're all fairly familiar with computers such as this one, and we can now remember with some amusement the fears that many of us expressed that machines such as these might someday take over the world. Today we recognize them for what they are... huge calculators, arithmetic machines, no more capable of acting for themselves than a desktop adding machine. However, a totally new class of computing

machine has come into being. It's called an adaptive computer, and it's important because it can learn from its own experience.[3]

Widrow called his learning machine a neural network because it was loosely based on the 1943 McCulloch-Pitts model of the biological neuron. Like a string with balls attached on each end, neuron pairs are connected with a weighted interconnect. According to Hebbian learning published in 1949, the strength between neurons is determined by how often the connected neurons simultaneously fire. Today we simulate such weights using a computer program. But during the early 1960s, when computers were still wet behind the ears, Widrow used thin pencil leads suspended in a solution appropriate for electroplating for his interconnection weights.

Electroplating was a more familiar concept in the '50s and '60s than it is now. Odd though it may seem to today's families, fond parents used to bronze their children's baby shoes using electroplating. The shoes—the more wrinkled the better—were dipped into a copper-based solution and dried. Then the shoes, able now to conduct electricity, were submerged in a plating solution and voltage was applied. Atom by atom, the shoes were plated in a thin coat of hard metal.

In high school I did a science project in silver plating where silver nitrate in solution was supposed to deposit a thin silver coating on submerged metal objects when a voltage was applied. I should have used gloves. I learned later that silver nitrate can be used to remove warts, treat nosebleeds, and cure gonorrhea; but when in contact with skin for long periods of time, silver nitrate is toxic, corrosive, and can cause burning. My electroplating worked but was far from meeting my expectations, and my fingers turned black from prolonged handling of the silver nitrate. My blackened fingers and I won no blue ribbons at the high school science fair.

The silver nitrate for silver plating is toxic, but is nothing compared to copper plating using a copper-cyanide solution. Copper-cyanide can cause headaches, dizziness, pounding of the heart, and vomiting.[4] Adolf Hitler famously committed suicide by biting into a cyanide capsule.

Copper plating is used for coins.[5] Pennies these days are not copper all the way through.[6] Why? Because copper is expensive. Many years ago my uncle Ed Hersman, a NASA engineer and stock market watcher, saw that the value of the copper in a penny was soon going to exceed a penny in cost. So he purchased ten thousand dollars in copper pennies that he stored in his basement in Doylestown, Ohio, in thirty-three gallon drums.[7] That's a million pennies! And Uncle Ed was right. A penny's worth of copper today is not enough to make a penny made of copper.[8] So the United States Treasury makes today's pennies out of less expensive zinc and plates them with a thin veneer of copper.

The electroplating process can be reversed by changing the voltage polarity. The copper surface of a penny can thereby be removed. The copper simply goes back into the liquid solution.

Bernie Widrow used electroplating to make his neuron interconnects. The Hebbian model of learning said a synaptic connection between two neurons grows stronger the more often the connected neurons simultaneously fired. The catchphrase summarizing Hebb's law for biological neurons is: "Neurons that fire together wire together."

Widrow used metal-plated pencil leads to simulate this effect. The more plating was on the pencil lead, the thicker the pencil lead and the better it conducted. Widrow called the ever-changing pencil lead a "memristor," which stands for "memory resistor." Why? Because the pencil lead conductance depends on the history of the pencil lead plating. In a sense, the current conductivity of the pencil lead was a function of its past plating history. Hence, the pencil lead was said to have memory. Widrow founded a company, *Memristor*, to promote and sell his ADALINE and MADALINE adaptive learning machine. The company ran from 1960 to 1980. Widrow's memristor was analog and suffered from all the shortcomings in all analog computing, including poor accuracy. Updating neural interconnects digitally in software is much more precise.

Neural Network Applications

In the old *Science in Action* episode, which you can watch for yourself,[9] black-and-white buzz-cut Bernie walks his audience through a number of applications of his neural network that remain impressive today.

For one thing, the speech recognition systems of today are not new. Widrow's 1960 neural network was able to process a phrase spoken into a microphone and immediately type out the English. The machine also translated other languages to English. A French phrase spoken into a microphone was translated and printed in English. Japanese too. Today's voice recognition technology and language translation machines are more technically sophisticated and powerful, but Widrow was first.

Widrow's neural network also was trained to play the casino game of twenty-one (also called blackjack). The neural network played against the dealer. The dealer followed fixed rules and the job of ADALINE was to adapt around the fixed set of rules. At each stage, the network decided on either another hit or to stop and hold.

In the game, you see one of the dealer's two cards. Your goal is to get as close to twenty-one as possible without going over. You can ask for additional cards to add to your score. If, though, your card count exceeds twenty-one, you automatically lose. If your card count does not exceed twenty-one and you stop then it's the dealer's turn. The dealer must take additional cards until her score is seventeen or more. If the dealer flips a card and exceeds twenty-one, you win. If the dealer has between seventeen and twenty-one points, the game is over. Whoever has the most points without going over twenty-one wins. If there is a tie, the dealer wins. There are many variations and nuances to the rules, but these are the fundamentals.

ADALINE was trained by observing many blackjack games and seeing which betting strategies failed and which were successful. From this, ADALINE learned how to play blackjack and was able to nearly achieve the known optimal performance level.

Then there's physical balance. Balancing an upright broom handle on your index finger is called the "inverted pendulum" problem in control theory. Recall our discussion of the marketing hype surrounding introduction of the Segway two-wheeled self-balancing scooter. The control of the Segway parallels that of the inverted pendulum. You are the broomstick being balanced by the Segway. Forty years before the 2001 introduction of the Segway, Widrow trained ADALINE to balance a broom placed on a movable cart. Give the broom a slight shove at the top to push the broom off of equilibrium, and the balancing cart, mimicking a human's movement to regain balance of a broom on a fingertip, moves back and forth in ever decreasing steps to reposition the broom in a stable upright position.

And then there's weather forecasting. Using data provided by the San Francisco airport, Widrow trained his neural networks to forecast weather. Training looked at pressure patterns for one day—say Monday—and forecast whether or not it would rain on Tuesday. ADALINE beat the official forecast accuracy of the human weatherman. ADALINE was accurate 83 percent of the time verses 67 percent for the weatherman.

Transcription of voice to text, broom balancing, weather forecasting, and winning card games were demonstrated using a rudimentary neural network AI over sixty years ago. Today's AI machine does a better job due to speed and sophistication. But the fundamental algorithms for these AI tasks were being used on a computer in the 1960s.

And we must note that Widrow's ADALINE wasn't the only early neural network attempt. There were others. Notably, in 1957 Frank Rosenblatt introduced the perceptron,[10] an algorithm which was also based on biological models, and for which he received international recognition.[11] The perceptron and ADALINE were not exactly alike,[12] but both were based on human brain neuron connectivity and both relied on training data.

Cage Match: Expert Systems versus Neural Networks

ADALINE, a neural network, learned blackjack. (In case you're wondering, ADALINE did not count cards, a no-no in blackjack.) As we've mentioned before, neural networks aren't the only game in town. Another AI approach to playing blackjack is an expert system. An expert system uses so-called symbolic artificial intelligence where rules define the decision process.

Here's an example of a rule in an expert system: "If a blackjack dealer's shown card is a seven, and you have to date been dealt a three, a six, and a four, then ask for another card." The fundamental idea behind expert systems is, as the name suggests, querying human experts and replicating these rules in computer code. For example, we can ask the professional gambler Bart Maverick what he would do if the dealer's card were a seven and the player's cards a three, a six, and a four. The human expert, Bart Maverick, might respond, "I would ask for another card." The AI expert system records this in its big list of rules. Since there are a lot of different ways cards can be dealt, there can be a lot of rules. From a long session with Bart Maverick, an expert system can be built with expertise equivalent to Bart's.

We can now speak of two ways for AI to learn blackjack. Blackjack can be captured by AI either by learning, as is done in neural networks, or by repeated querying of an expert and capturing the answer in code.

As we have seen in our discussion of hype, in the field of engineering, the true test of the success of a technology is the reduction to practice. Widrow's ADALINE was reduced to practice but not in the game of blackjack. Remember the Concorde airplane that used to cross the Atlantic at supersonic speed and reach an altitude of 60,000 feet? An ADALINE-type neural network was used to optimize the engine control on the Concorde.

You might be old enough to remember dial-up modems, where computers connected to the internet over phone lines. Back then you could use your landline phone or the internet, but not both at once. When first connecting, there would be a sound not unlike a duck choking on a kazoo. The sound was caused in part by an ADALINE-type system equalizing the phone line to allow optimal uploading and downloading speeds.

Using an engineering metric, ADALINE was successful because it was reduced to practice. Not so with early expert systems. As discussed previously, rule-based expert systems were used to write a short western play in the early 1960s. But the effort was academic and never reduced to practice.

The existence of two types of AI should have been an altogether good thing—we learn by trying different approaches, noting the advantages and disadvantages of each, and so forth. But the way the two camps treated each other led to a rather different outcome.

Imagine a world where clowns drive around in tiny crowded clown cars looking for mimes to beat up. An observant clown car passenger yells "Mimes!" when he spots a group of mimes. Brakes screech as the clown car comes to an abrupt stop. Angry clowns begin to climb out of the clown car and run angrily at the mimes, brandishing pool noodles for beating sticks. More clowns emerge from the car than seems physically possible. The mimes see the clowns coming and know they are in for a beating. They begin to silently and busily construct imaginary protective air walls using their hands. The clowns, eager for conflict, burst through the air walls and both sides break into slap fights.

Why would clowns and mimes be in conflict? After all, both are working towards the common goal of entertaining. But they end up hating each other because their approaches differ. Such was the case between those backing expert systems and those backing neural-type systems like ADALINE, which learned from data. Both approaches had AI as the common goal, but petty tribal conflict between the two methodologies led to the downfall of the first wave of research into artificial intelligence.

Such battles in academia—costly and much less funny than the conflict between clowns and mimes—are due to prideful ego, prestige seeking, and the never-ending pursuit of research money from an often cliquish federal budgetary process.

The Expert Experts

The leader of the rule-based expert system cult was MIT professor Marvin Minsky. In 1959, with John McCarthy, Minsky founded what is known today as the MIT Computer Science and Artificial Intelligence Laboratory. Minsky started out working with neural networks. In fact, in 1951 he invented one of the first artificial neural networks, called SNARC for "Stochastic Neural Analog Reinforcement Calculator." SNARC simulated a rat finding its way through a maze, learning from its mistakes until it made it out.

"It turned out that because of an electronic accident in our design we could put two or three rats in the same maze and follow them all," Minsky told a reporter in 1981. "The rats actually interacted with one another. If one of them found a good path, the others would tend to follow it. We sort of quit science for a while to watch the machine."[13]

Despite this early enthusiasm, Minsky became disenchanted with neural networks (he saw the limitations all too clearly, but didn't see that there could and indeed would be a way past those limitations) and began embracing symbolic artificial intelligence like expert systems.

Expert systems have some advantages over neural network systems. But they also have their drawbacks. Despite the drawbacks, Minsky embraced symbolic AI and turned against neural network training—so much so that he and his colleague Seymour Papert went to war against what they referred to as the connectionists (supporters of neural networks like ADALINE). Minsky and Papert were two clowns in the clown car; Rosenblatt and Widrow were enemy mimes.

To dis the work of those embracing neural network training, Minsky along with his colleague Papert wrote the book *Perceptrons*, first published in 1969.[14] In the book, Minsky and Papert collegially give kudos to the learning systems of Rosenblatt, Widrow, and others. This is characteristic in the halls of academia where opponents jockeying for recognition call each other honored and distinguished scholars while snarling and brandishing knives behind their backs. We also see this in Congress where political opponents call hated opponents "good friends" and label them "distinguished." In this spirit, Minsky and Papert even dedicate their expanded second edition of *Perceptrons* to their nemesis, Frank Rosenblatt, who died before its publication.

But in the body of the book, Minsky and Papert move from praise to snark. They claim "most of this writing" about perceptrons "is without scientific value," and they use terms like "vacuous" and "sterile" to describe the approach.

In 1988, almost two decades after the publication of *Perceptrons*, Papert published a peer-reviewed paper titled "One AI or Many?" in which he confessed to behind-the-scenes emotions. He says, "There was *some* hostility... and there is *some* degree of annoyance at the way the new movement [in neural networks] has developed."[15]

In recounting his version of what happened during the clown/mime fight, Papert composed a fairy tale, a sort of conflation of Cinderella and Snow White:

Once upon a time two daughter sciences were born to the new science of cybernetics. One sister was natural, with features inherited from the study of the brain, from the way nature does things. The other was artificial, related from the beginning to the use of computers. Each of the sister sciences tried to build models of intelligence, but from very different materials. The natural sister built models (called neural networks) out of mathematically purified neurones. The artificial sister built her models out of computer programs.

In their first bloom of youth the two were equally successful and equally pursued by suitors from other fields of knowledge. They got on very well together. Their relationship changed in the early sixties when a new monarch appeared, one with the largest coffers ever seen in the kingdom of the sciences: Lord DARPA, the Defense Department's Advanced Research Projects Agency.[16] The artificial sister grew jealous and was determined to keep for herself the access to Lord DARPA's research funds. The natural [neural network] sister would have to be slain.

The bloody work was attempted by two staunch followers of the artificial sister, Marvin Minsky and Seymour Papert, cast in the role of the huntsman sent to slay Snow White and bring back her heart as proof of the deed. Their weapon was not the dagger but the mightier pen, from which came a book—*Perceptrons*—purporting to prove that neural nets could never fill their promise of building models of mind: *only computer programs could do this.* Victory seemed assured for the artificial [symbolic AI] sister.... But Snow White was not dead. What Minsky and Papert had shown the world as proof was not the heart of the princess; it was the heart of a pig.[17]

Some of the criticisms of neural networks by Minsky and Papert were valid but, in retrospect, applied to the then-current development of the neural network and not the neural network's future. Many of Minsky and Papert's principal objections were ultimately overcome. Nevertheless, the impact of the book *Perceptrons* was immediate and brought funding of neural networks research in the United States to a screeching halt. Snow White, it seemed, had been slain.

Europe was not far behind the US. The publication of *Perceptrons* in 1969 was followed in 1973 by the so-called Lighthill Report, penned by Sir James Lighthill.[18] The report, requested by the United Kingdom's Science Research Council, was critical of the accomplishments of AI in light of initial exuberance. According to Lighthill, the promises made at the peak of the hype curve were grandiose claims that could never be achieved, because of mathematically insurmountable obstacles. The Lighthill Report caused the British government to stop funding AI research and development in most universities.[19]

What followed has been called the dark age of neural network research. Even though Minsky and Papert took aim only at neural networks, they were wounded by the ricochet of their own shotgun blasts. Not only was neural network research axed, their own funding got cut as well. In fact, all AI funding in the United States shriveled and all but disappeared. The period after the publication of *Perceptrons* and the Lighthill Report is therefore known as the AI Winter.[20]

This winter lasted for about a decade. Then, as we will talk about in the next chapter, came an explosive AI revival.

8. The AI Revival

AI will continue to solve particular, set problems brilliantly, as it has been doing with slowly increasing prowess since the 1950s, but AI software won't show a glimmer of originality or creativity, which are essential to the very idea of thought, until it can simulate emotion as accurately as it does other mental phenomena.

—David Gelernter, Yale University[1]

After infighting between AI factions brought about cuts in funding across the board, not much progress was made in the field until Cornell University's John Hopfield began resurrecting the comatose neural network in the early 1980s. By this time I was involved in AI research, so I got to see the resurgence of AI firsthand. This wave of progress saw exciting innovations still in use today.

Hopfield and His Neural Network of Little Worth

With evangelistic zeal, Hopfield spoke loudly and frequently about what is today known as Hopfield neural networks. Hopfield's neural network was markedly different from Widrow's ADALINE and the Rosenblatt perceptron. Using adaptive processes, classic problems were tackled. Here's one, known as the traveling salesman problem: Place a bunch of dots on a map and identify one as home. Starting from home, what's the shortest distance so that all of the dots are visited once and you end up back at home? This is the traveling salesman problem. Finding the shortest round-trip path becomes more and more difficult as the number of dots increases.

Although not immediately obvious, the traveling salesman problem is related to what is known as the queens problem. My group at the University of Washington used a Hopfield neural network to solve the eight-queens version of this puzzle.[2] The idea is to place eight queens on an eight-by-eight chessboard so that no queen can capture any other queen. The problem on a standard chessboard is mildly difficult. (You can try it.) Watching the Hopfield neural network solve the queens problem was fun. During the iteration to solution, a queen would appear and the neural network would notice the queen could be captured by another queen. So one of the queens would disappear and the neural network would take another stab at the problem. Queens at different locations on the chessboard faded in and out until a solution was found.

Hopfield's neural network was a hit. His papers were subsequently cited many thousands of times.[3] Some of these citations were from me.[4]

Here's an illustration of a basic Hopfield neural network that stores images. If you get close to a computer screen you see that images are not continuous but are represented by small discrete dots called pixels. Imagine, then, a bunch of pixels in an image that are only black and white. Just like turning a white LED light off and on, black pixels are said to be off and white pixels on. Each pixel corresponds to a neuron in a Hopfield neural network. Every pixel neuron is connected to every other pixel neuron with a weighted connection. Whether or not a pixel is off or on depends on (1) whether the neurons connected to it are on or off and (2) the weights of the connections between neurons. These fixed weights carry information about a large number of images stored in the neural network.

Suppose one of these stored images is a picture of a smiling baby using only white and black pixels. If we only know the baby's picture around his nose and right eye, that's okay. The known pixels can be enough information for the Hopfield neural network to construct the rest of the picture of the baby.[5] We turn on the white pixels in the region where the eye and nose are. Ideally neurons in the Hopfield neural network will

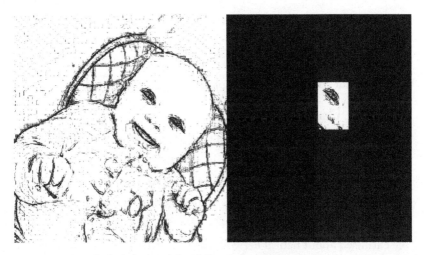

Figure 8.1. Left: A picture of a smiling baby using only white and black pixels. Right: The same picture with only right eye and nose of the baby shown.

spend time flickering as pixels turn off and on but will ultimately end up with the full picture of the baby. This type of Hopfield neural network is called a *content addressable memory* or an *associative memory*.

To understand the terminology, we can think of computer memory as an array of mailboxes, each with an address. A picture of the baby might be stored in a mailbox labeled baby-dot-jpg, i.e., a JPEG image labeled "baby." A traditional memory would access the stored baby image by the memory location's address. The mailbox with the right number is identified and the contents retrieved.

For a content addressable memory, we don't know the mailbox address but we do know about some of the contents of the mailbox. In the mailbox labeled baby-dot-jpg, for example, we know the pixel values corresponding to the baby's nose and right eye. This is ideally enough for the Hopfield neural network to turn on the remaining pixels and completely specify the contents of the baby-dot-jpg mailbox. Hence the name *content addressable memory*. The memory is not accessed by knowing the address of the mailbox but by examining part of the contents of the mailbox.

Note that that the neural network is not actually originating information about the baby's picture. It doesn't accurately "imagine" what the baby looks like based on a nose and eye. It accesses other files with information about the image and completes the photo that way.

Of Little Use

THERE WERE other applications of the Hopfield neural network besides the content addressable memory. Researchers got excited about them. These were new and exciting ideas and everyone wanted a piece of the action. Hopfield neural networks were generalized, made into circuits, and even implemented optically. The Hopfield neural networks got people enthused about neural networks again, leading to a new peak on the hype curve.

But closer inspection revealed the Hopfield neural network had a number of problems. For one thing, it didn't scale well. The idea of scaling is best illustrated by a human body. If a copy were made of you that was twice your height, your belt size would also increase by a factor of two. The surface of your skin, though, would increase by a factor of four and your weight by a factor of eight. If you weigh one hundred pounds and were scaled to be twice your height, your weight would increase to eight hundred pounds. That's why an ant, if scaled to the size of an elephant, would break its skinny ant legs. The ant's legs would need to be closer in structure to the stocky legs of an elephant.

Like the ant, the Hopfield neural network did not scale well. If the number of neurons doubled, the number of images able to be stored in the neural network less than doubled. Also, the number of interconnections between neurons grew as the square of the number of neurons. For an eight-by-eight chessboard with every square acting as a neuron, there are only sixty-four neurons but about four thousand interconnects if every pixel neuron is connected to every other neuron. Increase this to a chessboard with dimensions of a thousand by a thousand, and over a thousand billion weights are required. This scaling problem was a showstopper for the Hopfield neural network.

Hopfield neural networks theory is in analog rather than digital form and was implemented in analog using both silicon and optics. People into analog circuits got pumped. They thought they had another application for their craft. Today's neural networks are nearly exclusively implemented digitally. The reason is that analog systems are both inexact and prone to errors.

Analog works fine in many situations. Most physical phenomena seem to be analog—that is, composed of continuous varying properties. The acoustic waves you hear, the electromagnetic light waves you see, the microwaves that cook your food, and even the rough surface of a wooden desk are examples. An exception in nature is digital DNA that encodes life. DNA has a sequence of four bases that combine in base pairs, each of which can be viewed as two bits of information. Reproduction is largely a digital operation. We might be degrading due to deleterious mutations and DNA locations,[6] but not as fast as we would with analog reproduction.

Which brings us back to the Hopfield neural network implemented with analog electronics and optics that were prominent during the Hopfield hype peak. Because of its scaling problems and explosive increase in interconnects, analog Hopfield neural network popularity tumbled down from its hype peak. The asymptote-of-reality for the Hopfield neural network, as it turned out, is zero. There are more straightforward and better ways to implement content addressable memories and solve the traveling salesman problem.

I know of no Hopfield neural network reduced to practice today.

The Awesome Layered Perceptron

REMEMBER THE perceptron, attacked by Marvin Minsky and Seymour Papert in their book of the same name? Neural networks got better, so much so that the so-called "layered perceptron" gave lasting impetus to the second wave of serious interest in neural networks.

Whereas early perceptrons were "single layer" (the input was fed directly to the output nodes), multi-layer perceptrons have hidden middle

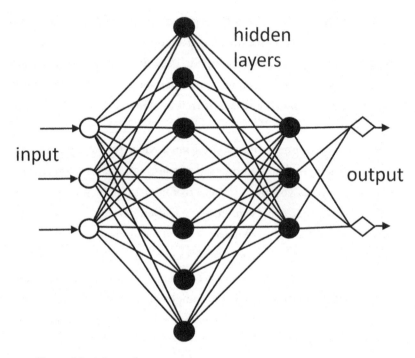

Figure 8.2. A layered perceptron.

layers. They're called "hidden" because they don't connect directly with the outside world, but instead transfer information between the input and output layers.[7]

The most basic multi-layered perceptron is a *feedforward* neural network, which means the data is transmitted from the input layer to the output layer in the forward direction. Things really get hopping with *backpropagation*, a training algorithm that uses outputs as inputs. That is, the algorithm calculates the difference between the expected output and the actual output (the *error*) and feeds it back through the network to tune the neural interconnect weights so the neural network performs a bit better next time. By doing this multiple times, the error between actual and expected output is minimized. In effect, the machine notices and corrects its own mistakes. It "learns." (We'll take a more in-depth look at how error backpropagation works in just a moment.)

The error backpropagation training algorithm was first reported in 1974 by Paul Werbos in his Harvard PhD dissertation,[8] but it wasn't widely popularized until a 1986 two-book set titled *Parallel Distributed Processing*.[9] I suspect that error backpropagation would make the list of the top ten most commonly used algorithms in the world. When I asked Paul Werbos whether he agreed, his response was simply "Easily."[10]

Error backpropagation generalized the idea of Frank Rosenblatt's perceptron and Bernard Widrow's ADALINE. It did so by allowing those hidden neurons in the neural network's structure. Previously every input node and every output node were connected; now, to get from the input to the output in a layered perceptron, one typically must go through one or more hidden neurons. The generalization of the perceptron to the layered perceptron was so named because the hidden neurons were often grouped into layers.

Adding hidden neuron layers vastly increased the types of data the neural network could learn. The layered perceptron was nonlinear and was able to classify nonlinearly. It overcame the main objections made in Minsky and Papert's book *Perceptrons*.

In Entertainment Media

THE IMPACT of the layered perceptron filled the media and spilled over into entertainment.

Dick Tracy was a syndicated newspaper cartoon strip that premiered on October 4, 1931. It was so popular that "Dick" became an American slang for detective. In a series printed January 27–29, 1991, Dick Tracy is on the track of a cybercriminal. In the strip, Tracy speaks to the character Data Banks about her brother.

Tracy says, "Your brother was working on a 'neural network' computer? You mean a type of artificial intelligence?"

Data Banks replies, "A neural network computer functions more like a person than an overgrown calculator."

Ever-informed Dick Tracy responds, "I understand the federal government sank 40 million into neural network research recently."

Data Banks then mentions her brother Memory Banks: "Yes. But they won't make the strides Memory did."[11]

Dick Tracy was right about the interest of the US government in neural networks. DARPA, "The Department of Mad Scientists,"[12] commissioned an in-depth study of the state of the art in neural networks in 1988.[13]

Neural networks also made it into the movies. Arnold Schwarzenegger's character in *Terminator 2: Judgment Day* (1991) tells the boy he's sent to protect, "My CPU is a neural network processor, a learning computer."[14]

Supervised Training

AS WE'VE seen, the breakthrough causing resurgence of interest in neural networks was the *error backpropagation* algorithm. This is a good place to pause and talk about supervised learning. Supervised learning is used by Widrow's ADALINE, Rosenblatt's perceptron, and our current topic of the layered perceptron. It is also applicable to more advanced training like convolutional neural network deep learning.

To train a neural network or any other learning machine, we need training data. Suppose, for example, we have a bunch of data on the heights and weights of numerous sumo wrestlers and basketball players. We choose these two features because we suspect the weights and heights of sumo wrestlers will be relatively far removed from the weights and heights of basketball players. The height and weight measures are therefore useful in differentiating between the two types of athletes.

On a data spreadsheet, imagine three columns: height, weight, and sport. The height and weight numbers are the inputs to the neural networks. They are called *features* of the image. The output is the sport— either basketball or sumo wrestling. For the purposes of this discussion, we'll assign the output +1 to a basketball player and -1 to a sumo wrestler.

Like the Hopfield neural network, the information in a layered perceptron is stored in the weights connecting the neurons. Recall Bernie Widrow's clever use of memristors (memory resistors) to vary the strength of connections between two neurons. As Hebb put it, "Neurons that fire together wire together." Each connection weight is assigned a single number dictating how strongly the neurons are connected. Given the data concerning the basketball players and the sumo wrestlers, our job is to find weights such that any time a sumo wrestler's height and weight are input into the neural network, the neural network outputs a minus one, meaning, "This is a sumo wrestler." If basketball player data is input, we would like the neural network to output a one, or "This is a basketball player." The question is how we figure out the weights in the neural network to achieve this goal.

During training, each weight connecting neuron pairs can be considered a tunable knob on a big board of knobs. Each knob can be tweaked up or down. But how do we tweak them to achieve the sumo wrestlers versus basketball classification? Some intelligent way to tweak the knobs is needed. Doing so is called *supervised training* and the process is referred to as *supervised learning*.

The term *supervised* means that each input data, for example weight and height, has a corresponding classification label. In our example the classification labels are sumo wrestler and basketball player. If we didn't have the labels, could we still learn from the data? Yes, but we would need to use *unsupervised learning* or *clustering*.[15] With unsupervised learning (without labels), we might look at the data and announce, "Hey! This data looks like it separates into tall skinny people and shorter fat people." We are not told that the data comes from basketball players and sumo wrestlers. The height and weight data alone hopefully has naturally separated into two classes without being told what the classes are.

Supervised training where each piece of data has an associated tag is easier to learn. Generally, the more information brought to any problem, the better the results. So, use of tags in supervised learning will give a better result than no tags of unsupervised learning.

There is an analogy to be made between supervised learning and the 1956 black-and-white science fiction classic *Invasion of the Body Snatchers*. In the movie, giant five-foot pods from outer space are laid alongside a human. Slowly the pods begin to morph into human form. Soon, the former pods resemble the human almost exactly. Imagine, then, a list of data lying next to a neural network being trained using supervised learning. Like the pod from outer space, the neural network slowly changes its weights to match the data. In the end, the neural network becomes a clone that generates numbers like the data lying next to it.

Here's another way to look at it. The input-output data used to train a neural network can be thought of as the result of an unknown system. In warfare, spotters for mortars help zero-in the launched mortars on their targets. Consider parameters from a mortar launching system. The input to the system is (1) the angle of the launcher, (2) the speed and direction of the wind, and (3) the launch velocity of the shell. The output label is how far the mortar travels.

A layered perceptron could learn to simulate mortar statistics if we wanted it to. If we have a large amount of data from previous mortar firings, a neural network can be trained under ideal conditions to hit the target every time. But in this example, we don't need to train a neural network. The relation between the mortar input and output data is easily determined by fundamental laws of classic physics. Why spend time training a neural network when we can plug numbers into a simple equation? Domain expertise here trumps AI.

Knowing a model like the physics behind the mortar launcher is a luxury. There is no well-defined equation describing the height and the weight of an athlete and his profession. The neural network constructs a system to map inputs to outputs in the absence of such knowledge.

The Beauty of Error Backpropagation

ERROR BACKPROPAGATION is a mathematically beautiful and effective method of training a neural network with hidden neurons.

Training of neural networks is typically iterative. The weights in a neural network are slightly nudged each training iteration so that learning the input/output data becomes more and more accurate.

Error backpropagation begins by providing an input. The weights connecting each neuron pair, not yet trained, will typically give a neural network output totally inconsistent with what the output should be. Whatever it is, we'll call the output "what we get." We know the output is wrong, because it differs from the data label that tells us "what we want." The difference between "what we want" and "what we get" (squared) is the error. To train, we wish to tweak the weights so that, next time, "what we get" is closer to "what we want." This is equivalent to pushing the output error closer to zero. This is the job of the neural network training algorithm.

Training a dog illustrates this process. You tell your dog, "Bring me the potato chips." Your dog brings instead the bag of Doritos. You shake your finger at the dog and say, "Bad dog. Bring me the potato chips." The dog delivers a bag of Cheetos and the scolding is repeated. Finally, the dog retrieves the bag of potato chips, and you scratch her behind the ears and give her the rest of your Slim Jim. In the rewarding, the dog's neurons are being wired so the potato chips are recognized in the confusion of the plethora of other salty and crunchy snacks. This is roughly what happens when you train a classification neural network.

When an input is fed to a layered perceptron neural network, every neuron is assigned a number. The state of neuron X is determined only by all the other neurons that connect directly to neuron X and the values of the interconnecting weights. Visualize, then, every neuron in the neural network being assigned a number. This number is called the neuron's *state* and is determined by a flowing wave of activation starting from the neural network's input to its output. The input values determine the states of the neurons in the first hidden layer, which then determine the states of the neurons in the next hidden layer, etc. Eventually the wave reaches the output layer and every neuron has a state number assigned to it.

The states of all the neurons are remembered. At the output of the layered perceptron the result is "what you get." This is compared to "what you want" and the error is computed from the difference.[16] The error at the output then flows in a wave backwards from the output to the input. This is the source of the term *error backpropagation*. While the error wave flows backwards, each neuron is assigned a second error number called its *delta value*. Now every neuron has two numbers assigned to it: its state and its delta value.

Here's the beauty of error backpropagation. Each weight in the neural network can be updated only knowing the numbers of the two neurons it connects. The multiplication of the state of one neuron by the delta value of the other is sufficient to tweak the connecting weight so that, next time, "what we get" is closer to "what we want." Error backpropagation is mathematically beautiful.

This is a big deal. Recall Hebbian learning where weights between two neurons were only determined by the degree the two neurons simultaneously fired—"Neurons that fire together wire together." This is not exactly what is happening in error backpropagation, but it's similar in that weights are tweaked only as a result of numbers associated with the two connected neurons. This is a highly satisfying result for neurologists and psychologists like error backpropagation popularizer David Rumelhart.

In biology, one interconnect weight in a neural network will not directly know what another weight is doing unless there is a communication path going through numerous neurons. There is no overseer that views all the weights and, based on this global knowledge, provides updates to all the weights. The weights only know what is happening locally, and locally the only thing happening is the action of the two connected neurons. This is the same thing that happens in error backpropagation training of layered perceptrons. In this narrow sense, the neurons in human brains and the "neurons" in algorithmic neural networks are indeed alike.

Computer scientists and engineers, though, have no reason to be constrained by the biologically friendly updates provided by error back-propagation. Other effective tweaking techniques can be used to update a weight as a function of another far-removed neuron or weight. Many training algorithms have been proposed and used that require other than local information. Error backpropagation, though, has made resurgence in the training of deep learning convolutional neural networks where the number of weights are so large that dealing with neurons two at a time is more efficient than any training that requires global knowledge of everything prior to updating.

There are numerous generalizations of error backpropagation. Those interested in learning more or in wading through the beautiful math might want to take a look at the MIT Press book *Neural Smithing* by Russ Reed and me.[17]

Exponential Interest

LARGELY DUE to Hopfield's evangelical zeal and the development of the layered perceptron, interest in neural networks swelled in the engineering and computer science communities. A key by-invitation-only conference dedicated to neural networks was held in 1986 at Snowbird, Utah, and was attended by the top researchers in the field. An open neural network conference, held the following year, attracted thousands of technical attendees from industry and academia. The sponsoring organization was the IEEE Neural Networks Council (NNC). IEEE, pronounced "eye triple e," stands for the *Institute of Electrical and Electronic Engineers*. It is the largest professional society in the world, with over 400,000 members. IEEE is carved up into several specialties, including computer science, power, cybernetics, signal processing, and electronics. With the Neural Networks Council, IEEE designated a specific spot for neural networks. I was elected Secretary of the NNC and, when the committee chair resigned in 1988, I became the chair. Another independent professional organization, the International Neural Network Society (INNS) was formed at the same time. Neural network pioneer Bernard Widrow was its first president.

The first large open neural network conference was titled "The IEEE International Conference on Neural Networks." The conference continues to this day but has been renamed the "International Joint Conference on Neural Networks" because it is now sponsored by both the IEEE and the INNS.

As you might guess from all these conferences and new organizations, the hype curve for neural networks went vertical in the mid 1980s. The media took notice. Headlines screamed:

- "First Annual ICNN Meeting Will Draw 2,000 or More to San Diego"
- "Nerves of Silicon: Design of Neural-Network Computers Are Trying to Capture the Most Ordinary–And Elusive–Powers of the Human Brain"
- "A Long-Existing Goal of Computer Science Is Met by Neurocomputers That Learn"
- "Changing Synapses: Teaching Old Neurons New Tricks"
- "Institute Gathering Demystifies Neural Networks: IEEE Puts Neural Nets into Focus"

Government-funded researchers climbed on board. Other headlines read:

- "Lockheed Targets Neural Networks"
- "European Community Begins Esprit II Neural Network Program"
- "Japanese Developing a Thinking Computer"

As neural networks climbed the hype curve in the technical journals, there were some useful applications reduced to practice. And there were some silly ones, which we'll talk about first.

Early Hype

HERE ARE some curious uses of neural networks reported during the excitement period of the early layered perceptron. Like many headlines we see today, they are hype.

Did Family Bowlers Elect Bill Clinton?

The United States presidential campaign in 1996 was between incumbent Bill Clinton and Senator Bob Dole. Dole's right arm and back had been riddled with machine-gun fire when he was a soldier in Italy during World War II. His right arm was visibly useless. Bill Clinton, by contrast, was famous for playing saxophone on the Arsenio Hall show and participating in the fall of American morality with a well-publicized indiscretion with a White House intern. The Clinton campaign bought into neural network hype and enlisted the help of a neural network hypester we will call Barnum.

I know a former employee of Barnum who calls Barnum a compulsive liar and says Barnum would stand in a torrential downpour and declare it a sunshiny day. I have spoken to a Department of Defense engineer who says dealing with Barnum left a vile sour taste in his mouth about neural networks. Barnum funded his neural network company with numerous small federal grants.

The Bill Clinton campaign asked Barnum to crunch some data to help Clinton win his second term in the White House. We quote from the late syndicated columnist Robert Novak, who reported the story February 18, 1996: "President Clinton's pollsters have identified the voters who will determine whether he will be elected to a second term: two-parent families whose members bowl for recreation. Using a technique they call the 'neural network,' Clinton advisors contend that these family bowlers are quintessential undecided voters. Therefore, these are the people who must be targeted by the president."[18]

I am not privy to the details of the neural network used to finger the bowling family voting block. The claim has the feeling of careless hand-waving bordering on the ludicrous.

Novak, a conservative opposed to Clinton's election, ended with a snarky footnote: "Two decades ago, Illinois Democratic Gov. Dan Walker campaigned heavily in bowling alleys in the belief he would find swing voters there. Walker had national political ambitions but ended up in federal prison."

Bill Clinton was elected to a second term as United States president. The questionable role of family bowlers in Clinton's reelection was never explored. It was too silly an explanation.

Can Neural Networks Prevent Riots?

Here's another story about Bill Clinton and neural networks.

The 1996 Democratic National Convention that nominated Bill Clinton for president was held in Chicago. Twenty-four years earlier, in 1968, the Democrats also held their national convention in Chicago, and it was a disaster. To prevent a repeat, the Internal Affairs Department of the Chicago Police Department turned to neural networks for help.

Why was the 1968 Democratic National Convention such a disaster? That was a volatile year. A few months before the convention, civil rights leader Martin Luther King, Jr., was assassinated, as was presidential hopeful Bobby Kennedy. (Kennedy's assassination opened the way for the nomination of the sitting vice president, Hubert Humphrey, who ultimately lost the election to Republican Richard Nixon.)

Then there were the Yippie protests, which were everywhere in 1968. Anarchist Yippies were amusingly dangerous. They spread their strange brand of chaos by giving away free bologna sandwiches outside of thousand-dollars-per-plate political fundraisers. From the spectator balcony of the New York Stock Exchange, Yippies mockingly showered traders with fluttering dollar bills, hoping to show that the traders below on the floor were greedy. They were. Some traders scrambled and grabbed for the floating bills and were mocked by the Yippies. Yippies protested Vietnam. Yippies also spread rumors that smoking dried banana peels could get you high. The pop singer Donovan popularized the rumor with his hit *Mellow Yellow*, which included the line "electrical banana is gonna be a sudden craze."

What motivated the Yippies? The same thing that motivated Marlon Brando's character in the 1953 motorcycle outlaw gang classic *The Wild One*. Asked what he was rebelling against, he replied, "Whadaya got?"

The Yippies brought their antics to the 1968 Democratic National Convention and contributed to loud noisy protests against the Vietnam War and various other things. They decided to nominate a 145-pound pig for president, naming him "Pigasus the Immortal" and saying, "They nominate a president and he eats the people. We nominate a president and the people eat him." (Pigasus was confiscated when his backers were arrested for disorderly conduct. Reportedly he was transferred to a farm.[19] His ultimate fate remains unknown.)

The Yippie protesters at the 1968 Chicago convention butted heads with political strongman and Chicago mayor legend Richard J. Daley. Daley thought the protestors fouled his city, and he released his police department like a pack of attack dogs. On the streets outside of Chicago's International Amphitheatre, where the Democratic convention was being held, there were violent clashes between the protestors and the Chicago police.[20] Blood was shed. Protestors and police officers alike were injured. More than 650 protestors were arrested. A presidential commission later called the conflict a "police riot," though the commission did state that most officers had behaved responsibly.

So, yes. The Democrats of 1996 wanted to avoid a repeat of 1968.

In 1996 Richard J. Daley was no longer mayor, but his son Richard M. Daley was. What could be done to assure there was no repeat of the "police riot"?

Enter the neural network. The task of the neural network was to identify bad cops who might become enraged and start cracking skulls. The neural network was trained using data from 12,500 police officers. They were compared to about two hundred officers who had previously

192 / Non-Computable You /

been dismissed or who had resigned under investigation. The charges of troubled cops in the database ranged from insubordination to criminal misconduct.

After the neural network was trained with historical data, a total of ninety-one of the 12,500 currently serving Chicago police officers were identified as potential risks by the neural network. Those identified were asked to enroll in a counseling program.

But the union representing the police officers did not like the decree and challenged it in court. The objection raised by the police union remains a weakness of neural networks even to this day: the neural network is basically a black box. When the computer programmer was asked why a cop was classified as a bad cop, the only explanation was "because I trained the neural network to detect bad cops and the neural network did what I trained it to do." That's apparently not a good enough legal reason. Specifics must be cited, like "The officer regularly attends dog fights" or "The police officer we fingered as dangerous regularly beats her husband." The trained neural networks couldn't give officer-specific reasons.

The generic neural network lacks what is called an *explanation facility*, which assigns reasons as to why a conclusion is reached. Although there is some research into constructing explanation facilities for neural networks, the layered perceptron and the convolutional neural network used in deep learning remain fundamentally black boxes.

All the fuss about the 1996 Democratic National Convention was much ado about nothing. Key Yippies were out of commission—Jerry Rubin died in 1994, Abbie Hoffman committed suicide in 1989, and Tom Hayden (after divorcing Jane Fonda) served in the California State Senate. The Vietnam War was long over and there seemed to be nothing much to protest, except Bill Clinton's extramarital affairs. So insofar as the 1996 Democratic National Convention was concerned, all went smoothly—even though the neural network results were ignored by legal decree.

Reduction to Practice

Now LET's talk about some success stories. The first AI wave in the 1960s gave us a method to equalize phone lines for modem and fax transmission. Widrow's ADALINE was used in the supersonic trans-Atlantic Concorde aircraft. The second wave of AI in the 1990s also spawned technologies that were reduced to practice.

Power to the People

To schedule generation of electricity, your power company likes to forecast future demand. If a forecast overestimates demand, the power company has to sell any excess power it generates at whatever price the power market says. If future power usage is underestimated, the power company must buy power at whatever the market price is. Removing this uncertainty is good.

I'm not an expert in power, but in 1991 I was able to team with some of the best power engineers in the country. That's the way some great research gets done. Experts from orthogonal fields get together and do great things.

Our goal was to train a neural network to forecast power usage. The historical data we used to train the neural network came from the Puget Power and Light Company in Seattle. Prior to neural networks, the power forecast for that region was performed by a Puget Power employee name Lloyd. To estimate the power demand for the next day, Lloyd looked at the day of the week, the current temperature, the forecasted temperature, and some other relevant variables. He then placed his moistened finger into the air, furrowed his brow, thought hard, and announced his forecast.

My colleagues and I first applied the layered perceptron to forecasting the load demand for power companies in 1991.[21] Six years later neural networks were being used by thirty-two major North American utilities.[22]

The neural network forecasting did the same thing as Lloyd, except more methodologically. We had gobs of historical data from Puget Power. From Mondays past, for example, we knew power usage, times, and temperatures. We also knew the temperature forecasts for Tuesday. So the input to the neural network was all the data we knew on Monday, and the output was the Tuesday power forecast. We also trained the same neural network for data from the other days of the week. Like the pod in *Invasion of the Body Snatchers*, the neural network soon morphed into a system with a similar input-output relationship as the training data. Once trained, the neural network, when presented today's information about time, power, and temperature, will output a forecast of what happens tomorrow. The neural network worked and worked well.

Our paper was not the first used to forecast using neural networks. We've mentioned Bernie Widrow's use of ADALINE to forecast weather in the 1960s. For power load forecasting, the technique used in our paper has been tweaked, addended, and expanded numerous times by others. Our paper has been referenced over 1,700 times by those expanding or improving on our initial effort.[23]

Our paper on power load forecasting was not well written. But it was the first on the topic. My wife's grandfather often quipped, "If I knew I was going to live this long, I would have taken better care of myself." In hindsight, if I'd known our paper would be cited so often, I'd have spent more time polishing it. Even now, three decades after its publication, somebody somewhere references our paper on average more than once a week.

Robert Hecht-Nielsen Checks Your Wallet

A leader in the second wave of AI popularity was Robert Hecht-Nielsen. Hecht-Nielsen held an adjunct professorship at the University of California, San Diego. He co-organized the first few major conferences on neural networks in the late 1980s and was a prolific contributor to the field. Hecht-Nielsen Corporation (HNC) specialized in the application of AI to financial fraud. When you swiped your credit card at 7-11, HNC software cataloged the transaction and checked for fraud.

I acted as an expert witness for HNC in a patent conflict. The software they used was before kick-ass computers. One of my jobs was to examine HNC code. Did you know that you can subtract the zip code of one town from that of another to get a rough estimate of the east-to-west separation of the locations? One of New York City's zip codes is 10001; Chicago's is 60007; LA's is 90001. The further west you go in the continental United States, the bigger the zip codes. Before more powerful computers, this was one of the metrics used by HNC software. Credit card transactions occurring close together in time but separated in distance raised one of many flags monitored by the HNC credit fraud code.

Fair Isaac sounds like a character in a Charles Dickens novel, but is in fact a large financial company named after its two founders.[24] The first two letters in the acronym FICO, as in your FICO score, are for Fair Isaac. HNC Software was sold to Fair Isaac in 2006 in an $810 million deal.[25] Robert Hecht-Nielsen reduced his AI to practice very successfully and was rewarded handsomely for his success.

I received an unexpected phone call from Robert a few years after the Fair Isaac deal. He'd had a near-death experience that transformed him spiritually. I never shy away from confessing my faith professionally when appropriate, and Robert knew I was a Christian. That's why he called me. He wanted to share the joy of his spiritual transformation. Robert, now rich and free, was flying his own plane around the world living a full life in the peace he had found. He passed away in 2019 and would be the first to say he couldn't take his millions with him. Nor, because of his transformative experience, did he care.

Based on impact, Robert Hecht-Nielsen was by far the most successful individual to reduce neural networks to practice in the second wave of AI popularity.

Enter Fuzzy Systems

FUZZY LOGIC jumped aboard the neural network hype bandwagon as a technique to implement simple expert systems. Yes, believe it or not, "fuzzy" is an oft-used technical term giving rise to other curious terms such as "fuzzification" and "defuzzification."

During a 2000 presidential campaign debate, Republican George W. Bush dissed Democratic candidate Al Gore's economic plan as "fuzzy math." I was listening to the debate in my office, and I recall looking at my bookshelf at a book titled *Introduction to Fuzzy Arithmetic*. The book was a serious scholarly treatment of performing arithmetic operations on uncertain numbers. Addition, for example, is performed using a complex mathematical operation called convolution. This wasn't, of course, what Bush meant.

Fuzzy arithmetic is a well-defined discipline in mathematics. It is built on the idea of fuzzy sets. The application is so broad that journals and international conferences are still exclusively dedicated to the topic. Fuzzy logic and fuzzy arithmetic are based on fuzzy sets.

Here's how it works. In regular or Boolean set theory, an object is either a member of a set or isn't. Ants and beetles are members of the set of all insects. Elephants and anteaters are not. What, then, do we say about the set of tall men? Is a man measuring six feet in height in the set of tall men? In a way, yes. Certainly a man seven feet tall is *more* a member of the set of tall men than is a six-footer. Someone who is five foot eleven would rank lower in the set of tall men, though he'd still be partially in the set.

That's the idea of fuzzy sets. Something isn't totally within the set or external to the set. There are, rather, degrees of membership.

Fuzzy set membership is used any time a judge at an athletic event gives a heuristic judgment call. After ice-skating performances there is a ranking of how well the skaters performed. Judges offer a number from one to ten based on their opinion of the performance. The numbers are combined for an aggregate score. Each judge's scores are often not the same, but that's okay. The mathematics of fuzzy logic takes care of that.

For the set of tall men, the key word is "tall." "Tall" is called a *fuzzy linguistic variable*. Your idea about the membership of a six-footer in the

set of tall men might be different from mine. I might say the membership is 70 percent and you might say 75 percent. But this difference does
not prohibit you and me from talking about tall men. Indeed, we communicate using fuzzy linguistic variables all the time.

Fuzzy linguistic terms include ugly, hot, cold, fat, shiny, long, short,
beautiful, fast, faster, slow, slower, hot, cold, smart, dumb, and thirsty.
In each case, we define a fuzzy set. For example, consider the set of "hot
foods" in terms of temperature. You and I might differ in the exact numerical estimate of membership, but our relative rankings would be the
same. Both you and I would have a larger membership in the set of hot
foods for freshly brewed coffee than we would for ice cream straight
out of the freezer. Given a list of foods, our specific membership might
differ. But if we were to make a list of highest to lowest membership,
we would expect the lists would be in the same order or at least show a
strong resemblance.

The ranking of the performance measure of ice skaters to fuzzy
membership is straightforward. With a rating of one to ten, judges are
asking: What is the membership of the skaters in the set of perfect performances? In terms of percent, membership in a set ranges from 0 to
100 percent. When a judge gives a ruling of zero to ten, simply multiply
by ten to get the percentage. A judge's ruling of five out of ten becomes a
membership of 50 percent in the set of perfect performances. A perfect
score of ten translates to a membership of 100 percent. In ice skating,
a ranking of ten means total excellence. In fuzzy logic, the equivalent
membership 100 percent means the skaters are totally in the set of excellent skaters.

There is an old saying among statisticians: If you can't measure it,
you can't manage it. Fuzzy sets apply to measures that are not ordinal—
in other words, to measures you can't assign a numerical value to. Fuzzy
linguistic variables like "tall" and "fat" have numerical values of feet and
pounds to help with assignment of a fuzzy membership function. Non-
ordinals can't be numerically measured. Examples include beauty, pain

level, and cleverness. Things not ordinal can't be definitively measured but can be described using a fuzzy membership value.

Describing the membership of a three-year-old in the set of "cute three-year-olds" does not have an associated number to back the membership. The fuzzy membership is based solely on the heuristics of experience and judgment.

Pain is likewise not ordinal. Pain, as discussed in Chapter 1, is an example of qualia and thus non-computable. Pain is also a fuzzy linguistic variable. On Saturday, June 5, 2013, I was running and tripped on a teeny three-inch-wide, half-inch-deep sinkhole in the parking lot of The Coffee Shop in McGregor, Texas. My head was in front of my body as momentum pushed me forward. I tried to get my feet under my head. Unfortunately, I have a very large head not unlike Jack Box (sorry mom) and the faster I ran, the greater the horizontal distance between my head and my feet. Soon I was sprinting. I blocked my gravitationally induced transition from vertical to horizontal primarily with my right hand.

The collision was neither graceful nor elastic. I fortunately had the instinctual foresight to distribute the load of the impact to my right knee, right ribs, left hand, nose, and upper lip. When my nose first made contact with the concrete, my glasses escaped their perch and bounced a couple of feet beyond my head. They landed unscathed facing me and seemed to mock my newly sore ribs, skinned knee, two injured wrists, and freshly grated face. It was the first time I had ever felt contempt for the glasses.

I lay motionless on the parking lot taking inventory. Was I dizzy? No. Was I unconscious? I don't think so. Pain? Maybe. The assessment was mine because initially there was no one around to assist. Face down, spread-eagled, and lying still for a good half minute, I heard a woman's tiny voice from afar ask, "Are you okay?" Me kowtowing to a pair of glasses in an open parking lot apparently left her room for doubt. I slowly raised myself to my knees, then stood. A little dizzy. But okay as far as it goes. "Sure," I said in the most macho voice I could muster. Fortunately, my brother Ray was at The Coffee Shop. I told him I was fine and just needed my overstuffed Lazy Boy, a Diet Dr Pepper, and a Tylenol. My wrist heard the exchange and protested. It communicated in Morse code using intense short and long throbs. So brother Ray drove me to the Hillcrest Hospital emergency room. We walked in, registered, and were ushered to an examination room.

After the paperwork, the first guy I met was a medical technician. He asked me on a scale of one to ten how much pain I felt. Aha! A fuzzy non-ordinal linguistic variable!

I told him eight, which meant I was 80 percent in the set of maximal pain. With the technician was a mobile aluminum pole on wheels where IVs are hung. There were some strange-looking things like inverted hollow cow nipples hanging on strings, and a long thin bag on which "10 pounds" was written. Have you ever played with Chinese finger traps as a child? The Chinese finger traps are long tubes in which you stick your fingers, usually the pointer fingers on both hands. Then when you pull the tube, it squeezes tighter around both your fingers and you are trapped. That's what the inverted nipples were. They were open on one end only.

There were numerous hanging nipples of all sizes. Little fingers, big fingers, and just right fingers. The technician found some inverted nipples that looked like they would fit my fingers. My middle finger and the finger next to my pinky were inserted. As I lay reclined, my arm was hanging with my elbow at 90 degrees in midair, supported by my two digits pulling against the one-sided Chinese finger traps. To increase the tension the ten-pound weight was placed across my bicep. This made the downward pressure on my fingers even more intense. Oh my goodness. It felt wonderful! The throbbing diminished and the pain took a break. When asked, I told the technician the pain had gone down to two on a scale of ten. The technician explained to me that the muscles around my broken wrist were trying to adapt. The downward pull in my fingers aligned my wrist and placed less stress on my muscles to conform to a new and novel bone geometry.

I hoped my wrist was not broken. But the doctor came in, felt about, and announced I did have a broken wrist. In rolled the mobile x-ray apparatus. My wrist was x-rayed from the side and from the top. After x-ray development, the doctor reentered and said he had to set the bone. I had heard the phrase "set the bone" numerous times before—mostly on TV. But never again will I underestimate the pain associated with such an act. If your bone breaks and is no longer aligned, mechanical force must be applied to align the bones. The doctor first gave me a shot of some numbing agent in my joint at the break. He grabbed my wrist and began feeling my bones through my skin. I thought he was setting the bone and told him the shot had really worked—there was next to no pain. Then came the unannounced bone alignment jerk. In hindsight I should have asked for a stick on which to bite. Man did it hurt. I turned to the technician and through clenched teeth muttered "TEN!"

Pain on a scale of one to ten is an effective non-ordinal measurable by fuzzy membership functions.

As seen when talking to a doctor about pain, we communicate effectively using fuzzy linguistic variables. Or consider the problem of backing a car into a parking space. A computer-based instruction might be "back up at a speed of two miles per hour for seven feet. Then linearly decelerate to a speed of zero for four feet." But this is not the way we do it. Suppose I'm the driver and you're standing outside watching the car as I back in. Your instructions would sound like, "Come on back. A bit faster. Okay. Start slowing down. Slower, slower, stop!" (In my native West Virginia, "come on back" is pronounced "mon-back.") Notice the use of fuzzy linguistic variables in the instructions—faster, slow down, slower. In these instructions, it doesn't matter that your membership in the fuzzy linguistic variable "slower" is not the same as mine. In fact, numbers aren't even considered in the set of instructions. All that is required is a general agreement on the meaning of the fuzzy linguistic variables.

The idea of fuzzy sets was introduced in 1965 in a seminal paper by UC Berkeley electrical engineer Lotfi Zadeh.[26] Zadeh was an affable, energetic man who relished the success of his founding of fuzzy logic. Until his death in 2017 at the age of ninety-three, Zadeh traveled across the globe accepting awards and giving keynote talks at conferences. I once edited a book of fuzzy logic[27] and asked Zadeh to write a foreword. His response was "I always say yes."[28]

Zadeh chose the term "fuzzy" to describe his mathematics. His choice was not without consequence. To soften the negative reaction to the word "fuzzy," some literature began to refer to the field in other terms like "soft logic." Nevertheless, Zadeh defended his choice of the term "fuzzy" to the very end, even though it caused image problems for the field.

Zadeh's choice of the term "fuzzy" caused me problems. While at the University of Washington, I did a lot of work with Boeing. Boeing research had a big footprint in Seattle. The engineering team I worked with was concerned with airplane anti-skid and automatic braking systems. Boeing's legacy anti-skid and automatic braking systems were described to me as mechanistic. The basic systems had small faults, so they were updated over the years with various Band-Aid fixes. My team of cutting-edge Boeing engineers formulated a new simple and highly effective replacement expert system based on fuzzy logic. A detailed fuzzy system hardware mock-up was shown to outperform the systems currently used. For future airplanes, use of fuzzy seemed to be a no-brainer.

But when the engineers ran the idea up the management flagpole, the idea was nixed. The fuzzy solution was DOA. Why? A Boeing engineer told me that top management felt their customers would not want to ride on airplanes whose automatic braking and anti-skid systems were based on "fuzzy logic." Boeing management was unfortunately interpreting the word "fuzzy" the same way George W. Bush did when he called Al Gore's economic policy "fuzzy math."

Hey, at least Zadeh's choice of the term "fuzzy" cannot be accused of seductive semantics.

I lost contact with the status of Boeing's anti-skid and automatic braking systems. I admit to not even thinking about such things when flying on Boeing planes today. Whatever is there seems to work well.

Fuzzy Applications

Fuzzy logic expert systems emerged as an application-rich approach for AI control.[29] Consider a washing machine with two sensors. One sensor shines a light through the wash water to a simple photoreceptor. If the water is dirty, not a lot of light gets through. If the water is clear, a lot of light gets through. This simple light detection system measures how dirty the water is. A fancy word for the measure is the water's *turbidity*. A second sensor measures how heavy the wash load is. The weight and the water turgidity are the inputs, or antecedents, to controlling how long to wash the clothes. The output, or consequent, is how long to wash the clothes. The idea is similar to a neural network where input data gives some result at the output. For the neural network, the mapping from input to output is determined by training data. For the fuzzy system, the mapping is determined by coding an expert system using fuzzy logic. After establishing the fuzzy expert system, the input-output relationship might not be close to that desired. The fuzzy system can then be tuned using a training algorithm to give results closer to those desired.

It doesn't take a genius to figure out the rules for washing clothes. For example, one rule would be, "If the water is highly turbid and the load is heavy, then wash the clothes for a very long time." Note the fuzzy linguistic variables: highly, heavy, and a very long time.

To have a complete set of rules, all contingencies would need to be covered. Another contingency might be, "If the water is highly turbid, and the load weight is medium, then wash for a long time." Since the weight has changed from the first rule from "heavy" to "medium," the consequent has changed from "a very long time" to "a long time." An exhaustive list of all these fuzzy if-then rules is required to cover all possibilities. Suppose the turbidity is described by three linguistic variables: lightly turgid, medium turgid, and highly turgid. If the laundry weight were likewise described by the fuzzy linguistic variables light, medium, and heavy, then a total of nine fuzzy if-then rules describe all possible contingencies. Each contingency must be assigned a fuzzy consequent describing how long the clothes need washing. An example of fuzzy linguistic variables for the consequent might be a very short time, a short time, a medium amount of time, a long time, and a very long time.

There you have it! An expert system totally expressed in fuzzy if-then rules.

Lotfi Zadeh showed us how to express fuzzy linguistic variables using fuzzy membership function math that could be straightforwardly reduced to computer code. He also showed how to combine memberships using logic operations like "and" and "or." Notice the logical "and" in the rule, "If the water is highly turbid *and* the load is heavy..." Two fuzzy linguistic variables need to be combined using what is known as a fuzzy "and" operation. Zadeh showed how to do this in his seminal 1965 paper. When done, the results of all the if-then rules must be reduced to a single member. Specifically, how long the clothes are washed. This is the output consequence of the fuzzy control system. This was figured out by Ebrahim Mamdani and S. Assilian[30] about a decade after the first publication of Zadeh's 1965 paper.

The bottom line is this. Writing out fuzzy if-then rules can be straightforwardly intuitive. Once written down, Zadeh, Mamdani, and Assilian have given us the mathematics to reduce the linguistics to computer code. It could be that the initial attempt at codifying the if-then rules doesn't work out exactly as desired. That's okay. All design, including the design of fuzzy control systems, is iterative. The designer can tweak the contributing parameters. Perhaps the membership of one or more of the fuzzy linguistic variables needs to be increased or decreased.

Alternatively, if the desired system performance can be defined beforehand, the parameters of the fuzzy system can be tuned automatically using procedures like those used in training neural networks. The desired system performance is the "what we want" part of neural network type training. The parameters of the fuzzy system are adapted until the fuzzy system output, the "what we get," matches "what we want."

The washing machine timing example we explained is easy to set up. Another fuzzy expert system can be designed to determine other operations such as how much laundry soap to add. For example, "If the water is highly turbid and the laundry weight is very heavy, then add a lot of laundry soap."

Reduce these fuzzy linguistic variables to computer code using Zadeh's mathematics, tune the result, and you have a great expert system to run your washing machine.

Analytic Clowns and Fuzzy Mimes

THE PARADIGM shift to fuzzy and neural systems was not without resistance. Many applications of fuzzy AI were in the area of control theory. The washing machine is an example of controlling washing time given sensor inputs of laundry weight and water turbidity. Classic control theory was anything but linguistic. Journals published highly theoretical articles on control theory; many of these papers are so esoteric they will never find any real-world application. Undergraduate engineers are still taught sophisticated mathematics using impressive-sounding tools like Laplace transforms and solution of simultaneous differential equations. Then along comes simple fuzzy logic control that translates control linguistics used by humans to perform control theory. Some of the entrenched classic control theorists were outraged.

Piero Bonissone, PhD, a chief scientist at GE Global Research, was involved in the fuzzy redesign of General Electric appliances such as washers and dryers. He tells about being approached by an academic who suggested that conventional classic control could accomplish fuzzy design's goals in a possibly more efficient way. Bonissone recognized—

rightly—that arguing with academics with no skin in the game can often be futile. So instead of engaging, he deflected with the equivalent of a skillful judo move and replied, "Hey, that's great! Why don't you go do it?" (The academic didn't.)

Among the fuzzy logic naysayers was Australian professor Bob Bitmead, who liked classic mathy control and disliked AI. At the peak of the fuzzy AI hype curve, he conveyed his disdain of fuzzy systems in no uncertain terms: "The image that is portrayed is of the ability to perform magically well by the incorporation of 'new age' technologies of fuzzy logic, neural networks, expert systems, approximate reasoning, and self-organization.... This is pure unsupported claptrap which is pretentious and idolatrous in the extreme, and has no place in the scientific literature."[31]

In our running analogy, Bob Bitmead was one of the classic control clowns attacking the fuzzy mimes of AI. Both were trying to supply the world with effective control technology, but one did not like the cut of the other's jib.

One of the AI mimes under Bitmead's attack, fuzzy control pioneer Mamdani, countered.[32] He noted that fuzzy AI solutions were unduly criticized by those in the "cult of analyticity" who swore any contribution to control theory must be described by sophisticated mathematics. Professor Bitmead was apparently in that cult, and his cult was found to be misguided. Fuzzy technology has been reduced to practice.

Reduction to Practice

As WE have seen, arguments about technology are often solved by reduction to practice. When the market makes use of technology, most arguments about the validity of this or that academic approach become moot.

In the AI boom of the 1990s, a wave of AI-based consumer products appeared on the open market in Japan. Many were later adapted worldwide by companies like GE. A partial list of such Japanese products from 1991 includes air conditioners, washing machines, vacuum cleaners, rice cookers, microwave ovens, clothes dryers, electric fans, and refrigerators.[33] All incorporated neural network and fuzzy logic AI components.

Recall that Bernie Widrow's ADALINE neural network was used in the supersonic Concorde passenger airplanes. In the second wave of AI, fuzzy AI was used in the US Space Shuttle's attitude control.[34] AI also found uses in industrial process control vehicular technology such as cruise control, motor control, bioengineering, and as we have discussed, power engineering. These were stairs in an ascending staircase of AI technology that, as we discuss next, continues to amaze.

9. AI Matures

Computers aren't intelligent, they only think they are.
—ATTRIBUTED TO COMEDIAN EMO PHILIPS

THE TERM AI IS USED A LOT IN THE MEDIA, BUT RARELY DEFINED. When it is defined, the definitions are often in conflict. In circles of scholars, disciplines such as artificial intelligence, computational intelligence, and machine intelligence are teased apart. But in the popular media, AI seems to be defined as any "gee whiz" application of computers that surprises and amazes. I like the "gee whiz" definition. It's a thread that connects all the definitions.

There are towers of AI accomplishment like Deep Blue's chess program, DeepMind's Alpha-Go, deep fakes, GTP writing prose, and the victory of IBM's Watson at *Jeopardy*. All these accomplishments were exciting at first. Now, in many cases, that initial "gee whiz" response has been numbed by familiarity. But for those of us who experienced the first unveilings of AI, remnants of the magic remain.

In this chapter, I reflect briefly on a few "gee whiz" highlights of AI's teenage growth spurt before moving into an examination of where it stands today.

Technical Nostalgia

MY GRANDPARENTS' generation was blown away by the introduction of the automobile, the talking motion picture, commercial air flight, electricity, air conditioning, and affordable motorcars. My generation takes such astonishing technology for granted.

Here, colored by some of my personal memories, are a few of the astonishing AI-related developments that today's generation takes for granted. These innovations have all happened in my lifetime and, upon reflection, still leave me in awe.

Dear Mom

Here's an old riddle that some youth today might not get: What starts with an e, ends with an e and contains one letter? The answer is (drum roll) an envelope.

When I was a boy, we took detailed lessons in how to write a letter. Where does the address go? In what order do you write the address elements? What are proper salutations? How should the letter be folded? Where does the stamp go on the envelope? Then along came email, which was amazing. Instant communication! No more shopping expeditions to collect paper, envelopes, and stamps. No more searching for a pen that worked.

I remember thinking how much simpler email was going to make life. How wrong I was.

Phone Home

A few decades ago Max Hitchens, a former engineering classmate of mine from Rose-Hulman, visited me in Seattle with a prototype of a cell phone. It was the size of a brick. He drove me to downtown Seattle and, while still in his car, I called my mother in Cleveland. This was mind blowing! I still remember the beginning of the conversation. "Mom! You won't believe where I'm calling you from!" At the time, calling Mom from home on a wired phone racked up big long-distance phone charges. Now long distance is no distance at all.

The magic of the cell phone is lost on today's generation. Like the opposable thumb, it's simply another appendage we take for granted.

Lost No More

I'm severely directionally challenged, and I don't know how I ever lived without GPS and Google maps. Think of the magic technology behind

GPS. From satellites orbiting Earth, GPS fingers your location. On your cell phone you enter where you want to go, and an algorithm in the cloud calculates the best route. The cell phone even talks to you, giving turn-by-turn instructions! Incredible when you think about it. GPS is among the few commonly used technologies that require Einsteinian relativity adjustments.

And yet I have become too familiar and unappreciative of this AI magic; I can become peeved if all this pinpointing and calculation doesn't happen in a few seconds.

Catch a Ride

Today I take an Uber from my home to the DFW airport because it's cheaper, more reliable, and more convenient than flying out of the unpredictable Waco airport to DFW. The service is taken for granted and I am no longer in awe of computers behind the business.

Happy with the convenience, I also don't tend to think about the way Uber and its imitators have threatened the livelihoods of many. Consider this: Taxi drivers in New York City at one time paid up to a million dollars for their medallions and the right to operate cabs in the city. Many cabbies borrowed from the bank to pay their fees. In London, cabbies must pass an extremely difficult test called The Knowledge, proving they know their way around the intricate and sprawling city. This grueling test requires years of study.[1]

Then Uber and LYFT changed the rules. Free from the regulations imposed on cab drivers, powered by GPS and cell phones, drivers in these new ride services have a definite edge over traditional cab drivers.

The *New York Times* reports that "in the past year and a half, eight professional drivers, including three taxi medallion owners, have died by suicide. Since 2016, over 950 taxi drivers have filed for bankruptcy."[2] Huge protests brought London traffic to a stop as cab drivers there protested Uber.[3] Uber currently operates in London but is heavily taxed.[4]

Disruptive AI is going to take us into a lot of troubled waters of this sort.

Goodbye Brick and Mortar

In the early '90s I did some expert witness work for a company called Neopath. The technical head of Neopath said there was this new web business called Amazon that sold books. He had just read a book titled *The History of Pi* and wanted to buy a copy for me. I gave him my address and watched him enter information on the Amazon website. I was astonished. The book selection on this new Amazon website was broader than Barnes & Noble, Borders Bookstore, and Waldenbooks combined.

Amazon has of course ballooned into a site where you can buy almost anything. Today I use it weekly and get prompt delivery. This is incredible technology except for the annoying part where Amazon tries to analyze me and pitch products.

Today most of us take Amazon for granted. Gone are the days when finding a particular book required physically searching through libraries and bookstores.

Talk to Me

When I broke my wrist and couldn't type, I purchased Dragon voice recognition software. Stanford's Bernie Widrow trained a voice recognition system in the 1960s that typed spoken words into a microphone. Today's technology is far better but still has a long way to go. AI still has no common sense and has a rough time with homonyms. "But it's not!" from the mouth comes out as "But it's snot" on the computer screen. If you've ever used voice-to-text dictation on your cell phone, you've no doubt experienced similar problems.

Speaking of speaking, Alexa and Google Home are impressive but amusingly dumb. I recently asked Alexa to play "I'll Do Anything for Love" by Meatloaf. It kept playing a redo of the rock classic; no matter what I said, I could not budge Alexa off its decision.

Some of the jokes generated by Alexa are pretty good, though. And Siri has proven to be a boon to kids with autism, who can practice conversations with the technology. It requires them to speak clearly; and, as one researcher put it, "Humans are not patient. Machines are very, very patient." One mother says that her son's "practice conversations with Siri are translating into more facility with actual humans."[5]

Again, this voice recognition technology is nowadays taken for granted.

Entertainment at Your Fingertips

Streamed media remains jaw-dropping to me. My brother Ray spent years collecting every recording in history that appeared in Billboard's charts. Along comes Spotify and, except for the market value of the physical recordings, my brother's effort has little musical worth.

When I was a boy my friend Art Porrello had an uncle who belonged to a movie club that swapped classic celluloid reels among members. I once went to Art's house to watch the classic Hollywood movie *King Kong*. Even with the projector clunking away in the background, I remember what a wonderful experience this was. We stopped the movie in the middle for a bathroom break. What a treat! I couldn't stop a movie at the theater. I wanted to be a member of this movie-swapping club when I grew up.

Television likewise required exercising bladder control until the next set of commercials. Now, with Amazon video, nearly every movie ever made is available instantaneously for a small fee. And I can pause it any time I want.

I now take the service for granted.

Trivia Titan

When a question arises in a conversation and no one knows the answer, I pull out my cell phone and announce, "Fortunately, I have all the world's knowledge at my fingertips. Let's find out the answer." I then do a Google search.

While going to graduate school, I spent hours in the library looking for journal papers. I have pulled a bound volume of journals down from the library stacks and flipped to the article I wanted, only to discover some lazy jerk has ripped the entire paper from the volume. No more!

Everything in my university library and more is at my fingertips on a cell phone.

I haven't been inside a library for twenty years.

Hello, World!

The comic strip detective Dick Tracy was introduced in the 1930s. Dick Tracy used a wristwatch that shared real time images during phone calls. Tracy's wristwatch was a prophecy of Skype, Zoom, and the other real time video we have today. I've had Zoom calls from Texas to Nigeria, Scotland, Australia, Sweden, and Indonesia. I continue to be amazed that this can be done with almost no delay.

Building on the Past

EVEN WITH all this technology behind us and taken for granted, we are still awestruck with new advances in computer technology. It's interesting to note, however, that contemporary accomplishments of trained AI, such as neural networks, that get celebrated in the media often are related to algorithms formulated way back in the 1960s and before, but which can now be effectively implemented. Faster computers, instant communication, and more memory allow neural networks and related AI to be trained more quickly. The increased speed of computers made possible smart exploration of large databases stored in the bowels of cyberspace.

Looking into Deep Blue's Eyes

The first big news story of modern AI is IBM's Deep Blue. Russian Gary Kasparov was indisputably the world's chess champ. Except for three months, he ranked the number one chess player in the world for nineteen years, ending with his 2005 retirement. Deep Blue first beat Kasparov on February 10, 1996, and later defeated him in match play in May 1997.[6] The world was astonished.

Deep Blue's playing strategy was not new. It was a suggested strategy for winning at chess by Bell Lab's Claude Shannon, who is more famous for founding the field of information theory in 1948.[7] (Application of Shannon's genius theory allows today's cell phones to work so well.)

In 1950, Shannon published a paper entitled "Programming a Computer for Playing Chess."[8] The strategy proposed by Shannon, called minimax, was simple in concept. First, the current chessboard layout is assessed and the worst damage your opponent can do is identified. Then, from the options available, the move that minimizes the worst-case scenario is chosen. In other words, you want to minimize the maximum damage. Hence the term minimax. Often the number of cases to be considered becomes prohibitively large to look at all worst cases, so methods have been developed to only look at the most suspected worst cases.

To demonstrate his chess playing theory, Shannon invented a device in 1948 that could handle up to six chess pieces. One hundred and fifty relay operations were required to complete a move and required ten to fifteen seconds to compute.[9] In 1997, algorithm polishing and faster electronics used Shannon's minimax approach to eventually beat the world chess champion.[10]

More modern breakthroughs in AI already discussed include generative adversarial networks, or GANs, and the writer of short bursts of coherent prose, GPT. Two other remarkable AI algorithms are deep convolutional neural networks and reinforcement learning. We discuss them next.

Deep Convolutional Neural Networks

ONE MAJOR leap contemporary artificial intelligence has made is in the area of deep learning. Deep learning generates astonishing results. Modern deep convolutional neural networks[11] are a clever generalization of the layered perceptron popularized in the late 1980s.

With the traditional layered perceptron, features of training data had to be used to train the neural network. Early neural nets could only handle a few inputs, so outstanding features needed to be identified to limit the number of inputs. For example, two good features to differentiate between sumo wrestlers and basketball players are height and weight.

This changed with deep learning. The deep convolutional neural network allows classification of sumo wrestlers and basketball players using raw pixels from pictures of sumo wrestlers and basketball players. Instead of only two features (height and weight) thousands of inputs can be handled. Each pixel is an input.

Looking at how nature uses raw pixels for classification can help explain this process. In the mid 1980s I attended a workshop of optical computing practitioners and entomologists (bug scientists). There I learned about a fascinating property of the dragonfly. Dragonflies have extraordinary color vision,[12] but sometimes the enormity of data can be overwhelming. So dragonflies have a hierarchical system whereby, one step at a time, unneeded information is discarded. Eventually a binary sensor tells the dragonfly whether the light it sees is polarized or not. Light reflecting from water is polarized, so the dragonfly knows it is hovering above water if the detected light is polarized. If the light is not polarized, the dragonfly knows it is over land. This remarkable feature of discarding unusable information is hardwired into the dragonfly's physiology.

The categorization of information as useful or not useful is determined by the ultimate goal of the information discarding process. For the dragonfly, the ultimate goal is determining whether or not light was polarized.

Removal of unusable information is what neural networks do in general and what the deep learning convolutional neural networks do in particular. Scads of pictures of sumo wrestlers and basketball players are shown to the deep neural network. The neural network is told to discard all the information not relevant to the identification of a picture as a sumo wrestler or a basketball player. All other information, like the background in the picture or the image's contrast, is not useful and is ideally discarded.

This is useful stuff. However, research has now exposed fundamental limitations of deep convolutional neural networks. The Peak of Hype on the hype curve has been reached and enthusiasm for convolutional neural networks is on its way down. It remains to be seen how deep the dive will be and where opinion will plateau. There are niche applications of deep convolutional neural networks, but dreams of more universal application are being crushed. Below are a couple reasons why.

The Curse of Dimensionality

One fundamental issue constraining AI is the curse of dimensionality.

A neural network or any regression machine requires tagged data. Inputs of features of sumo wrestlers must be tagged "Sumo Wrestler" and basketball players tagged "Basketball Player." If we use athlete height and weight, the neural network uses two inputs. We can add a third feature, say annual income, and the number of inputs increases to three. As we will now illustrate, a rule of thumb says the amount of training data needed can increase exponentially with respect to the number of inputs. This is the so-called curse of dimensionality.[13]

Consider attempts to identify a prespecified short line segment inside a longer line segment. Visualize a short freshly painted stripe on a long asphalt strip of the same width. We can choose a point at random on the asphalt strip and ask, "Does this point lie on the part of the asphalt strip just painted?" If the point is inside the painted segment, we write an X. If outside the painted region but still on the longer road, we write an O. The more points we identify, the better the guess will be. There is no precise answer, but if the line segment is about a third the length of the longer line segment in which it is imbedded, let's say we need ten Xs and Os to estimate the location of the painted region.

The painted stripe example is functionally one-dimensional. For two dimensions and two inputs, imagine a circle inscribed inside a square. How many points do we have to know to see there is a circle inside a square? We need enough points to visually see that the underlying shape is a circle. The training data is, again, little Xs and little Os written within a square on a sheet of paper. The Xs and Os are randomly chosen. Little Xs are inside the circle and Os outside. How many Xs and Os are needed to see that the Xs roughly define the interior of a circle? Again, there is no right answer, but one hundred points sampled on the two-dimensional square seem reasonable.

For three dimensions, we have a sphere imbedded in a cube. The number of required X and O samples to recognize there is roughly a sphere inside a cube is clearly larger than the two-dimensional case. If we slice the cube into ten planes, we have ten circle problems each requiring a hundred samples. The three-dimensional sphere-in-a-box example therefore needs about a thousand samples.

There is enough here to see a trend. One input in one dimension requires ten samples, two dimensions require one hundred samples, and three need one thousand samples. The number of dimensions tells how many zeros there are after the one. Two dimensions require a one followed by two zeros. Three dimensions require a one followed by three zeros. In other words, a thousand samples. If there are nine inputs, a billion samples are needed. That's a one followed by nine zeros.

So in general, the more inputs there are to a neural network, the more data is needed, with the increase occurring exponentially.

The curse of dimensionality is only a rule of thumb and is not applicable when the target being learned has certain properties. When the shape within a box is not a circle but resembles a long-coiled snake with Xs inside the snake and Os outside, more samples will be needed to see the pattern of the snake. The data training set here must be much larger. Russ Reed and I used the spiral coil picture on the cover of our *Neural Smithing* book as an example of this difficult shape to learn.[14]

Visualizing hyperspheres in higher dimensions is difficult if not impossible. But we don't have to. We know by the pattern established that, in ten dimensions, the number of sample points required is one followed by ten zeros, or ten billion.

Deep convolutional neural networks have figured out how to learn directly from image pixels. Since the number of pixels in an image can number in the millions, it looks like the number of training examples would be on the order of one followed by a million zeros. Since one followed by eighty zeros is about the number of atoms in the universe, a million zeros looks to be insurmountable. The genius behind convolutional neural networks is avoidance of this problem. A much smaller set of pixels, called a window, is used to scan the image up and down and right to left, and the neural network trains how strongly each section of the image is connected to the smaller set of roaming pixels in the window. With some additional pixel pushing, this process is repeated again and again in different layers of the convolutional neural network. The curse of dimensionality in this case, it turns out, relates to the number of pixels in the windows and not the number of pixels in the image. The number of training examples needed to train the neural network is still very high but not anywhere near the colossal number required if every image pixel were supplied as an input.

The Problem of Sensitivity

Another major problem is sensitivity. The accuracy of some deep convolutional neural networks can be derailed by changing a handful of pixels on an image. In fact, a 2019 paper titled "One Pixel Attack for Fooling Deep Neural Networks"[15] showed that deep neural networks trained on popular databases can be fooled by changing only one pixel in an image.

This ill-conditioned property resident in some deep neural networks gives the military (and others) concern about developing deep neural networks. In his book *An Army of None*, Paul Scharre authoritatively explores use of AI in the military. He warns that in battle situations, deep neural networks can be gamed by the enemy to make the AI ineffective. "Deliberately feeding a machine false data to manipulate its behavior is known as a spoofing attack," Scharre writes, "and the current state-of-the-art image classifiers have known weakness to spoofing attacks that can be exploited by adversaries."[16]

Using such technology for actions based on autonomous target detection "could lead to tremendous harm," AI researcher Jeff Clune says.[17] Scharre explains, "An adversary could manipulate the [deep convolutional neural network] system's behavior, leading it to attack the wrong targets. If you're trying to classify, target, and kill autonomously with no human in the loop, then this sort of adversarial hacking could get fatal and tragic extremely quickly."[18]

Can this problem be overcome? We'll see. For now, as Scharre notes, "The vulnerability of deep neural nets to adversarial images is a major problem. In the near term, it casts doubt on the wisdom of using the current class of visual object recognition AIs for military applications—or for that matter any high-risk applications in adversarial environments."[19]

Testing the Black Box

Use of deep convolutional neural networks in the military is not verboten, however. Their use, as in the case of medical diagnosis, needs a human to verify the black box output. For instance, Scharre relates how a deep neural network trained in image recognition was able to locate a crashed helicopter. A human was needed to verify.

Trained neural networks are black boxes whose performance must always be verified. This is often done by testing whether the neural network has learned or memorized. This is accomplished by showing the trained neural network data not yet considered. Will the neural network respond correctly? Even though this process, called cross-validation, is necessary, it's not always sufficient.[20]

When assessed by an expert, the debunking of an AI program can sometimes occur immediately. I once served as a program co-chair for a conference titled Computational Intelligence for Financial Engineering.[21] The conference co-chair was John Marshall, who later became the world's first professor of financial engineering. Marshall was repeatedly approached by people who claimed they had trained an artificial neural network to successfully forecast the stock market from tick data. He told me he didn't even need to look at their computer code or results. He assessed the true success of their software with the simple question, "What kind of car do you drive?"

In other words, if they could predict the stock market with their software, they should be driving a Lamborghini. Maybe their neural network worked well with cross-validation data, but the true test is how the software performed when applied to the market in real time. The technology must be successful in field tests and when reduced to practice.

Other AI performance assessment requires closer, more in-depth scrutiny. There is a story that the Pentagon trained a neural network to determine whether there were enemy tanks in surveillance pictures.[22] Numerous photos with and without enemy tanks were collected. Not all the images were used to train the neural network. Some were set aside for cross-validation after the neural network was trained. The experiment was successful. The cross-validation worked and everyone was happy, until some spoiler noticed a deal breaker. All the pictures with tanks had been taken on a cloudy day and the tankless pictures on a sunny day. This included both training and cross-validation data. The neural network was not learning whether a tank was or was not present, but rather whether the sun was shining or not.

In engineering, we emphasize that for reduction to practice, field tests must be performed. If the cloud cover problem had not been identified in the lab, the tank-trained neural network would have performed poorly in field tests.

Similarly, robotics researcher Peter Haas recounts a confusion in a classifier that differentiates dogs from wolves using deep convolutional neural networks.[23] A husky dog was misclassified as a wolf, but why? When further investigation was performed, neural smiths discovered the classifier's attention was on the snow in the background of the picture of the dog. Pictures of wolves used to train the neural network always had snow in the background. The pictures of dogs had no snow. When the picture of the husky was presented with snow in the background, the neural network saw snow and immediately figured that the husky in the picture was a wolf. None of the characteristics of the husky was important in making this decision. The husky pixels were discarded as not useful.

The tank and dog examples are blatant failures of classification—what would be obvious to a human confused the neural network. But remember that ambiguities always exist in classification. Consider differentiating a bush from a tree. After the neural network is trained, a bonsai tree is supplied as an input. The bonsai tree is small like a bush but is actually a tree. The classification here is not a problem of the neural network. There are always ambiguous cases where both a human and the neural network will have problems. Like any detection scheme, success is determined by the frequency of false positives and false negatives.

Reinforcement Learning

DEEP CONVOLUTIONAL neural networks require training data. There are other problems where AI is trained to win a game. No training data is used. Only the rules of the game. Reinforcement learning explores use of different strategies to win the game. AI trained to play checkers, chess, and GO use reinforcement learning. Training consists of exploring different strategies to win the game. As different winning strategies are tried, results of attempts are remembered.

Reinforcement learning uses incremental neural networks; each new piece of data allows the AI to "learn," adjusting its behavior with every new bit of feedback. Reinforcement learning has been used to beat world champions at GO and beat legacy Atari video arcade games trained on pixels only. These are astonishing accomplishments.

In pure reinforcement learning, there is no training data per se. In winning at board games like checkers, chess, or GO, there are only rules and the goal of winning. Reinforcement learning explores and ultimately decides on the best winning methodology.

Reinforcement learning is given an environment and a goal. How is the environment to be explored to best achieve the goal? Ants run around individually foraging for food. They are exploring. When food is found, the ants form a line back and forth from the food to their nest.

They are exploiting their discovery. Exploration and exploitation are the fundamental components of reinforcement learning.

In the ant foraging example, the environment is fixed but unknown. Similarly, in GO, the environment is the GO board accompanied by the rules of GO. The goal is to explore and exploit different move combinations for different board configurations, and reinforcement learning is the procedure to achieve this goal.

A simple example of reinforcement learning involves a row of slot machines, nick-named one-armed bandits. A coin is inserted in one and a lever pulled. Three simple images spin, slow down, and then stop. If all three images are cherries, you win. If the three images are all diamonds, you win bigger. If the images all differ, the investment of the coin dropped into the machine is lost.

Now, there's a row of twenty slot machines, and some of them pay off better than others. One machine pays off 60 percent of the time and another 70 percent. The rest pay off 50 percent of the time. At the start, you have no idea how well any of the slot machines operate. The only way to find out is to insert coins and see how the machines pay off. After spending a lot of money, the machine with the best payoff can be identified. To maximize winnings, all your money should then be used on the most generous machine.

What is the best way to do this? How much money should be invested in each machine to identify the most generous machine? If a machine is paying well, is confirming the statistics of the win by playing the machine some more the best investment of your coins? Or is it better to try some of the other machines to see if they are better? This is an example of a problem addressed by reinforcement learning.

There are two basic aspects of reinforcement learning: exploration and exploitation. In the slot machine example, exploration is the testing of various machines to see which one pays off the best. Once one slot machine is thought to be superior to all the others, it is exploited. All the gambler's nickels go into the favored machine. Once the best one-armed bandit is identified, there is no reason to explore the others.

One can, however, never be 100 percent sure that the slot machine chosen is the best. Maybe some more nickels should be spent in the other machines to be sure. In other words, maybe you should explore more. If you are limited to a single bag of nickels and have no other money, how is the money best divided between exploration and exploitation? Reinforcement learning manages this tradeoff to hopefully maximize winnings.

Here's another example of reinforcement learning. Imagine you are a general in the seventeenth century looking for a path to a harbor through a thickly grown rainforest. First, you send an expedition into the rainforest. The team hacks through the vegetation and ends up against a massive cliff that cannot be crossed. The expedition team returns and reports the path and how far they got.

You send another team in a totally different direction. They also fail but report some progress for the chosen path. Maybe a variation of this path will give a better result.

A third team is available and ready to go. As the leader, you must decide whether to use information about a previous path or take a brand-new path. Or you can do a mix, combining what is known with a little bit of new exploration risk.

Repeated excursions eventually find a path to the harbor. But even then, can a better path be found? You continue your search, always using a trade-off between what you know and new risk, i.e., between the exploration of new paths and the exploitation of the paths you already know. Given enough time, you'll eventually find the best path.

Making Money with Reinforcement Learning

The ultimate test of technology is reduction to practice. So how is Deep-Mind, the AI that mastered GO using reinforcement learning, doing? How about other hot topics in AI? Many formerly hot AI developments like the Hopfield neural networks are on the scrap heap of failed ideas.

In projects other than reinforcement learning, DeepMind has sharpened the ability to make recommendations to us like which tune to play next on our music app. DeepMind is also training tomorrow's cyber salesman. And DeepMind's Text-to-Speech converts text into human-like speech in more than one hundred voices across more than twenty languages and variants. I wonder if their Text-to-Speech will soon be reading books for Audible or replacing voice actors in audio plays? Many websites, including MindMatters.AI, can now read text automatically. The renderings are not without flaws.

Like IBM's *Jeopardy*-winning software, DeepMind is looking to apply AI to medicine, specifically by applying algorithms to diagnose eye diseases, spot cancers on medical images, and predict which patients are at risk of various conditions.[24] As you may recall, Watson has no common sense and has thus far failed in its medical ventures. Will Deep-Mind fare any better? That remains to be seen.[25] There are, however, some strong indications things are not going well.

In 2014 the company behind DeepMind was purchased by Google for about a half billion dollars. DeepMind is still chugging away on AI applications, including reinforcement learning, in competition with Amazon, Apple, Facebook, and Microsoft to produce AI that generates big bucks in the market. But in 2018, DeepMind lost $570 million. Forbes reported, "DeepMind's losses are growing because it continues to hire hundreds of expensive researchers and data scientists but isn't generating any significant revenue."[26]

In August of 2019, DeepMind's three-year debt reached a billion dollars, and it also had more than one billion in debt due in the twelve months following, causing industry watchers to ask whether DeepMind was on the right track. "There is reason for skepticism," Wired reporter Gary Marcus wrote. "DeepMind has been putting most of its eggs in one basket, a technique known as deep reinforcement learning.... The trouble is, the technique is very specific to narrow circumstances."[27]

In 2020 DeepMind scored a profit of $60 million. But some are skeptical of the figure. DeepMind is owned by Alphabet, Google's parent company. And Alphabet and its subsidiaries are the DeepMind's primary customers. "DeepMind does not directly sell products or services to consumers and companies," one reporter notes. "Its customers are Alphabet and its subsidiaries. It is not clear which one of DeepMind's ventures caused the spike in its revenue." One has to wonder if the sudden increase in DeepMind's revenue is nothing more than "creative accounting."[28]

Always hopeful, Google CEO Sundar Pichai claims not to be bothered by the lack of high-profit DeepMind applications. He says, "Looking at the pace of progress, I think we will have AI in a form in which it benefits a lot of users in the coming years, but I still think it's early days, and there's a long-term investment for us."[29]

This scrutiny-avoiding optimism is encouraging, but is it realistic? Is it just a matter of pouring enough time, money, and brainpower into the research, or are there hard barriers that will forever limit DeepMind's applications? Time will tell.

Until then, be wary of the hype. As Bradley Center Fellow Brendan Dixon says, for a clearer picture, follow the money consistently over time.[30] If it's not making money, chances are it isn't working in terms of real-life application.

The Need for Forecast Ergodicity

WHAT COULD be holding back reinforcement learning AI such as DeepMind? One barrier for certain advances is forecast ergodicity. Simply put, not all data can be used to train AI. This limits the scope of AI application.

Forecast ergodicity, a property of data, requires future performance to be captured by examining previous performance. Ergodicity is formally taught in introductory courses on stochastic processes. The term "stochastic process" is a fancy term for noise and random signals. If I flip a fair coin a million times and keep track of the number of heads, about

50 percent of these flips will be heads. The conclusion is that the probability of getting a heads is about 50–50. If you repeat the experiment and flip a coin a million times, you will also get about 50 percent heads. This is true even though the detailed record of my coin flips is different than yours.

Coin flipping is an example of a stationary stochastic process. It is mean ergodic in the sense you get about the same result as I do when looking at two different instantiations of the same stochastic process. The details of our flips are different, but both estimate a 50 percent chance of a heads.

For time series, a stationary process is one whose character does not change with respect to time. Coin flipping is stationary. The probability of getting heads or tails remains the same. The sound of rain on a metal roof or the shhhh sound of white noise are also stationary. In contrast, electromagnetic interference from a flash of lightning is not stationary. It is a onetime event.

With no inflationary pressure or disrupting news, stock market movement is modeled in finance as a stationary stochastic process.[31] The model was used in the Nobel Prize-winning mathematical derivation of the Black-Scholes model for options pricing in finance.[32] The naïve stock market model is stationary but famously cannot be profitably forecast from tick data. The next occurrence in the market, like the next flip of a coin, cannot be forecast from previous events.

Ergodicity comes in many flavors. The coin flipping process just described is mean ergodic since the mean can always be extracted from any sufficiently long realization of the process. The mean of the flipping of a fair coin is 50 percent heads. A process can be ergodic for measuring one thing, like the mean, from an arbitrary realization of the stochastic process, and not ergodic for some other measure like the ability to forecast.

In the AI treatment of time series, we are interested in whether a process is forecast ergodic. Can future values of a time series be forecast from past values? The coin-flipping problem is clearly not forecast ergodic. The result of the next flip is independent from all previous flips. This may seem obvious but is not an idea widely embraced among those seeking to get rich at a Vegas casino. At roulette wheel stations, results of previous winning numbers are sometimes displayed for players. A naïve player might examine the board and think, "Number thirty-one on the black hasn't won for the last two hundred games. It's overdue!" A large bet is then placed on the number thirty-one. But like coin flipping, the next outcome of the roulette spin is independent from and has nothing to do with the spin results in the past.

This is hard for some to believe, but it's true. If ten sequential flips of a fair coin are heads, the chance of getting a tails on the next flip is not increased. Getting a tails cannot be considered overdue. The probability the next flip will be a tails remains 50–50.

Forecast ergodicity can also be subtle. Reflect upon the following game considered by the founders of probability, French mathematicians Blaise Pascal and Pierre de Fermat. Assume Pascal and Fermat agree to flip a fair coin five times. If the majority of the coin flips are heads, Pascal gets one hundred dollars. If there are more tails than heads, the pot of money goes to Fermat. The coin is flipped three times and the results are heads, heads, tails (HHT). Before the last two flips can be made, a Covid pandemic occurs and prevents the game from being finished. How then should the pot be split between Fermat and Pascal in the unfinished game?

There are four possible outcomes for the remaining two flips: HH, HT, TH, and TT. Since Fermat has only one tails to date, he needs two successive tails to win. This is his only path to victory. This is one of the four possible scenarios of the remaining flips. The other three outcomes give the pot to Pascal who, with two heads, only needs one more heads to win. So since there are three out of four scenarios where the pot goes to Pascal, three-fourths of the pot should go to Pascal and one-fourth of the pot to Fermat. The fair solution to the problem is that Fermat gets twenty-five dollars and Pascal seventy-five dollars.

The unfinished coin flipping game is the problem considered in a series of letters between Fermat and Pascal in the seventeenth century. Their correspondence and subsequent solution to the problem, nicely described in the book *The Unfinished Game*,[33] is credited with the founding of the field of probability theory.

So, although the sequence of coin flips is not forecast ergodic, wagers of the type between Pascal and Fermat can tell us to bet more heavily on Pascal when he is two successes ahead on a best-of-five coin flipping contest.

Ergodic Examples

BEFORE APPLYING AI, practitioners need to address whether the problem under consideration is forecast ergodic or not.[34]

We are amazed when reinforcement learning can be used to win Atari arcade games using only display pixels. But in doing so, the AI is exposed to the same game again and again. The game scenarios change as the human opponent makes different moves, but the game itself does not change in time. It is time invariant. The same is true with chess or GO. The same game is played over and over and over. When trained, the AI will be playing this same game. No rules are changed. A time-invariant system is one where the rules remain the same, and the AI's response to inputs does not change over time. Today, tomorrow, whenever—the game always remains the same.

To illustrate time invariance, consider training AI to win at the game of checkers. When a boy, I played a variation of checkers called "give-away" where the winner is whoever gets all his checkers jumped. Needless to say, AI trained to win at conventional checkers would not do well in the game of give-away. The rules have been changed. Changing the rules violates time invariance and thus forecast ergodicity is not applicable.

Remember our rainforest example, where you're sending out teams seeking the best path? If the terrain is continually being changed by earthquakes, tsunamis, and volcano eruptions, then results from previous explorations can no longer be trusted. Reinforcement learning will no longer be applicable because the problem under consideration no longer displays forecast ergodicity.

Likewise, if I train machine intelligence to play GO and then switch to the game of chess, the trained GO-playing program will sit up and flub its lips in confusion. The future performance in playing chess cannot be assessed by analysis of past performance in playing GO. Similarly, strategy in GO cannot be learned if the rules of GO are randomly changed during the training process.

All board games from simple Parcheesi to GO are time invariant and forecast ergodic. The rules are fixed. Note the terminology differences: While stationarity applies to data such as that used in load forecasting, time invariant applies to fixed systems like the games of GO and checkers. Stationarity indicates that the character of the data doesn't change. Future data has the same character as past data. Time invariance dictates that the rules of the game don't change.

Power Ergodics

A REAL-WORLD example of a stationary forecast ergodic process is prediction of power load demand for a power company.[35] As we discussed in Chapter 8, if a power company produces too little power, it must purchase power off the grid at the prevailing price. If the forecast is too high, too much power is generated and the power company must sell its excess at an uncertain market price. Because of the uncertainty of the power market, power companies wish to avoid both underestimating and overestimating future demand. Power companies like to reduce this uncertainty as much as possible with accurate power consumption forecasts.

Fortunately for power companies, data for power load forecasting is forecast ergodic. Data from the past is indicative of data of the future. The secret is identification of data to train a forecasting neural network. For the forecast of Tuesday's power demand, we know the power usage for Monday. Another relevant parameter is Tuesday's forecasted temperature. Air conditioners are turned on when the temperature is high and electric heaters when the temperature is low. Both these tempera-ture extremes increase power consumption. There is access to a lot of historical data for power consumption on Mondays and Tuesdays. A neural network is trained with the historical data using Monday's data and Tuesday's weather forecast on the input and Tuesday's power con-sumption at the output. Once trained, we can ideally provide inputs to the neural network on Monday and forecast the power usage on Tues-day. This, in fact, works quite well. Many power companies use neural networks to forecast load demand.[36] The success of the load forecasting neural network is proof that the underlying forecasting data was forecast ergodic.

Note that in describing the load forecasting neural network, we spec-ified forecasting power consumption for Tuesday. The power load char-acter for some days is different than for others. Weekends differ from weekdays. Holidays are also outliers. Holidays do not fit the statistics of normal day usage. My friend and colleague Mohamed El-Sharkawi worked on this problem. He called a spike in power usage on Thanksgiv-ing "The Turkey Effect." Everyone turned on their electric ovens to cook their turkeys about the same time on Thanksgiving, manifesting a big spike in power consumption.

Some processes can be described as displaying slowly changing (or variation limited) stationarity.[37] The historical data for training the pow-er forecasting becomes more unreliable the farther it is removed from the present. New housing developments, factories, and offices affecting power consumption might have been built. Old power-inefficient build-ings might have been torn down. In training a neural network for power consumption forecast, care must be taken when using older data that might pre-date such changes.[38]

Another example of short-term forecast ergodicity is predicting the weather from meteorological data. Generally, the nearer the future event is from now, the more accurate the forecast. We can be pretty sure of the weather a minute from now. Forecasts of weather details two months from now will be less accurate. But seasonal history can provide relevant data, even if the data is from a year ago. If it's August in Waco, Texas, it's going to be hot.

Meteorologists' forecast accuracy based on data has increased remarkably as more and more data is gathered and analyzed by more powerful computers. Some practitioners believe, though, that there remains a lot of room for improvement.[39]

Forecast ergodicity is not guaranteed by either stationarity or time invariance. Nor is forecast ergodicity guaranteed by ergodicity in some other sense. The coin flip process is mean ergodic but not forecast ergodic. The 50 percent heads-tails chance can be estimated using any history of a flipped coin. This is mean ergodicity. Forecast ergodicity would require that past flips give you more than a random guess of the next flip. Since the outcome of a coin flip cannot be forecast, the process is not forecast ergodic.

Although stationarity and time invariance do not guarantee forecast ergodicity, the converse sets up a necessary condition for forecast ergodicity. If data is non-stationary, or the system time variant, it is not forecast ergodic. A game whose rules are changed in a non-forecastable manner is time variant and cannot be mastered by AI.

Takeaways

ENGINEERS AND computer scientists have been seriously studying AI for over seventy years. During this time, many new ideas have bit the dust. Other AI innovations have taken root and are commonly used today. We take many of them for granted. The jury is still out on some more recent AI.

Reinforcement learning has been wondrously applied to board games like GO and arcade games like Space Invaders. These problems are time invariant and strongly forecast ergodic. The same game with the same rules is played again and again. However, many real-world problems involve human creativity and insight and are not forecast ergodic. Battlefield conditions and CEO leadership can require that decisions be made about situations not formerly considered. This is a problem for AI. Reinforcement learning will fail in such cases. Reinforcement learning has no ability to "think on its feet."

The absence of ergodicity stymies successful application of AI, such as reinforcement learning, to strategy on the battlefield. Commander Bradley A. Alaniz, a military professor at the US Navy War College, writes that "at the strategic and operational levels of warfare—the realm of human decision-making that requires creativity and original thought in order to compel or dissuade other humans—there are very few defined states. Furthermore, the number of non-defined, ambiguous states is essentially infinite."[40]

To apply AI, reinforcement learning would at minimum need to be privy to all of Commander Alaniz's "non-defined, ambiguous states." But as we have seen in previous chapters, creativity is beyond the reach of AI. A clever enemy would seek to guide a military conflict into unexpected contingencies not considered in the training of the AI.

AI is good at fixed strategies. But any fixed military strategy can be gamed by the enemy. In World War II, General George Patton beat the top Nazi, General Rommel, in Germany's North African campaign. How? Patton had studied Rommel. He knew Rommel's strategy and gamed it. The 1970 movie *Patton* captures this reality with a fun but fictitious line where Patton says, "Rommel, you magnificent bastard! I read your book!"[41] Likewise, military adversaries with knowledge about an enemy's AI strategy can game the weak point of the AI strategy and win the day.

In sum, deep convolutional neural networks have found niche applications but suffer from performance problems in broader, more complicated applications. At this writing, these limitations are still being sorted out. In many applications, AI may serve as an effective advisor, but final decisions will need to be made by a human. One perhaps insurmountable barrier to AI moving beyond "advisory" capacity is that time variant systems and nonstationary data are not forecast ergodic and cannot be captured by AI.

We will dig deep into other reasons why AI is limited in the next chapter.

PART FOUR: GÖDEL TO TURING TO CHAITIN TO THE UNKNOWABLE

10. It's All Gödel's Fault

> Either mathematics is too big for the human mind or the human
> mind is more than a machine.
>
> —Kurt Gödel[1]

Algorithmic information theory is the science that addresses what algorithms and therefore computers (including AI) can and can't do. The field may sound stuffy and even tedious, but when understood, is more fascinating than the best science fiction you could ever read.

Computable Means Algorithmic

AI often produces surprises. Self-driving cars may crash. In such cases the car-driving computer program must be bettered to address this contingency. Sometimes, though, surprising results from a well-written computer program may cohere with the goals of the programmer. AlphaGo, programmed to play the board game GO, might make surprising moves but will never self-evolve to give investment advice. What else can the program do? Oren Etzioni, chief executive officer of the Allen Institute for Artificial Intelligence, notes AlphaGo can't even answer simple questions like, Do you play poker? Can you cross the street? Can you explain the game of GO to me?[2]

As we've discussed, computers only do what they're programmed to do, by way of step-by-step procedures called algorithms. A recipe for baking a cake is an algorithm. Google Maps generates an algorithm—a set of instructions—to help you get from point A to point B.

Computers can only execute algorithms. If a task can be described using computer code, it is algorithmic. In other words, computable implies algorithmic. In logic, the contrapositive or modus tollens of a true statement is also true. Since computable implies algorithmic, non-algorithmic implies non-computable. There are problems that are proven to be non-algorithmic. Therefore, no computer program can ever be written to solve these problems. This is not a proposition or an arguable issue. It is a mathematical fact. As discussed earlier, humans display non-algorithmic properties that no AI will ever compute.

The Non-Algorithmic

WE ARE so used to thinking algorithmically using step-by-step procedures that non-algorithmic tasks can be difficult to grasp. But they do exist.

For example, undergraduate students in computer science are taught about the Turing halting problem, encapsulated by this question: can a computer algorithm be written that can determine whether another arbitrary computer program will stop running (halt) or will run forever? As will be explained in the next chapter, the answer is no. The Turing halting problem is non-algorithmic and therefore not computable. Alan Turing proved this mathematically in 1936. The Turing halting problem is the poster child for the non-algorithmic and therefore the non-computable. Sometimes people talk about a hypothetical program called the Turing halting oracle that can decide whether an arbitrary computer program will stop or run forever. Computer code for a Turing halting oracle can never be written.

We have already shown humans can have non-algorithmic capacities such as compassion and creativity. Humans are therefore beyond the capability of a computer. This is not to say humans can do all non-algorithmic tasks. We can't, for example, look at an arbitrary computer program and solve the halting problem in many cases. Answering the question as to whether a computer program halts or runs forever currently looks to be beyond the ability of both man and machine.

Axioms and the Non-Algorithmic

RELATED TO the non-algorithmic are limitations resident in a finite set of assumptions called axioms or postulates. These are the foundational assumptions upon which all else is built.

The concept of axiomatic foundations and their consequences should be familiar to you from everyday life. Your beliefs and behavior are based on an axiomatic core. Jews have the Ten Commandments as their axioms. There are five pillars to the Muslim faith and, for some Christians, the five points of Calvinism are captured in the TULIP acronym. These are the foundational assumptions (axioms) that blossom into a system of belief. They also limit what follows. If your foundational assumption is that the Earth is round, you are limited or prevented from worrying about sailing off the Earth's edge.

Definitions always accompany axioms. For instance, both Muslims and Christians claim belief in Jesus, but the meaning differs when defined by the two groups. Definitions must be precise to remove ambiguity.

Some strict mathematicians might claim any connection between mathematical axioms and the more malleable foundations of religion is troublesome—and they are right to a degree. But the analogy is there and, although not perfect, is strong.

Because of its direct and visible connection to rigid rules and inflexible logic, mathematics is highly specified compared to the more interpretive social commandments. Mathematical axioms are truths so evident that they need not be proved. In mathematics, axioms are first established using precisely defined terms. Then, using laws of logic, these axioms are expanded into lemmas, corollaries, and theorems. Mathematical systems can be developed formally from a handful of definitions and axioms. A mighty oak of mathematics can grow from the acorn of the foundational axioms. But, as Kurt Gödel showed, there are limits. An oak tree can grow from an acorn, but can only grow so high. The trees, mathematical or religious, are dependent on the choice of axioms.

Euclid of Alexandria developed planar geometry three hundred years before the birth of Christ. Planar geometry is the mathematics describing geometrical figures on a two-dimensional plane like a flat floor or a tabletop. Before talking about any of Euclid's axioms, a common understanding of some definitions must be established. These include the meaning of a point on a plane or the concept of a line in the plane. After agreeing on definitions, some obvious self-evident truths of geometry on a flat plane can be addressed. To develop his theory of planar geometry, Euclid proposed five such axioms.[3]

His first axiom claimed that between any two points a unique single line can be drawn.

Duh! Yes, axioms are often seemingly obvious to the point of being trivial.

Euclid's second axiom claimed any line segment can be extended indefinitely in both directions.

Again... Duh! This is obvious.

Euclid's remaining three axioms deal with the nature of circles, right angles, and parallel lines. From these five axioms, all Euclidean geometry emerges. Euclid's axioms expanded by common logic lead to theorems that prove truths such as (a) the three angles in any triangle add to 180° and (b) the Pythagorean Theorem. These and other truths are not immediately obvious from Euclid's five little axioms.

Euclid's book *Elements* describes his beautiful axiomatic development of planar geometry. It is a landmark work in the development of mathematics. Mathematics today still relies on Euclid's axiomatic approach. Modern probability theory, for example, is a field of mathematics built on axioms by the extraordinary twentieth-century Russian mathematician Andrey Kolmogorov.

The first of the five probability axioms states that a probability is either zero or greater. Obviously! Talking about a probability of minus one-half makes no sense. Another axiom requires that the probability of something happening when a random event occurs is one. Obviously! Axioms are obvious.

Euclid's axiomatic approach can be applied in many places. But though it is powerful, axiomatic development has limitations.

Euclid had flatness in mind when he developed his theory. Suppose instead of a plane we live on the surface of a sphere. (Come to think of it, we do, more or less.) Between the North Pole and the South Pole there is no unique shortest path on the earth's surface. Just like there are many ways to slice a perfectly round tomato into two equal halves, there are an infinite number of lines connecting the sphere poles, and they are all the same length.

Euclid's first axiom requires that a single unique line connect two points, but on the sphere there are cases where the number of lines connecting two points is infinite. Thus Euclid's first axiom is violated, and no subsequent theorem based on this axiom can be trusted. This illustrates that although powerful, any set of axioms will not solve all problems. A new set of axioms is needed if we are to talk about the geometry on the surface of a sphere.

The Big Challenge

WE NOW come to the moment that eventually catapulted young Kurt Gödel to fame. In 1928 the great German mathematician David Hilbert offered a challenge to his fellow nerds: find a set of axioms that can be used to develop theorems that ultimately prove any mathematical proposition. Hilbert's *Entscheidungsproblem* (German for "decision problem") asks for an algorithm that takes as input a mathematical proposition and, using axioms and logic, outputs whether the proposition is true or not. Having such a tool would essentially solve all mathematics.

Hilbert's challenge was accepted by Sir Alfred North Whitehead and Bertrand Russell. They launched their journey with a three-volume work titled *Principia Mathematica*. Like digging a tunnel through hard rock, the going was slow and tedious. Several hundred pages are required to prove the validity of the simple proposition $1 + 1 = 2$. The book was ranked by the Modern Library as twenty-third of the top one hundred English-language nonfiction books of the twentieth century. *Principia Mathematica* also has the distinction of being called the most important twentieth-century non-fiction book no one has read. I suspect even those who highly ranked the tome never read it cover to cover.

Whitehead and Russell had not yet reached their goal but felt they were approaching success. Their dream, however, was permanently derailed by a young Austrian math punk named Kurt Gödel.

Gödel showed that Hilbert's challenge and Russell and Whitehead's ultimate goal was not possible. There is no way to create an algorithm that can consider all mathematical statements and decide whether they are valid.

Gödel demonstrated this mathematically using a logical tool fancifully named *reductio ad absurdum*, which translates to "reduction to the absurd." The principle of reductio ad absurdum is also called "proof by contradiction." It works like this: if assuming a proposition is false leads to a contradiction or absurdity, then the proposition must be true. Reductio ad absurdum has been used extensively in the fields of philosophy and mathematics since at least the time of the ancient Greeks.

Here's an example of a proof using reductio ad absurdum. Our goal is to prove the proposition that "all positive numbers are interesting." To prove that "all positive numbers are interesting," we make a contrary assumption: there are positive numbers that are not interesting. If this is true we can assume there exists a smallest non-interesting positive number.

But hmmm. This is interesting!

The observation contradicts the assumption that all positive numbers are not interesting. Therefore, the initial proposition "all positive numbers are interesting" is true because its contrary assumption was shown to logically "reduce to the absurd." We have thus proved that all positive numbers are interesting.

Self-Refuting Statements

THE PROOF dealing with interesting positive numbers is whimsical. More serious self-refuting statements like "There is no truth" also can disprove themselves using reductio ad absurdum. Using meta-analysis, we simply apply the claim to itself. The statement "There is no truth" by its own application is not true. The statement is presented as true. But if there is no truth, the statement itself cannot be true. The claim contradicts itself. When a simple claim applied to itself causes a contradiction, the claim is said to be self-refuting.

The Cretan Paradox

One famous self-refuting statement comes from the Bible, where in Titus 1:12 the Apostle Paul writes, "One of Crete's own prophets has said it: 'Cretans are always liars...'"

This claim, first credited to the Cretan philosopher Epimenides of Knossos around six hundred BC, is known as the Cretan Paradox or the Epimenides Paradox. Since Epimenides was a Cretan, his statement applies to himself. We can thus exaggerate a bit and say Epimenides is claiming that "everything I say is a lie." The restatement has taken the original claim to the extreme.

Applying meta-analysis to the statement, Epimenides's statement is a lie. So applying "everything I say is a lie" to itself says that Epimenides is lying about his claim. If he is lying, Epimenides must be telling the truth. But if the statement is true, then he is telling a lie. But if he is lying, Epimenides must be telling the truth. Around and around we go. Like an unstable flip-flop in electronics, the reasoning in the Cretan Paradox flips without end from one conclusion to another.

Electrical engineer Bart Kosko calls this cycle a bipolar paradox.[4] Douglas R. Hofstadter in his classic book *Gödel, Escher, Bach*, refers to such recursive flip-flop in logic as "strange loops" and notes their occurrence in drawings and music.[5] The unresolvable Cretan paradox can also be interpreted as a logical illusion.

Logical Illusions

Illusions are ubiquitous. M.C. Escher draws surrealistic strange loops. In Escher's 1960 sketch "Ascending and Descending," we find ourselves always climbing the stairs but, by some remarkable fluke, find ourselves at the bottom of the staircase, ready again to ascend. Escher accomplishes this by drawing a clever optical illusion that does not exist in reality.

Strange loops happen in music. The Shepard-Risset glissando seems to ever increase in pitch. Up and up the tone seems to go. But if the tone frequency were always increasing, the tone would soon be out of range of human hearing and become irritating to dogs. This doesn't happen. Ten hours of a Shepard glissando can be experienced on YouTube[6] and no such thing occurs. No matter where the ten-hour timeline is clicked the tone seems to ever increase in pitch. Hofstadter relates the tone to the work of Bach, which is why Bach appears in the title of Hofstadter's book *Gödel, Escher, Bach.*

Escher's sketches are optical illusions. The Shepard-Risset glissando is an audio illusion. The illusion is accomplished by increasing the frequencies of a number of notes simultaneously. As the notes get higher, their volume is slowly decreased and then faded. At the same time lower frequency notes are introduced quietly and slowly increased in volume. All this happens seamlessly, giving the listener the audio illusion that the pitch of the ensemble of frequencies is ever increasing. The effect can be compared to a rotating barber pole. When the pole rotates, the red stripe pattern seems to move up the pole even though the spiral stripe itself does not move.

Hearing the Shepard-Risset glissando described with words falls far short of hearing the music itself. I encourage you to go to YouTube and listen.[7] The spooky glissando was used in the Hans Zimmer score for the movie *Dunkirk*[8] and also makes an appearance in the 1996 Super Mario Nintendo Game as Mario climbs the stairs. The band Pink Floyd uses the Shepard-Risset glissando in its 1971 recording title "Echoes."

Weird Shepard glissando tones can also be heard in movies like *The Dark Knight* and *The Dark Knight Rises*.

Another audio illusion is the Risset rhythm, where the speed of a drumbeat sounds like it is getting faster while, in fact, the beats per second remain the same. It's fun to listen to as well.[9]

Optical and audio illusions create the impression that something exists when it doesn't. Escher's optical illusion stairs are contradictory. If I continue to climb stairs, I cannot end up in the same place I started. The two conclusions are in conflict and we have an optical illusion. The Shepard-Risset glissando cannot simultaneously increase in frequency and forever remain in the frequency range of human hearing. The two observations are in conflict; the Shepard-Risset glissando is an audio illusion.

There are also logical illusions consisting of contradicting statements that cannot simultaneously exist. Saying "There is no truth" while simultaneously affirming that statement to be true is a logical contradiction. If true, the statement "There is no truth" is not a truth. Holding two conflicting ideas to be true at the same time isn't logical.

The Meta Test

Meta statements can sometimes be self-refuting. They are statements that can refer to the statement being made. An example of an obvious meta-statement is, "This sentence uses five words." The meta sentence is true since the statement contains five words. But the meta statement, "This sentence uses twenty words," since it contains only five words, is false. Meta statements like these are easy to analyze. Others are not.

A particularly curious example of a self-referential sentence is Curry's Paradox,[10] introduced by Haskell B. Curry to demonstrate the inconsistency of certain systems of formal logic using conditionals like "if A, then B." An example of a Curry paradox is the sentence, "If this sentence is true, then fire is a liquid." Is this sentence true?

What if we changed the statement to: "If this sentence is true, then Texas borders Oklahoma"? Texas does border Oklahoma, so is the statement true? What about the variation where bordering Oklahoma is changed to far-away Australia? We now have, "If this sentence is true, then Texas borders Australia."

Curry's Paradox is curious.

The truth table of Boolean logic implication states that a falsehood implying something true is true.[11] For example, the statement "a throbbing toe implies it's raining outside" is true if it's raining outside. It matters not whether a toe is throbbing or not. So the truth in Curry's paradox has nothing to do with whether the sentence is true or not. "If this sentence is true, then Texas borders Oklahoma" is true because Texas borders Oklahoma. "If this sentence is true, then Texas borders Australia" is false since Texas does not border Australia.

Here is a less-curious statement from the Bible that appears to be self-refuting. In Matthew 19:36b, we read, "With God, all things are possible." Let's apply a meta test.

If the claim made in Matthew is true, then God should be able to create a task impossible for God to do. If God can do anything, He should be able to do this. Has meta-analysis discovered a self-referential contradiction in the Bible? Biblical scholars will say no. The statement must be placed in context. Invoking context can dissolve a logical conflict. A more complete statement would be, "With God all things are possible that are consistent with His nature."

God is said to be righteous, so He cannot be unrighteous. Titus 1:1, for example, refers to a "God, who cannot lie." By adding context, the meta self-referential that refuted itself is transformed into a statement without conflict.

Context can likewise be used to remove self-referential conflict from many troublesome claims. The problem with the Cretan can be removed if the statement is augmented to read, "Everything I say, except for this sentence, is a lie." The validity of the revised claim can still be debated, but not because meta-analysis reveals it as inconsistent.

Here's another common self-defeating claim, one made by some atheists: given enough time science can account for everything. The claim is self-refuting because science cannot demonstrate (cannot account for) the claim that science will account for everything. In other words, the claim itself cannot be proven scientifically. Such a claim lies beyond scientific scrutiny and is therefore, according to the claim itself, unworthy of consideration. The faith that science can explain all is called *scientism*.

Consider next the pantheistic claim that "all religion should be accepted as true." The problem is that nearly all religions claim some degree of exclusivity. And their truth claims are often contradictory. If Hinduism claims there are millions of gods and the Abrahamic religions claim a single God, both propositions cannot be accepted as true. Any claim that "all religions are true" is like claiming any liquid from a cow, when chilled, goes well with a chocolate chip cookie.

A more severe meta claim is "there is no right or wrong." Proponents of this viewpoint will argue its truth. Imagine a rebel pounding his fist on the table and yelling, "There is no right or wrong!" You softly counter, "You are wrong." The fist repeats its pounding and the rebel yells "No! I'm right!" If there is no right or wrong, how can the rebel claim he is right?

The claim "there is no right or wrong" is self-refuting. A philosophy that asserts "there is no right or wrong" must therefore be discarded onto the scrap heap of nonsense. It is a logical illusion.

Here's another example. There are those who believe faith and religious belief are a cover for insecurity. Others do not agree. I think true belief is based on explanatory power and supporting evidence. New Age guru Deepak Chopra does not agree and thinks his New Age philosophy frees him from insecurity without the need of beliefs.

Chopra was confronted in a public forum Q&A where a questioner destroyed Chopra's claim with a short and pointed reductio ad absurdum smackdown.[12] After being recognized to ask a question, a man standing at the audience microphone first restates Chopra's position. He says, "Now you stated before that all belief is a cover-up for insecurity. Right?"

Deepak Chopra responds with "uh huh," meaning "yes, this is my position." The questioner responds with a question. "Do you believe that?"

With no hesitation, Chopra responds, "Yes."

"Thank you," the questioner says, and with this mic-drop moment returns to his seat in the audience sits down.

The crowd responds with a long communal belly laugh while Chopra, victim of the reductio ad absurdum smackdown, squirms uncomfortably on stage. Chopra's belief that his position allows him escape from insecurities was a belief that, according to Chopra's own precept, was itself a cover-up for insecurity. The contradiction exposed Chopra's philosophy on this matter as self-refuting.

Russell's Paradox

E. Kasner and J. Newman once noted, "Perhaps the greatest paradox of all is that there are paradoxes in mathematics."[13] Russell's Paradox is a famous example of self-refutation that leads to an unexpected and curious result. It takes a bit of buildup to appreciate Russell's Paradox, so let's get started.

We all have an idea of what a set is. We can have sets of dogs, sets of geometrical shapes on a plane, and even sets of sets.

Some sets contain themselves. We will call such sets inclusive. An example is the set of all things that are not skunks. The set of all things not skunks is itself not a skunk. Let's give this set a name. Call it the NOTSKUNKS set. The NOTSKUNKS set is a set. It is therefore not a skunk and is a member of the set NOTSKUNKS. NOTSKUNKS is therefore an inclusive set. The set includes itself as a subset.

Another inclusive set is the set of all sets with more than three elements. This set contains more than three elements and will therefore contain itself as a subset.

Sets that do not contain themselves will be called exclusive because they exclude themselves from being in the set. An example is the set of all apples. The set of all apples is itself not an apple. A set isn't an apple. Therefore, the set of all apples is exclusive because the set does not contain itself as a subset.

So there are two types of sets—sets that contain themselves as subsets and those that don't. If a set includes itself, it is inclusive. If a set does not contain itself as a subset, it is called an exclusive set.

Russell's paradox reveals these simple definitions lead to a theory that is a logical illusion. The paradox arises from considering the meta question: "Is the set of all exclusive sets itself an exclusive set? Or is it an inclusive set?"

For reference, let's call the set of all exclusive sets the AllEx set for All Exclusive. We consider both possibilities one at a time.

1.   If the set of all exclusive sets contains itself, it is an inclusive set. But AllEx is limited to only contain exclusive sets. There are no inclusive sets in AllEx. We have reached a contradiction and are forced to conclude that AllEx is not an inclusive set.

2.   Consider the alternative. If the set of all exclusive sets does not contain itself, AllEx is an exclusive set. But AllEx contains all the exclusive sets in the universe, so it must therefore contain itself. We have reached another contradiction and are forced to conclude that AllEx is not an exclusive set.

This weird result may require a couple of readings to understand.[14] The bottom line is that the AllEx set leads to contradictions. The set of all exclusive sets, AllEx, is neither inclusive nor exclusive. The question, when we try to answer it, leads to a logical illusion.

What's a mathematician to do? Have we stumbled on a third type of set that is neither inclusive nor exclusive? Or maybe we are the victims of bad thinking.

When a conflict of this sort is reached, we must conclude a mistake has been made somewhere. If you prove 2 plus 2 is 5, you made a mistake somewhere.

To avoid problems of this sort, mathematicians set aside so-called intuitive set theory that gave rise to Russell's Paradox in favor of greater rigor. Because of Russell's Paradox, set theory was derived from scratch using an axiomatic approach—just like Euclidean geometry and probability. Russell's Paradox is avoided by careful development from foundational axioms. Reasoning of the type leading to Russell's Paradox is now derogatorily called "naïve set theory." Zermelo, Fraenkel, and Skolem (ZFS) developed the axiomatic foundation for set theory. The ZFC formalism is still taught today. Within the ZFC structure, Russell's paradox about the AllEx set is no longer a problem.

Apparently our naïve intuition about sets cannot be trusted if we wish to avoid curiosities like Russell's paradox. Mathematicians, after all, need to establish axioms that give rise to consistent results.

No logical illusions are allowed in mathematical truth.

Gödel's Theorems

SPEAKING OF consistent, we now address Gödel's theorems that show that all mathematical systems built on axioms must either be incomplete or inconsistent. Gödel's use of reductio ad absurdum self-contradiction is cleverly parodied in an XKCD cartoon panel in which someone taking a survey holds a pad of paper and happens upon Kurt Gödel.

Survey-taker: "Hey Gödel—we're computing a comprehensive list of fetishes. What turns you on?"

Gödel: "Anything not on your list."

Think about that! Gödel's response means the questioner can never complete his survey. If one of Gödel's fetishes is added to the questioner's list, then it's no longer a Gödel fetish and must be removed from the list, in which case it again belongs on the list, and so forth forevermore. Cartoon Gödel's response has rendered completion of the list a logical

Figure 10.1. XKCD. Gödel is a dangerous guy to question.

illusion. His request that "anything not on your list" be added to the list is impossible to do.

Similarly, Gödel's proof demonstrated that Whitehead and Russell's task of axiomatically developing all mathematics would also never be completed.

Gödel's Proof

Gödel showed that Whitehead and Russell's attempt to derive all of mathematics from a group of axioms was not possible.[15] He used a reductio ad absurdum smackdown. Remember, Whitehead and Russell were attempting to formulate a set of axioms that would determine the truth or falseness of any mathematical statement. Gödel showed that in any such attempt, one must ultimately arrive at something like the following self-referential theorem:

Theorem X says Theorem X can't be proved.

The self-reference here is obvious. Theorem X explicitly refers to itself. But what are we to make of Theorem X? There are two possibilities.

1. Incompleteness: If Theorem X is true then there are truths (theorems) that cannot be proven using the foundational axioms. Theorem X is an example of something that can't be proved with the assumed axioms. The formal system defined by the axioms is therefore incomplete. There are truths beyond those able to be proved.

2. Inconsistency: If Theorem X is not true, then Theorem X, contrary to its claim, can be proved. So if Theorem X is not true, the system built on the foundational axioms is inconsistent. We are claiming at the same time that Theorem X can't be proved and can be proved.

The conclusion is this: any system built on axioms will either be incomplete or inconsistent. To avoid contradiction, mathematicians like Whitehead and Russell work hard to keep their system in *Principia Mathematica* consistent. They wanted no repeat of Russell's paradox. Gödel showed as a consequence of maintaining consistency, the work of Whitehead and Russell was doomed to be incomplete. They would never axiomatically develop all of mathematics. Whitehead and Russell raised a white flag and surrendered their work to Gödel's analysis.

The Theorem X statement is not a logical illusion if the derived theory is consistent. For the math system developed from axioms to be consistent, Theorem X must be true. Therefore there exist things that are true that lie above and beyond what can be proven from chosen foundational assumptions. To keep consistency, Theorem X must be true! It is a true theorem that can't be proved within the constraints of the chosen axioms.

Gödel published his first landmark papers when he was only twenty-five years old. His contributions were obscured by sophisticated mathematical details and not widely understood. Later that same decade, Alan Turing gave a more intuitive and understandable explanation of Gödel's result using computer science mathematics. Turing's result unveiled limitations about what computers can and cannot do. The list of cannots reveals part of non-computable you.

This is the astonishing material covered next.

11. TURING MAKES GÖDEL SIMPLE

> Even though such machines might do some things as well as we do them, or perhaps even better, they would inevitably fail in others, which would reveal that they were acting not through understanding but only from the disposition of their organs. For whereas reason is a universal instrument which can be used in all kinds of situations, these organs need some particular disposition for each particular action; hence it is for all practical purposes impossible for a machine to have enough different organs to make it act in all the contingencies of life in the way in which our reason makes us act.
>
> —RENÉ DESCARTES (1637)[1]

POLYMATH CHARLES BABBAGE CONCEIVED OF THE PROGRAMMABLE digital computer in the nineteenth century, but Alan Turing formalized modern theoretical computer science a few years after Gödel's landmark papers. In doing so Turing made Gödel's ideas more accessible by framing them in the context of a computer.

It's possible that Turing became interested in computers because of a personal tragedy. In high school, Turing lost his friend Christopher Morcum to bovine tuberculosis. There is speculation that Turing turned from God because of the incident and later concentrated on development of the automated human to demonstrate man's materialistic nature. As we discussed earlier, Turing used the imitation game in his proposal in 1950 of a "Turing test" to refer to whether computers can achieve the abilities of the human. Constructing a machine to imitate a human was Turing's imitation game.

Turing and His Machine

IN 1936 Turing invented the Turing machine, which uses operations that can be considered foundationally axiomatic.

A Turing machine is a mathematical model of computation that manipulates symbols on a strip of tape according to a table of rules. The tape is regarded as infinite and is divided into a sequential set of locations on which the machine can read, erase, and write. The action of the Turing machine is determined by the number read from the tape at its current location and the machine's state. The symbol on the tape might be a one and the machine might be in state twenty-two. State twenty-two says that if a one is on the tape, the read/write head should erase the one, write zero, move one position to the left, and change its state from twenty-two to state fifteen.

The process seems quite simple but is extremely powerful. The simple Turing Machine can be used to execute any computer program. This includes AI computer programs written for today's supercomputers. The Turing machine might take a long time to duplicate the supercomputer but will eventually get the job done.

Thus, Turing is the founder of modern theoretical computer science. His machine formalized the concepts of the algorithm and computation.

Turing Goes to Church

LATER IN the 1930s, after developing the Turing Machine, Turing traveled from Great Britain to study under mathematician Alonzo Church at Princeton. Church had developed a computational language he dubbed lambda calculus. The computational ability of lambda calculus was shown to be the same as that of the Turing machine. Both were said to be computationally universal. In other words, the Church-Turing thesis claims any computationally universal number cruncher can be performed on a Turing machine and visa versa. If something can be computed, the Turing machine can compute it.

The Church-Turing thesis has powerful implications. The blazingly fast computers we have now are amazing, but every algorithm performed by today's computers can be performed on a Turing machine.[2] Compared to early computers, the Turing machine calculation may take a million or a billion times as long. But if computing time and memory are sufficiently large, Turing's simple machine can sluggishly duplicate the performance of a supercomputer.

Don't miss the significance of this. The Turing machine established what can or cannot be computed. The speed of today's computer is blazingly fast, but the takeaway is this: any performance limitations identified on Turing's original machine applies equally to today's computers and therefore to modern AI.[3] If a task is algorithmic, it can be executed on a computer. Non-algorithmic tasks cannot be executed on a Turing machine or any other computer.

Looping Algorithms

RECALL THAT an algorithm is simply a step-by-step set of instructions to generate a desired result. Many algorithms have inputs. Take cooking recipes, for example. The ingredients for a recipe serve as recipe inputs, and then comes the algorithm that tells you what to do with the inputs.

Some step-by-step procedures don't qualify as algorithms. For example, software developer Alex Altair observes that the scientific method may look algorithmic, but isn't.[4] Here are the four steps in the scientific method:

1. Make an observation.
2. Form a hypothesis that explains the observation.
3. Conduct an experiment that will test the hypothesis.
4. If the experimental results disconfirm the hypothesis, return to step #2 and form a hypothesis not yet used. If the experi-

mental results confirm the hypothesis, provisionally accept the hypothesis.

This is a step-by-step procedure. So why isn't it an algorithm? Because step #2 reads "Form a hypothesis that explains the observation." Unless there is a hypothesis specified, the general scientific method cannot by coded on a computer. Doing so requires information outside of the rule list. So, Altair is right. The scientific method is not algorithmic.

Some algorithms can loop forever. For instance, there is an algorithm on your shampoo bottle that could prove dangerous if interpreted literally.

1. Lather
2. Rinse
3. Repeat

Followed literally, this algorithm will go on forever and your hair will be really clean. No matter how clean your hair, you will wash it again when the algorithm instructions are followed literally.

The intent of the shampoo instruction is made crystal clear by changing the last instruction from "Repeat" to "Repeat once." The instructions are now:

1. Lather
2. Rinse
3. Repeat once

With this revision, the hair washing procedure is only executed twice. Thus is the world of algorithms: a programmer must be very careful to specify an exact action without ambiguity.

The Turing Halting Problem

WE MENTIONED Turing's halting problem in the previous chapter. Now we will address it more thoroughly.

In 1936 Turing proved the so-called halting problem is non-algorithmic and therefore cannot be solved using any computer program.[5]

The halting problem addresses whether there exists a computer program called a halting oracle. A halting oracle could examine an arbitrary computer program and answer the question of whether that program will halt or loop forever. As we said before, the halting oracle does not exist. Such a computer program can never be written.

A key word describing the program under analysis is "arbitrary." Some computer programs obviously halt. If computer code consists of "Print Hello World then stop," halting is obvious. Likewise, a computer program that says "Print Hello World and, as long as two is greater than one, do it again" will be printing Hello World forever. The condition that two is greater than one is always true, so the program will perpetually loop.

Sometimes it's easy to tell whether a computer program will halt or continue forever, as with the lather/rinse/repeat algorithm. But telling whether a computer program halts or loops for more complex programs is sometimes difficult. There's always the option of running the program. If a program runs for a while and stops, the problem is solved. But what if it doesn't stop? If a program runs for a year, we might be tempted to announce that it will run forever. But the program might halt after running for one year and five seconds. The halting problem is therefore described as a semi-decidable problem. We can often know whether a program halts, but we can never be sure if a program that is still running loops forever.

How can the Turing halting oracle be shown to be non-computable? Turing, acknowledging he was building on Gödel's paper published a few years earlier,[6] used Gödel's reductio ad absurdum smackdown. The proof first assumes the halting oracle is computable and then shows, as a consequence, that a contradiction occurs. The initial computable assumption is revealed as wrong and the computable halting oracle is exposed as a logical illusion.

258 / Non-Computable You /

A short proof appreciated by nerds is in the endnotes.[7] The proof that the Turing halting oracle is non-computable is beautiful for those who appreciate elegant reasoning.

The Incredible Uses of the Halting Oracle

IF THE Turing halting oracle did exist, it would have all sorts of wonderful applications. The oracle could be used to solve many open problems in mathematics. Proofs for some of these problems have large cash prizes.

May the Fours Be with You

Here's a fun example illustrating how a halting oracle could be effectively used—if it were computable.

Let's start by defining the operation of "crunch" as spelling out a number and counting the number of letters.[8] For example, the number three has five letters: T-H-R-E-E. So when we crunch three, we get five letters. For larger numbers, numbers are spelled out one number at a time. For example, the number sixteen is written as ONE, SIX. Both numbers have three letters for a total of six letters. Therefore, crunching sixteen gives six. This works for really big numbers too. Consider a million, which is one followed by six zeros. ONE has three letters and ZERO has four letters. So one million is ONE, ZERO, ZERO, ZERO, ZERO, ZERO, ZERO. That's a total of twenty-seven letters to write one million. We don't include spaces or commas in the count. Therefore, one million crunches to twenty-seven.

Here is the interesting part. If we keep on crunching any number, it looks like we always end up at four. Watch how this happens:

One million, as we have seen, crunches to twenty-seven letters.

Twenty-seven, written as TWO SEVEN (three letters plus five letters) has eight as its crunch number.

The word EIGHT has five letters.

The word FIVE has four letters.

The word FOUR has four letters.

Since FOUR crunches to four, it looks like we're in an endless loop of doing the same thing over and over.[9]

What is interesting is that, no matter what number we start with, we always seem to end up with the number four. Let's try another.

The number 377, as THREE SEVEN SEVEN (five plus five plus five), crunches to fifteen.

Fifteen as ONE FIVE has eight letters when spelled out and crunches to eight.

EIGHT crunches to five.

FIVE crunches to four.

Repeated crunching again converged to four. Could it be that every number eventually crunches to four?

Let's write the crunch operation as an algorithm. Since we always seem to end at four, we'll call the algorithm "May the Fours Be with You."

An input is needed to start things. Let's call the input X. X can be any number. The steps are as follows:

Input X

Replace X by its crunched number

if X = 4 stop

Otherwise, repeat

As you can see from our steps, when the "May the Fours Be with You" algorithm sees four, it halts. If not, it will run forever.

Does the "May the Fours Be with You" algorithm always halt no matter what number X we start with?[10] One counterexample is all that is needed.

We write a computer program that repeatedly uses the "May the Fours Be with You" program. We apply to the number X=1 and see if it crunches to four. If it does so we move on to X=2 and see it also eventually crunches to four. Then to X=3. On and on we go testing each number in sequence. If we happen on a number that does not crunch to four, we exit the program and the program HALTS. But if all numbers do eventually crunch to four, it would take forever to prove this, because there are an infinite number of numbers.

Enter the Turing halting oracle. Our program is presented to the halting oracle. The oracle examines the code and without running the code decides whether the program HALTS or LOOPS forever. If the oracle announces looping through all numbers HALTS, a counterexample has been found and there is a number that doesn't crunch to four. If the halting oracle outputs LOOPS, then the program will run forever. This would mean no counterexamples are ever found and the "May the Fours Be with You" has been proven.

This is not the only problem the halting oracle could solve. If it existed, the halting oracle could prove or disprove every conjecture where a single counterexample proves the conjecture false.

Here are some examples.

Goldbach's Conjecture

Goldbach's conjecture is a more serious application of the Turing halting oracle—if the Turing halting oracle were computable.

In a letter dated June 7, 1748, addressed to possibly the greatest mathematician of all time, Leonard Euler, fellow mathematician Christian Goldbach noted that every even number looked like it could be expressed as the sum of two prime numbers.[11] For example, the even number ten can be written as the sum of seven and three. Both seven and three are prime numbers. Another example is one hundred, which is the sum of prime numbers ninety-seven and three. Larger even numbers are more difficult to parse into two prime numbers, but so far no one has found a counterexample. Goldbach's conjecture has been tested for all even numbers up to 4×10^{13} or 4,000,000,000,000,000,000 or four billion billion. In every case, an even number was shown to be able to be expressed as the sum of two prime numbers.

But no matter how many even numbers tested Goldbach's conjecture, the conjecture will never be proved. No matter how long the search and no matter how large the even numbers, there can always be a larger number that violates Goldbach's conjecture. And we never run out of larger numbers.

So what does this have to do with the Turing halting oracle? Any student in introductory programming can write a program to step through all the even numbers one at a time and see if they are sums of two primes. The program will find that ten is the sum of the prime numbers seven and three, and then move on to the next even number, twelve. The even number twelve can be written as the sum of the two prime numbers five and seven. So we move on to fourteen, which is the sum of the prime numbers eleven and three. And on we go. The program is written so that if a counterexample is found to Goldbach's conjecture, the program will print Eureka! and print the even number that disproves Goldbach's conjecture.

If a single counterexample is found, Goldbach's conjecture will be proved to be wrong. If, on the other hand, Goldbach's conjecture is true, the Goldbach program will run forever. Unfortunately, forever is a long time and we are only able to check for a finite number of cases. Forever is still a long way from the four billion billion numbers already tested. In fact, the difficulty of starting to verify Goldbach's conjecture starting at four billion billion is just like starting over again. An infinite number of even numbers has yet to be tested.

But suppose a Turing oracle were able to analyze the computer program and announce whether the program would halt or run forever. The Goldbach program that steps through all even numbers is presented to the Turing oracle. If the Turing oracle says the Goldbach program runs forever, then Goldbach's conjecture is true. If the Turing oracle says the Goldbach program stops, it means there is a counterexample. The Goldbach program has found an even number that is not the sum of two primes and Goldbach's conjecture is false.

There have been prizes of up to one million dollars offered for anyone able to prove Goldbach's conjecture. So having a Turing oracle could earn us big bucks. But unfortunately, Turing has shown the Turing oracle is non-computable.

Here's the point. The halting oracle is non-algorithmic. It can't be written as a computer program. There are numerous other similar problems in computer science that are not computable. And according to the Church-Turing thesis, this limitation extends to today's hyper-performance AI engines.

Legendre's Conjecture

Goldbach's conjecture could be proved or disproved using a halting oracle, if such an oracle could exist. There are many other similar open problems. It helps to know about some of these before we consider Chaitin's number.

Take Legendre's conjecture, which is about prime numbers. Legendre claims at least one prime number always lives between the square of two consecutive numbers. Take, for example, the consecutive numbers two and three. Two squared (two times two) equals four. Three squared, or three times three, is nine. Between four and nine are the primes five and seven. Legendre's conjecture checks out here. What about ten and eleven? Ten squared is one hundred. Eleven squared is 121. Does a prime live between one hundred and 121? Yes. In fact, there are five prime numbers in this interval, namely 101, 103, 107, 109, and 113. Is this true for all numbers? Are there always prime numbers between the square of two consecutive positive numbers? To disprove Legendre's conjecture, we need only find one counterexample. Like the Goldbach conjecture, a computer program could be written to sequentially step through all consecutive positive numbers and check whether a prime lived between their squares. If a counterexample occurred, the program would stop and announce the answer. If no counterexample exists, the program would run in a never-ending search. This program could be submitted to a halting oracle (if one existed) to determine if the Legendre conjecture is true or not. But halting oracles don't exist so, to date, Legendre's conjecture remains unproven.

The Riemann Hypothesis

A $1,000,000 prize has been offered by the Clay Mathematics Institute for the first correct proof of the Riemann hypothesis.[12] The hypothesis deals with properties of the Riemann zeta function, conjecturing that all so-called zeros of the function have real parts equal to a half.[13] Don't worry if you don't understand the previous sentence; just know that many consider the Riemann hypothesis to be the most important unsolved problem in pure mathematics. You may recall Russell Crowe, as Nobel Laureate mathematician John Nash, discussing the Riemann hypothesis in the biopic motion picture *A Beautiful Mind*.

It would be great to be able to verify the Riemann hypothesis. A proof of the Reimann hypothesis would help solve many other open problems in mathematics. In 2004, Xavier Gourdon and Patrick Demichel verified the hypothesis through the first ten trillion non-trivial zeros. A single zero not displaying this property would disprove the hypothesis.

If the halting oracle existed, the Riemann hypothesis could be resolved as either right or wrong.

The Collatz Conjecture

Start with any positive number. If the number is even, divide by two. If odd, multiply by three and add one. The Collatz conjecture says that no matter what number you start with, you will end up at the number four.

Here's an example. Start with the number ten. It's even, so divide by two to get five. Five is odd. Multiply by three and add one, and you get sixteen. This is even so we divide by two. Sixteen divided by two is eight. Eight divided by two is the end: four. The destination of four has been reached—Collatz's conjecture works with an initial number of ten.

Does it work for all numbers? This is an open problem in mathematics. To disprove it, all that is required is a single counterexample. A computer program can be easily written to test the Collatz conjecture for ever-increasing numbers. The program would stop if a counterexample were found, but it would continue its search forever if the Collatz conjecture were true.

This would be solved if we had access to a halting oracle.

Conway's Game of Life

Conway's Game of Life is another interesting example illustrating how useful the halting oracle would be.

According to Conway, his Game of Life has its genesis with genius mathematician John von Neumann, who thought about a lot of things, including the settlement of Mars. As you no doubt know, Mars is hostile environment for humans. Von Neumann thought we could land a bunch of robots on Mars with the idea of preparing the planet for humans to visit. But sending a robot to Mars is expensive, and the number of robots needed would be cost-prohibitive. So von Neumann came up with a great idea. He first noted that Mars was red because there was lots of iron on the surface of the planet. Why not send robots up to build a smelter, process the iron ore, and manufacture more robots?

A serendipity of processing iron ore is the production of oxygen, which could then be used to fill a closed dome for future visiting astronauts. Von Neumann's idea required constructing robots that could, in turn, manufacture other robots. Von Neumann solved the problem mathematically and showed that, indeed, robots could be programmed to reproduce themselves.

Aware of von Neumann's work, John Conway experimented with a less ambitious project he called the Game of Life. As you may recall from Chapter 1, the Game of Life is laid out on a checkerboard grid that extends without bound in all directions. An arbitrary number of identical checkers (or lights) are placed on squares on the grid. Each square on the checkerboard is surrounded by eight squares: top, bottom, right, left, and the four squares touching the four corners. The initial placing of the checkers can be viewed as a computer program. The game's algorithm, recall, follows four simple rules that dictate how checkers are added or removed from a board.

Once a board is updated by removing and inserting checkers, the rules are applied again. The patterns able to be generated by the four simple rules are astonishing. There are patterns that do not change, patterns that repeat but do not move, and patterns that glide across the checkerboard. The diversity of patterns generated by Conway's four simple rules is unexpected. Significantly, in a crude realization of von Neumann's reproduction challenge, there are Game of Life patterns that iteratively generate an unbounded sequence of identical patterns that march off to the right of the generator.

The behavior of the Game of Life is determined solely by how the checkers are initially placed on the boundless board. The checker locations can be considered the input into the algorithm dictated by Conway's four rules. Here's the question: do the patterns launched by the initialization of the Game of Life continue forever? Or will all the checkers be eventually removed from the checkerboard and the game stop? This is the halting problem for the Game of Life.

There are some obvious cases. If only one checker is placed on the board, the checker is removed, the gameboard is empty, and the game is over. The same thing happens when many checkers are placed on the board such that no checker is in one of the eight squares surrounding any other checker.

Contrast this to the "blinker" where three checkers are placed horizontally in a row. Using Conway's rules, the next pattern will be three vertically adjacent checkers. The middle checker doesn't move. In the next step the pattern reverts to the original three horizontal checkers in a row, and the process repeats. The simple pattern is called a blinker because the same pattern oscillates back and forth forever. Even more fundamental is four checkers placed in a two-by-two square. According to Conway's rules, this pattern is stable. It never changes or moves.

Both the blinker and the two-by-two checker square are examples of patterns that will never go extinct. The patterns in isolation will always have checkers on the board and, in this sense, will never halt. In more complicated scenarios, a moving pattern such as the glider can collide with a two-by-two block and destroy the fragile balance that keeps the block alive. This can doom the block and the entire board to extinction.

Again, all action in the Game of Life is determined by the initial placement of the checkers on the grid. There is nothing random in the execution of the Game of Life. Conway's four rules can be interpreted as a computer program of sorts with the initial placement of checkers considered as the input to the program. For simple cases the program can be seen to eventually halt or run forever. But if we place a hundred, a thousand, or a million checkers on the grid, forecasting whether the Game of Life will halt or run forever becomes difficult if not impossible.

This is exacerbated by the brittleness of the future behavior as a function of initial positioning of the checkers. An elaborate distribution of checkers might result in a Game of Life pattern that runs forever. Move one checker and the subsequent process may become extinct and therefore halt.

A simple example is the blinker that oscillates back and forth forever. The blinker starts with three adjacent checkers placed in a horizontal row. Move the right most checker one square to the right so that there are now horizontally two adjacent checkers, an empty space, and a third checker. In the Game of Life, this new pattern goes extinct in the first iteration and the board is empty. Moving one square therefore transforms the immortal never-halting blinker into a pattern that immediately becomes extinct. The same initialization brittleness can be found in larger, more complex checker patterns.

Here, for our purposes, is the takeaway. The Game of Life results in patterns that go on forever or become extinct. If we had a halting oracle, we could write Conway's four rules and the initial checker pattern in a computer program and present the program to the halting oracle. The halting oracle would then tell us whether the future offers eternal life or extinction. But Turing has proved there is no computer program or, equivalently, no algorithm that can predict whether a computer program with an input will halt or run forever.

Rice's Generalization

IN HIS PhD dissertation at Syracuse University in the early 1950s, mathematician Henry Rice generalized Turing's halting problem and showed that no computer program behavior could be deduced by another computer program.[14] Not only is there no algorithm to determine whether a computer program will halt, there's no algorithm to determine anything non-trivial a computer program will do. There is no algorithm, for example, to determine whether an arbitrary computer program will print out the number three.

Although there is a formal mathematical development demonstrating Rice's theorem, its illustration is straightforward. Examples of Rice's theorem can often be seen by piggybacking on the Turing halting problem. Here's an example about the specific problem of printing a three or not. Consider again the computer program we wrote for Goldbach's conjecture. In the Goldbach program, even numbers are sequentially checked to see if they can be expressed as the sum of two primes. When presented to the halting oracle, Goldbach's conjecture will be disproved if the program halts, and proved if it doesn't. Now let's go back to the Goldbach computer program and make a small change. A line of code is inserted into the program that, prior to finding a counterexample and stopping, the program prints the number three. This is the only print command in the code. So if Goldbach's conjecture is false, the computer prints a three and stops. If the Goldbach program runs forever and Goldbach's conjecture is true, then the computer program will never print a three. Therefore, if there can exist no halting oracle, there can be no oracle that can examine an arbitrary computer program and announce whether the computer program will ever print a three.

Rice's theorem and the special case of the halting oracle are examples of the many things a computer cannot do.

Takeaways

Alan Turing proved there are truths outside of the capabilities of computers that cannot be algorithmically proven. Turing's proof of the non-algorithmic nature of the halting problem was the first of many problems shown to not be solvable by computer software, including AI. Goldbach's conjecture cannot be solved using a halting oracle. Nevertheless, Goldbach's conjecture is either true or false, and hope looms for a proof sometime in the future.

More interesting is the case where the truth of a proposition is provably unknowable. In the next chapter, Chaitin's number is introduced. It is a number between zero and one and is a function of the computer language under consideration. Chaitin's number can be used to prove or disprove every problem in mathematics requiring a single counterexample. These include Goldbach's conjecture, the Riemann hypothesis, and the conjectures of Collatz and Legendre. Remarkable as it sounds, Chaitin's single number does it all.

But Chaitin's number is provably unknowable. This means there are well-defined numbers that provably exist that are provably unknowable.

Showing there are provably unknowable realities is the topic of the next chapter.

12. The Unknowable

> The halting probability omega is maximally unstructured and maximally unknowable.... A religious person once in Vienna told me that he viewed it as a step closer to God because it shows something [in] the mind of God... a numerical value, but we can't get it.
>
> —Gregory Chaitin[1]

COMPUTERS AND COMPUTER PROGRAMS HAVE PROPERTIES THAT are unknowable. Non-computable you have even more remarkable unknowable properties. How do you know anything? What will your future self remember about you now? What are you capable of achieving?

Donald Rumsfeld knows about the unknowable. He served as the United States Secretary of Defense in the early 2000s. He offered the following word jumble: "There are known knowns; there are things we know we know. We also know there are known unknowns; that is to say, we know there are some things we do not know. But there are also unknown unknowns—the ones we don't know we don't know."[2]

Upon first hearing, Rumsfeld's quote sounds like doubletalk. But careful reading reveals insight. There are indeed things we don't know we don't know. In AI unexpected contingencies are something we don't know we don't know. AI engineers didn't know a windblown plastic bag would befuddle a self-driving car until it happened.

A case not considered in Rumsfeld's list is something knowably unknowable. In computer science, we can prove mathematically there are things that exist that are unknowable. Two examples are minimal computer program questions and Chaitin's number.

Are non-computable and unknowable synonymous? When I asked Gregory Chaitin this question, he responded affirmatively. He said, "There's no program to calculate it. There's no way to prove it."[3]

Chaitin is credited, along with Andrey Kolmogorov and Ray Solomonoff, as independently founding the field of Algorithmic Information Theory, also referred to as Kolmogorov-Chaitin-Solomonoff, or KCS, information theory.[4] Impressively, Chaitin formulated the basics of the theory while a senior in high school in the Bronx and published his initial contributions in a peer-reviewed journal papers while still a teenager.

KCS complexity is commonly referred to as Kolmogorov information. The reason for this is the Matthew principle. We read in Matthew 13:12, "Whoever has will be given more, and they will have an abundance. Whoever does not have, even what they have will be taken from them." Of the three men who independently discovered the principles of the theory, the Russian mathematician Kolmogorov was the most famous. He was a member of the Russian Academy of Science for his many contributions, including development of the axiomatic model of probability. At the age of five, he noted that the sum of odd numbers starting with one was always a perfect square. For example, $1 + 3 + 5 = 9$ and 9 is 3 times three, or three squared. Adding the first thirty-nine odd integers, $1 + 3 + 5 + ... + 39$ gives 400, which is equal to the square of 20. This is a pretty deep insight for a young lad of five.

On the other end of the celebrity spectrum, Solomonov was not as famous as Kolmogorov, and Chaitin was a teenager. According to the Matthew principle, all the glory usually goes to Kolmogorov. But we'll use the more historically fair term KCS information theory.

Foundational to KCS complexity is the length of elegant program.[5]

Elegant Programs

THE SHORTEST program for doing a specific task is called an elegant program. Unfortunately, for long programs, elegant programs are unknowable. One may stumble across an elegant program but never know it.

Consider a 3D printer. Amazingly, 3D printers can print body parts,[6] ceramic body armor,[7] toys,[8] firearms,[9] and who knows what else. These printers require programming. Consider a computer program to print a 3D image of the bust of Abraham Lincoln. The bust requires details of Lincoln ranging from his tussled hair to the mole-like bump on his left cheek. When written, this computer program will have a certain length in bits. Now consider a computer program to print a spherical bowling ball with three finger holes. Which program will be shorter?

The bowling ball is an easily described sphere with three holes. The program for the bust of Lincoln requires lots of details. The simpler bowling ball program will obviously be shorter when measured in bits.

If both you and I are tasked with writing a computer program to generate the same bust of Abraham Lincoln, our programs will be different. One of our programs will be shorter than the other. There must exist a shortest program for printing Lincoln's bust. Chaitin dubbed this shortest program the elegant program.[10] The length of the shortest program is a measure in bits of the KCS (or Kolmogorov) complexity of Lincoln's bust.

Since it is less complex, the elegant program for the bowling ball will be shorter than the elegant program for Lincoln's bust.

Those familiar with computers know about compression software that produces zip files and JPG images. Large images are made smaller by taking into account redundancy. Compressed files transmit more quickly and are then reconstructed by the receiver.

The compressing process can be compared to shipping dehydrated food. Water is removed at the factory. The waterless food is light and can be shipped less expensively. The customer rehydrates and, ideally, reconstructs the original food at the receiving end. Likewise, compressed files can be transmitted using limited bandwidth and be "rehydrated" at the receiver.

Rehydrated food rarely tastes as good as the original. The dehydration process often loses and even undesirably modifies the original food's taste, aroma, and texture. Some image compression techniques, such as JPG image compression, are likewise "lossy." The recovered image is a slightly corrupted version of the original. If an original computer file can be recovered from a compressed file exactly, the compression is said to be lossless. Lossless dehydration would result in reconstituted food that is indistinguishable from the original. Portable network graphic (PNG) images are examples of lossless compression.

For a given file, there is a way to compress maximally for given computational resources. The smallest lossless compression of a file, the elegant program, is the KCS complexity of the file measured in bits. The shortest file is the elegant program description of the image. The compression is typically cast in terms of a descriptive computer program able to reproduce the object.

Any large file can obviously not be compressed into a single bit. And any file can obviously be represented by its uncompressed version. Therefore, the KCS complexity of any file lies somewhere between one bit and the length of the uncompressed file in bits.

Here are some examples to help think in terms of KCS complexity. Structured sequences, like the repeating 01,

X = 01 01 01 01 ... 01,

have a small KCS information. A short program able to completely characterize the string is "repeat 01 a thousand times and halt."

A sequence of 0s and 1s formed by flipping a fair coin 1000 times will almost assuredly have KCS information close to 1000 bits. There is no structure or redundancy of which to take advantage. In other words, the coin flipping sequence is not compressible. We have to write the entire sequence of 0s and 1s in order to capture the sequence with no loss. The KCS complexity will be close to the length of the uncompressed file.

There are deceptive strings that look random, with seemingly large KCS complexity, but are not. One is the Champernowne constant.[11] The number is

0 1 2 3 4 5 6...

The constant is seen to be a list of sequential counting numbers side by side. In base ten the numbers do not look very random. The list in binary looks more ominous.

0 1 00 01 10 11 000 001 ...

What's so special about this number? Published when D. G. Champernowne was still an undergraduate, the number passes many tests for randomness, just like a repeated coin flip. But Champernowne's constant has a low KCS complexity. Like the coin flipping example, most lists of randomly appearing numbers are not compressible. But Champernowne's number has a short description, namely, "Write all integers side by side starting at zero."

Another example of a complex-looking sequence is the binary string describing the number pi.

$\pi = 3.14159...$

The string appears random. But π can be computed from many short looping algorithms. Its KCS complexity is very low.

Elegant Programs and Halting

Looping and halting are not relevant to whether a computer program is elegant or not. The number pi goes on forever without repeating. It can be computed using a looping program that runs forever. Every loop in the program generates pi to greater and greater precision. There must be a shortest elegant program to generate pi. No one of whom I am aware has claimed identification of this program.

Some real numbers are not computable even with finite unbounded resources. This interesting observation was made in 1937 by Alan Turing in a paper whose title begins "On Computable Numbers."[12] All integers are computable. Rational numbers, defined as the ratio of two integers, are likewise computable. Many irrational numbers like pi are computable by programs that loop forever.

But some irrational numbers cannot be computed. Imagine repeatedly choosing a number from zero through nine randomly, forever. The numbers are placed side by side, to the right of a decimal, to generate an irrational number between zero and one. The number might be 0.520913... etc., forever. This number will not be computable with a short computer program. The best the computer can do is say "X=0.520913... etc., forever. Print." There is finite memory in the universe, so this irrational number composed of random integers that goes on forever cannot be computed.

There is a continuum of numbers that can't be computed. A continuum, like all the real numbers from zero to one, can't be counted. Numbers able to be computed are countably infinite and, in this sense, smaller in number. As the name suggests, countably infinite is an infinity which can be counted. The integers, 1, 2, 3, 4, ... etc. are countably infinite. You can count them. All the numbers between zero and one is a larger infinity and can't be counted.

All computable numbers have a corresponding elegant computer program and, curiously, turn out to be countably infinite.

Translating Computer Languages

The KCS complexity of an object is the length of the object's elegant program. In other words, the amount of information of an object is the length of the smallest computer program able to reproduce the object exactly.

The length of any elegant program will depend on the computer language used. The shortest program to generate any object using the computer language Python will have a different length in bits than if the computer language Basic is used.

But there will always be a translating program to convert Python code into Basic code. The length of the translating program is fixed. If we have an elegant program in Python, the corresponding elegant program in Basic will have a shorter length that the sum of the length of the fixed translating Python-to-Basic program and the KCS complexity of the elegant Python program.

This doesn't specify the KCS complexity of the Basic program but does give a bound on the length of the elegant program written in Basic. So if an elegant program in Python is a billion bits and the translation program a hundred million bits, we are assured the KCS complexity of the elegant program in Basic is less than 1.1 billion bits.

Is a Program Elegant?

THE STATUS of a given program as elegant is unknowable for long programs. In other words, we can never know whether a program for a given task is the shortest possible program for that task. We might stumble across such an elegant program but won't know that it's elegant.

Furthermore, we can easily prove there can be no computer program to algorithmically show if any computer program above a given length is elegant.

The proof uses reasoning similar to that found in the Berry paradox.

The Berry Paradox

G. G. Berry, a librarian, told mathematician Bertrand Russell about a special number. Berry's number was "the smallest positive integer not definable in under sixty letters."[13]

Counting words is easier than counting letters, so let's change Berry's number to "the smallest positive integer not definable in under a dozen words."

As numbers get larger, their description in English can get longer. All numbers between zero and a hundred can be stated using only one or two words. For instance, the number 77 is stated in two words, "seventy-seven."

Numbers between a thousand and a hundred thousand need at most seven words. For example, the number 33,243 can be written as "thirty-three thousand two hundred forty-three."

Words above a million are longer. The number 1,234,560 can be stated as "one million two hundred thirty-four thousand five hundred sixty." The word count here is ten. So what is Berry's number? What is "the smallest positive integer not definable in under a dozen words"?

Berry's number thus defined seems innocent enough until the words in the sentence are counted and meta-analysis applied. The phrase "the smallest positive integer not definable in under a dozen words" has eleven words. Here's the rub. The sentence itself defines Berry's number but does so in eleven words. Asking for the smallest number requiring a dozen words using this sentence therefore reveals a logical illusion. Berry's statement of his number is nonsense. Finding "the smallest positive integer not definable in under a dozen words" defines the number in eleven words.

Similar reasoning can be applied to show there exists no computer program that can identify whether a computer program is elegant. Addressing whether a program is elegant reveals a logical illusion similar to Berry's paradox. The elegant program for a complex object is unknowable.

Let's unpack this claim.

Non-Computable Elegance

WE WILL now prove there is no computer program that can announce whether a long computer program is elegant.[14] This requires close attention and thinking, so if your brain is tired, you might want to skip this section. Otherwise, put on your thinking cap.

There are some caveats for proving a program is elegant, so let's make a precise statement: "Determining whether a program is elegant is not possible if its length is larger than a certain size." In other words, there is no universal elegant-program detector. Gregory Chaitin gives a wonderful (dare I say elegant?) proof of this unknowability theorem.

Chaitin's proof is beautifully simple.

Elegance Knows No Bounds

First, note there is no longest elegant program. No matter how long an elegant program, there is an elegant program for another object that is longer. The program for printing three busts of Lincoln is a teeny bit longer than that for printing only one. The three bust program is something like, "Print Lincoln's bust. Repeat twice. HALT."

There are better examples. We can have an elegant program that describes Lincoln's 3D bust and another elegant program that describes a specific 3D statue of Bugs Bunny. The elegant program describing both Lincoln's bust and Bugs Bunny will be longer than either one of the individual elegant programs. Likewise, a 3D elegant program for busts of all members of the US Senate will be longer than the shortest program for Lincoln's bust only.

There is no longest elegant program. Elegant program length can be arbitrarily large. The length of elegant programs for a given program language is unbounded.

Chaitin's Elegant Proof (Pun Intended)

A reductio ad absurdum smackdown can now be applied to prove the algorithmic unknowability of whether a program is elegant.

To apply the reductio ad absurdum smackdown or, equivalently, a proof by contradiction, an assumption must first be made. If the assumption is shown not to be true, then the opposite of the assumption must be true. So let's start out by assuming there is a computer program to tell whether a computer program is elegant. We'll call this program the elegance detector. If a program input as a sequence of bits is elegant, the elegance detector spits out a one. If not, the elegance detector outputs a value of zero.

If there is such an elegant-program detector, then it has a fixed length. Add to this the length of a binary counter of finite length. Starting at some initial point, the counter in the program sequentially adds one—like a digital odometer or the counter for the national debt. Assume the combined length of the elegance detector and the counter is, say, E (for elegant) bits.

All computer programs can be reduced to a sequence of bits. We start out the binary counter by inputting E bits that are all zero. This sequence of bits may correspond to some computer program, and the elegance detector outputs a one if it is elegant. If not elegant, or the sequence of zeros is nonsense as a computer program, the output is zero.

Next the counter generates another sequence of E zeros, except the last bit is changed from a zero to a one. This is a different possible elegant program and the elegant-program detector checks to see if it is. The counting continues. The next program is all zeros except the last two bits are 10. In other words, we are using a binary counter that, in binary, inputs all the programs of length E bits sequentially. Doing so can be done by a very short looping program that does the counting. This is a lot of programs to check, but this is okay. The concern here is not with how long programs take to run but only with the length of the computer program.

After a while all programs of length E have been checked. All have been tagged as elegant or not. The counter continues by checking all potential programs that are of length E+1 bits, starting with E+1 zeros. When this is done, all programs of length E+2 start to be checked.

Here's the rub. Since there are elegant programs of ever-increasing length, the elegance detector will eventually detect an elegant program of length greater than E bits. For purposes of discussion, let's say an elegant program is discovered that is E+100 bits long.

But wait a minute. A program of length E, the elegance detector, has generated and identified an elegant program of length E+100. Think about it. This is a contradiction similar to Berry's paradox.

The elegance of the program has been identified using the E bits of the elegant-program detector. Since the elegance detector is of length E bits and has generated the elegant program, any elegant program detected by the elegant-program detector cannot have an elegance above E bits. An E+100 length elegant program has been input into the elegant-program detector capable of generating the program using E bits. The elegant-program detector is, itself, the elegant program for generating the E+100 length elegant program. This cannot be! The elegant program is either E bits or E+100 bits. It can't be both.

This is the beautiful contradiction noted by Chaitin that proves that an elegant-program detector for checking all elegant programs cannot exist. The universal elegant program detector is not computable and therefore not algorithmic. For arbitrarily large computer programs, there is no way to determine the corresponding shortest program. The elegant program for a long program, like 3D printing of busts of all congressmen, in this sense is unknowable as such.

The length of an elegant program is its Kolmogorov or KCS information. We have just proved that the KCS information of an object is unknowable. This can include the shortest program for generating Lincoln's bust on a 3D printer or the maximum possible compression of a large image. Current compression algorithms, like PNG compression of images and zip algorithms for making big files smaller, do a good job but only provide an upper bound for the true KCS information. The true KCS information of long computer programs with long elegant programs is provably unknowable.

The Turing halting oracle and KCS information cannot be computed. They are unknowable. But the most compelling and mind-blowing non-computable unknowable is Chaitin's number.

Chaitin's Number

CHAITIN'S NUMBER, unknowable, is an intellectually stunning piece of mathematics ranking with Cantor's model of the infinite and Shannon's theory of information in terms of mind-bending brilliance. Chaitin's number exists. If you write programs in C++, Python, or Basic, your computer language has a Chaitin number. It's a feature of your computer programming language. We can prove that Chaitin's number exists, but also that it is unknowable.

The mathematically provable idea that something exists but is unknowable has clear philosophical and theological implications. There is a connection with Plato's cave allegory. Prisoners are chained together in a cave. They are only able to observe the wall of the cave. Behind the prisoners is a brightly burning fire, and between the prisoners and the fire there is activity. The prisoners can only see the shadows of activity on the cave walls. The shadows on the cave walls are their best view of true reality. The prisoners might expect there is true activity behind the shadows but, as long as they are chained and unable to look behind them, the true reality behind this activity is to them unknowable. Plato's allegory goes on, but the story thus far serves our purpose: there are things we know exist that are unknowable. We only know their shadows. Chaitin's number is one of those things. It exists, but it is provably unknowable.

Like Chaitin's number, elegant programs exist but can be unknowable. But when understood, Chaitin's number is more mind-blowing. Chaitin's number, one number, can be used to prove or disprove every known math conjecture that requires a single counterexample to disprove. We've previously listed a few of these open problems. They include Goldbach's conjecture, the Riemann hypothesis, the Collatz conjecture, and Legendre's conjecture.

This claim about Chaitin's number seems so outlandish we need to repeat it. Any open problem in mathematics that requires a single counterexample to disprove it can be proved or disproved using Chaitin's one number. Even though Chaitin's number is irrational and goes on forever without any pattern, it only needs to be known to finite precision to solve any arbitrarily long but finite list of open problems.

An Awkward Dance with Chaitin's Number

I was just learning about Chaitin's number when I heard a talk about the number at an invitation-only conference in 2006. When the talk was finished, I asked the speaker whether Chaitin's number changed depending on the computer language used. For example, is Chaitin's number different for the computer language Python than for the computer language C++? The speaker assured me that, just like KCS complexity, the number changed from language to language. In my role of pompous professor, I ignorantly informed the speaker I disagreed. He shrugged and went on to another question.[15]

On the plane trip home from the conference, I mentioned to my friend and fellow conference attendee William Dembski that Chaitin's number blew my mind. The number was an intellectually brilliant idea. I then mentioned to Bill that I would love to talk to Gregory Chaitin. In addition to formulating Chaitin's number, Chaitin was one of the three independent developers of algorithmic information theory. I told Bill I would love to meet this man and see what kind of mind thought such incredible thoughts.

Bill turned to me, his eyes wide with surprise.

"The speaker at the conference—the one you asked the question to. That was Gregory Chaitin!"

I was simultaneously surprised and embarrassed. I had corrected Gregory Chaitin on a property of Chaitin's number!

I came to find out—no surprise—I was wrong and Chaitin was right. Chaitin's number is different in Python than it is in C++. Some call Chaitin's number Chaitin's constant (as Wikipedia currently does).[16] But since the number changes from computer language to language, it is not a constant in the sense of Planck's constant or the speed of light. The term Chaitin's number is more appropriate.

I later met Dr. Chaitin, in 2011, at a conference in Italy and confessed about our first meeting. He was mildly amused. A decade later, in 2021, I recorded a wonderful two-hour podcast with Chaitin[17] where we talked about everything from his two children to his proof of KCS information unknowability, to Chaitin's number.

My wish to explore the mind of this intellectual giant had come true.

The Taxman's Deduction

The principle behind Chaitin's number can be boiled down to a simple illustration. There are two identically appearing bags of grain. One contains corn and the other contains beans. One sack is opened and it contains beans. The second bag doesn't need to be opened to identify its contents. It contains corn. Likewise, in the Taxman's Deduction example to be discussed, the payments of one taxpayer can tell us something about another taxpayer whose payment is not known. Chaitin's constant, we will see, informs us about programs that loop forever using information from computer programs that are seen to halt.

To more deeply understand Chaitin's number, consider the following tax collection problem. Again, you will need to put on your thinking cap.

A man gives Beggar Bob eight dollars with the instructions he should either keep it all or divide the money in two and give the two halves to two different people. And everybody who receives the money is told to do the same thing: keep the money or divide it in half and give to two different people.

Bob takes the money and starts the giveaway process. After all the sharing is done, the money ends up in the following hands:

$4 Shirley

$2 Goodness

$1 Ann

$1 spread among other people

The sum of the distributed money adds up to the eight dollars originally given to Beggar Bob. The taxman's job is to collect taxes on all the eight dollars according to who has what. He knows who has how much money. He also knows tax has been paid on five of the eight dollars but doesn't know who paid what. The five dollars, we will see, is analogous to Chaitin's number. We'll call five dollars the Tax Number.

To flush out the tax cheats, the taxman calls on his assistant to bring him individual records of tax payments. But the tax payment information comes in slowly. The assistant brings the taxman documents showing that Goodness ($2) paid her taxes. Immediately, the taxman knows that Shirley ($4) has not paid her taxes. Why? Because tax has been collected on $5 and Goodness has paid on $2 of the $5. The taxman knows Shirley has not paid her taxes on $4 because, if she had, the taxman would have collected more than $5, which he hasn't. Therefore, even though the taxman does not have a direct report about Shirley, he is justified in garnishing Shirley's wages to collect her back taxes.

One way to account for Beggar Bob's sharing is use of a string of bits. Every time sharing happens, an additional bit is added.[18] The table of taxpayers can be written in binary as:

Shirley: 0
Goodness: 10
Ann: 110
Binary strings of length four or more to other people

Goodness's string of 10 means sharing has occurred twice. So Goodness gets one half of one half, or a fourth, of the eight dollars. Ann's binary string is three bits long. She gets only an eight of the $8. The longer the string, the less the percent of money.

Here's how Chaitin's number relates to the tax example. Those who have paid taxes correspond to computer programs that have halted. Because of the Tax Number, some tax welchers can be identified when only a few payments from taxpayers have been identified. Likewise, with Chaitin's number, programs that will loop forever and never halt can be fingered when other programs have halted.

Let's drill down further.

Assigning a string of bits to each keeper of money can be thought of as a computer program. Assume Goodness's bit string of 10 is a computer program, as is Ann's 110. When reduced to a binary string, computer programs will be much longer than this, consisting of bit streams of a billion bits or more. Assuming the dollar can be subdivided into sub-penny units, sharing can continue as long as desired

Each subsequent split corresponds to adding a new bit,[19] and each split decreases the value of a program by one-half. This can be visualized as a tree. If there is sharing, a branch of a tree grows two more branches corresponding to the two persons shared with. If there is a decision not to split, the tree has a terminal leaf. The splitting continues until a program is complete and each branch is terminated in a leaf.[20] The splitting, or in case of the tax problem, the sharing, stops for that branch of the tree. The tree will be big and the programs will get quite long.

Each leaf of the tree corresponds to a computer program that will halt or loop forever. Like the taxman doesn't know who paid and who didn't, we have no idea which program halts and which loops forever.

Consider the task of running all the programs on the tree at the same time. Doing so will be a formidable but computable task. After a while a number of these programs will halt. Suppose we have our eye on a program that is still running. Is there any way we can ascertain whether that program will run forever? If the program's value when added to the accumulated value of all the other programs that have halted exceeds Chaitin's number, we know for a certainty the program under scrutiny will run forever! This can be determined before all the programs that will stop have stopped.

This is exactly analogous to the taxman's identifying tax cheats before all the tax paying records are collected. To make the identification, the taxman requires the Tax Number. For the computer programs, knowledge of Chaitin's number is needed.

Solving the World's Problems

As all programs corresponding to tree leaves are run, some will halt. If a program halts, its value is added to the tally of all the programs that have halted. This tally cannot exceed Chaitin's number. If the cost of a program added to the current tally exceeds Chaitin's number, that program will loop forever.

The tree of computer programs is enormous. One of the strings of zero and ones in a tree's leaves will correspond to a program written to evaluate Goldbach's conjecture about all even numbers being the sum of two primes. Recall that, if this program halts, the Goldbach conjecture is disproved. If not, Goldbach's conjecture is true. Chaitin's number can tell us if the Goldbach program will run forever if enough other programs in the tree have halted. If, as evidenced by all the programs that have halted, the Goldbach program when added to the tally exceeds Chaitin's number, then, like identifying the tax sheet, we know the Goldbach program will never halt. A counterexample will never be found. In this case, Goldbach's conjecture would be proven true.

But not only does the Goldbach program live as a sequence of ones and zeros on the computer program tree, so do the analogous programs evaluating such open problems as Legendre's conjecture, the Riemann hypothesis, the Collatz conjecture, and even the "May the Fours Be with You" conjecture. All these open problems can be solved by seeing if inclusion of their value in the tally of halted programs exceeds Chaitin's number. If Chaitin's number is exceeded by a running program, the program under inspection will loop forever and the conjecture irrefutably proved.

This is such an astonishing result it needs to be stated again. One number, Chaitin's number, can be used to solve all the open mathematics problems thus far proposed in the world that can be disproved with a single counterexample in an infinite list of possibilities.

So (drum roll) what is Chaitin's number?

Since the total value of all programs cannot exceed one and the value of programs that halt is a subset of these programs, Chaitin's number lies between zero and one. It will be very close to zero.

A catch, of course, is that Chaitin's number requires the accumulated value tally of all the programs that halt. This could be done by applying a halting oracle to every program. Doing so, though, would be overkill. We don't need to know specifically whether a program halts or loops. We only need the accumulated value of all the programs that halt. This is much less information than whether each individual program loops or halts. Besides, if we knew which programs loop or halt, we'd know whether the Goldbach program looped or halted. There would be no need to use Chaitin's number to determine this.

How might we determine Chaitin's number in a more direct fashion without repeated use of a halting oracle? No one knows.

So there you have it: Chaitin's number is extraordinary in what it can do. It exists but is unknowable.

Chaitin's number is appropriately called "mystical" and "magical" by the leading textbook in information theory.[21]

Notes and Limitations

HERE ARE some clarifications about Chaitin's number.

First, Chaitin's number is irrational, so it goes on forever with no repeating pattern. But to apply it to a given list of conjectures, Chaitin's number needs to be known to only finite precision. For any list of conjectures, the precision needed is determined by the longest computer program on the list of conjectures we are trying to resolve.

Secondly, there are numerous open problems that cannot be proved or disproved by a single counterexample. Chaitin's number isn't useful in answering such questions. An example is the twin prime problem. Two primes are said to be twin if they are two units apart. The number pairs (11,13), (41,43) and (101,103) are examples of twin primes. Are there an infinite number of twin primes? Knowing Chaitin's number does not solve this problem.

Thirdly, applying Chaitin's number would be an ominous task even if we knew Chaitin's number. Running all complete computer programs less than a given length is an unsurmountable undertaking even for the fastest parallel computers. And some programs can take eons to run before they halt. The extreme times required for certain programs to run explode into the unbelievably enormous busy beaver numbers[22] of Algorithmic Information Theory that are so large, a list of them can't be computed! So, the actual use of a knowable Chaitin's number to prove or disprove anything looks extremely doubtful.

The books of Gregory Chaitin, the source of Chaitin's number, are highly readable for the average nerd.[23] Included in Chaitin's book list is one entitled *The Unknowable*.

Non-Computable You

AI is executed by computers and there are barriers to what computer programs can do. That is why your most interesting properties are non-computable. Computer programs, themselves, have mysterious properties. Brilliant minds like Gödel, Turing, Kolmogorov, and Chaitin have explored these mysteries and have shown there are brick wall dead-ends to what can be known. Writing computer programs to solve the unknowables addressed in this chapter is impossible. They will forever remain unknowable—so abandon all hope. There is no way through, over, under, or around the brick wall of unknowability.

Computers can only analyze inside the box. Remarkable humans have the meta-ability to go outside ourselves, look back inside, and explore our abilities. We can understand understanding, think about thinking, and as seen in this chapter, know about the unknowable. These are astounding intellectual abilities beyond the capability of any computer. Our extraordinary meta-abilities provide more examples supporting both the limitations of computers and the non-computableness of you.

13. Randomness Happens

Anyone who considers arithmetical methods of producing
random digits is, of course, in a state of sin.
—John von Neumann[1]

Random numbers are used extensively in machine intelligence. Randomly assigned weights between neurons are typically used to initialize neural network training. In metallurgy, slow cooling of metal enhances the properties of the final product. The process is called annealing. Lots of heat means a lot of vibration of atoms—a lot of noise. Simulated annealing in AI schedules a reduction of random noise strength in the cooling of a computer search problem to make finding of the final optimal solution more probable. Evolution simulation in AI requires random mutation in each search generation.[2]

But generating true random numbers by computers is non-algorithmic. Computers are limited to deterministic operations and cannot generate random numbers. So-called random numbers generated by a computer program are not random. They are described, rather, as pseudo-random numbers. Pseudo-random numbers often work quite well as substitutes for true random numbers. But we must look to the quantum world for true randomness.

Random Numbers and Probability

One area in which randomness comes into play is in calculating probabilities. Numerical values for some probabilities are intuitively evident. The probability of getting a heads when flipping a fair coin is one-half. If a six-sided die is rolled, the probability of displaying three pips is one-sixth. Other probabilities are less evident. In the board game Monopoly, for example, what is the probability of landing on Free Parking after twenty moves? Figuring this out is possible but requires highly detailed analysis. An easier approach is to write a computer program to simulate playing the Monopoly board game. Run the computer program a billion times and count the number of times you land on Free Parking after twenty turns. Divide this number by a billion and you have a good estimate of the Free Parking probability.

Likewise, if a coin is flipped a billion times, you'd expect very close to half of the flips to result in a heads, giving an estimate of one-half as the probability of getting a head on the flip of a fair coin.

Estimating probabilities by repeated probabilistic simulations is called Monte Carlo simulation. The Monte Carlo name was coined by Stan Ulam and John Von Neumann during their classified thermonuclear bomb research at Los Alamos in 1946.[3] This was during the Jurassic period in the development of the computer.

I once applied Monte Carlo simulation to calculating the probability of winning the Cracker Barrel restaurant puzzle. In every Cracker Barrel restaurant I've ever visited, this triangularly shaped puzzle is on every dining table. There are fifteen holes in the board and a golf tee is inserted into all but one hole. As in checkers, the golf tees can be jumped as long as doing so lands you in an empty hole. The jumped peg is then removed. This solitaire game is won if you reach a point where only one peg remains on the triangular board.

What is the probability of winning the Cracker Barrel game? I wrote a simple Monte Carlo simulation to estimate the probability of winning. At every position, there are a small handful of possible jumps. I gave an equal probability to each jump. I published the result in the book *Introduction to Evolutionary Informatics*,[4] co-authored with William Dembski and Winston Ewert. A reader of our book independently wrote a Monte Carlo program for the same problem and claimed my results were wrong—and he was right. The results weren't off enough to alter the conclusions based on my simulation but were sufficiently off to be embarrassing.

Non-Random Calculations

My co-author Winston Ewert, programmer extraordinaire, came to the rescue by generating the exact probability of beating the puzzle. In his analysis, there were no repeated trials required in Monte Carlo simulation. He wrote a program that tracked every possible Cracker Barrel game using a branching tree. If there were three possible moves at some point, Ewert looked at each solution. If the first possible jump resulted in two possible jumps on the next move, he looked at each of these contingencies individually. The two possibilities correspond to a branch in the tree dividing into two other branches. By doing so for all cases, a tree of possibilities grew one sprouting branch at a time. When a game ends, there is no more branching. The branch is terminal and is called a leaf.

If there is one peg left at the end of the game, a Cracker Barrel victory is claimed. Otherwise, the game is lost. The number of tree leaves where the game terminates is equal to the number of games possible for the Cracker Barrel puzzle. We simply divide the number of winning games by the number of leaves. This is the probability of winning the Cracker Barrel game if, at each point, the next move is chosen with equal chance. Note there is nothing random in Ewert's algorithm, although the final answer should be about the same as the Monte Carlo simulation. Like reasoning the chance of getting three pips on a roll of a six-sided die is one-sixth, Ewert calculated all possible successes and divided by the total number of all possible Cracker Barrel games.

Similar search trees can be written for most board games, including Monopoly, checkers, chess, and GO. For any given board configuration in chess, for example, there are a finite number of possible moves. Each of the possible moves gives the next set of possible moves, and so forth. All of these possibilities can be ranked according to effectiveness. Based on this ranking a proper move is made.

The problem with trees in more complex board games like chess and GO is that the number of branches explodes and soon exceeds in number all the atoms in the universe. Most board games are also competitive and must factor in strategies of the competition. These factors mean that approaches much more sophisticated than exhaustive tree searches are needed. The most common method applied here is reinforcement learning, discussed in Chapter 9.

Generating Random Numbers

In Monte Carlo simulations, how are pseudo-random numbers generated by a computer algorithm? I learned a lot about this when I consulted as an expert witness for a Native American tribe in a lawsuit involving its casino. My job as an expert was to address the difference between gambling and sweepstakes. One distinction is that sweepstakes have a finite and fixed number of prizes. When you enter a sweepstakes of the type sponsored by McDonalds or the Publisher's Clearinghouse, there is a fixed list of prizes. Once the prizes are awarded, there is no chance of winning anything else. Gambling, on the other hand, allows repeated winning. Although highly improbable, winning at roulette ten times in a row is possible. There is no fixed number of prizes. Gambling has a different set of governmentally legislated laws than sweepstakes. The tribe I represented claimed its gaming establishments did not engage in gambling. They claimed they were running a legal sweepstakes.[5]

Another requirement of sweepstakes is that no purchase is required to enter the contest. This is usually written in small print on a sweepstake ticket. Small print because the sponsors of the sweepstakes want you to spend money to buy their product. If a purchase were required to gain a chance to win, the contest would be a lottery and not a sweepstakes. My mother, Lenore Marks, was part of a rebel community who repeatedly entered sweepstakes without buying the sponsor's product. A sweepstake entry typically requires only a postcard and a stamp. Mom won a few small prizes. She quit when I convinced her that any profit she claimed for herself must include deduction of the time spent filling out the postcards and the cost of postage stamps. There is no free lunch.

On the land of the tribe I represented, local establishments that offered sweepstakes machines allowed sweepstake players to offer a "donation" to the tribe by depositing money in the slot of the sweepstake machine. Because of the "no purchase required" sweepstakes requirement, requests for free sweepstake entries could be made at the establishment. Ask and you get a freebee.

My job for the tribe was to examine the proprietary code that controlled the automatic sweepstake units. In each case I examined, the software was always righteous. The software did what its developers said it did. Legally, the games were sweepstakes and not gambling. A fixed number of prizes were determined and randomly distributed to the sweepstake players. When the list was exhausted, the sweepstakes ended—and then a new list could be generated and a new sweepstakes started.

How did the program "randomly distribute" prizes? That was the element most interesting to me. The use of random numbers in AI is ubiquitous. But how do we generate random numbers on a computer?

Deterministic Random Numbers

As I've said, it turns out that almost all so-called random number generators are not truly random. Computers can only generate random numbers deterministically. This sounds like an oxymoron but is true.

Say you want a random number between zero and one. To do this mechanically, a wheel of fortune, much like a roulette wheel, can be calibrated between zero and one. The wheel is given a spin, and when it stops it points to 0.408. This is our first random number. Give another spin and we get 0.883. Repeated spins generate a sequence of random numbers.

But are the roulette random numbers truly random? Don't Newton's laws of motion always dictate the outcome? The spinning wheel and the behavior of the little ball dictated by its initial conditions and the interface with the roulette wheel can all be modeled by classic Newtonian physics. If I spin the wheel twice exactly the same way, drop the ball exactly the same way at the same point on the wheel, and there is no interference with the wheel, like vibration or heavy breezes, the outcome in both cases should be the same. The roulette wheel outcome is deterministic, but the interactions are so complicated that the outcome is more easily modeled probabilistically. The random outcome of the spin of a roulette wheel is perhaps better described as pseudo-random.

Computers are also unable to generate true random numbers. Random numbers generated by computers are also better described as pseudo-random. Here's a simple way to generate pseudo-random numbers between zero and one using what is called a linear congruential generator. Start with any number between zero and one. This is called the seed. Then add pi = 3.14159. Pi is a convenient number to add because it is complicated and usually available on the computer as a single symbol. Then discard everything to the left of the decimal and you have a random number between zero and one.

To illustrate, suppose we start with a seed equal to a half. Adding pi gives 3.6415. To generate the random number between zero and one, simply drop the 3. The number to the right of the decimal, 0.6415, remains. This is the first random number. We can then loop and use this random number to generate another random number. If we take 0.6415 and repeat the operation of adding pi and keeping only the numbers to the right of the decimal, we get yet another random number: 0.7832. Repeating this process again and again generates a decent list of random numbers between zero and one.

Notice that this procedure is deterministic. There is nothing random happening except for one subtle thing: the sequence of random numbers has to start at some point. What makes the string of numbers random is the choice of the first number, called the seed. If you and I started with the same seed and use the same random number-generating algorithm, we would generate the same random sequence of numbers.

For this reason, the random number generation process is a pseudo-random number generator.

If I choose a seed unknown to you, you will not generate the same sequence of numbers that I do. What makes the numbers look random is the choice of the initializing seed.

The linear congruential generator, once popular, has today been replaced by more sophisticated algorithms that also require a random seed. A truly random seed cannot be generated by a computer. One way to get a seed is to grab a random number off the computer's real-time clock. If you have ever seen a continuously updated tally of the US national debt, the digits corresponding to dollars, tens of dollars, and hundreds of dollars are changing so fast they appear blurred.[6] If "STOP" is hit at any time, these last three digits will be as if they are randomly chosen between 000 and 999. The computer's real-time clock is a place where a random number seed can likewise be generated. Grab a few of the least significant digits, stick a decimal point in front, and we have a seed to generate a string of pseudo-random numbers. Note that the seed is not generated by code. The seed is generated by reaching outside the code to, in this case, the computer's clock.

A problem with pseudo-random number generators is that, given a long enough sequence of numbers, they can be cracked. When random numbers are used in encryption, this is not good.

There are two cracking problem types. The most difficult, the non-parametric case, occurs when only a long sequence of random numbers is known. Nothing is known about how the sequence was generated. We have no idea whether a linear congruential generator or some other algorithm was used. Here, deep learning neural networks can be used to learn to duplicate the sequence of random numbers. Research in doing so is in its infancy but nothing stands in the way of more powerful computers solving the problem.[7]

Easier is the parametric problem where, in addition to a long line of pseudo-random numbers, the type of pseudo-random number generator is known. A given pseudo-random number generator will only have a handful of unknown parameters. Finding the numerical value of these parameters totally defines the operation of the pseudo-random number generator. The linear congruential generator has only one number that completely defines its operation. In the example we gave, the number pi was added to the previous random number. We'll call this the adder. The adder could be many other numbers. We could have used, for example, the square root of two for the adder instead of pi. The adder is the only number needed to define the sequence of random numbers. We don't even need to know the seed. Given a long line of numbers, jump in anywhere. The sequence of numbers to follow is determined by the adder and the number where you jumped in. This number acts as a seed for the random numbers that follow.

Pseudo-random number sequences have been cracked, allowing the exact forecast of future numbers from numbers past. George Marsaglia presented a crack for the primitive linear congruential random number generator using only a couple dozen consecutive pseudo-random numbers.[8] Certain types of a more sophisticated class of pseudo-random number generator called the Mersenne Twister have been cracked using 624 consecutive numbers.[9]

Care must be taken when using pseudo-random number generators in a program. I once wrote some code using the computer language of Matlab, a high-level user-friendly computer language. The program used pseudo-random numbers in a Monte Carlo simulation. I ran the simulation program for about a week and got a handful of successes over hundreds of thousands of trials. Then I ran the program again and got the exact same tally of successes. Suspicious, I looked closely and found that, unless told differently, Matlab always started their random number generator using the same seed. My two "random" simulations were therefore exactly the same because the initiating seed in both cases was the same. I had wasted a week's worth of computing time.

I fixed my code to force a new seed for the random number generator every time I started the program running. And I had learned an important lesson: software random number generators generate the same sequence of random numbers if initiated with the same seed. After the seed number was introduced, the "random number generator" used by Matlab was deterministic.

How to Recognize Truly Random Numbers

ARE PSEUDO-RANDOM numbers close to being random? How do we test to see if a string of numbers is truly random? The random numbers must be examined to see if they exhibit properties of truly random numbers.

George Marsaglia formulated the "diehard tests" to scrutinize the randomness of pseudo-random numbers.[10] The diehard tests are a battery of statistical tests assessing the quality of a random number generator.[11] An example easily understood is simple averaging. If the string of random numbers is uniform on zero to one, the average of a long list of random numbers should be about one half.

Regulatory agencies over gaming and sweepstakes require the random number generators used in one-armed bandits to pass the diehard or a similar battery of tests. The pseudo-random number generators don't always pass. For instance, the pseudo-random number generator used by Microsoft in Windows famously failed randomness tests in 2007.[12]

True Randomness Cannot Be Algorithmic

WE MUST be careful when talking about randomness because there are various definitions of randomness. In algorithmic (KCS) information theory, a sequence of ones and zeros is said to be random if it can't be compressed into a smaller file. We have seen that pseudo-random numbers can be generated if there is an initial random seed. But a long list of pseudo-random numbers can be compressed a lot. The compression consists of the typically short program used to generate the pseudo-random numbers and specification of the numerical value of the initializing seed.

As defined in the previous chapter, the elegant program to generate the sequence of pseudo-random numbers is the shortest program to do so.

In the world of classical Newtonian physics, true randomness does not exist. When I flip a coin, the measurable force applied to the coin is deterministic. When the coin hits the floor, well-established laws of elasticity and collision mechanics dictate how the coin will bounce. The outcome of the coin flip is dependably deterministic. Yet when I flip a fair coin on the fifty-yard line at the Super Bowl, the chance of getting heads or tails is modeled as 50/50. But probability theory is only a convenient model. It gives the general idea of what we should expect to happen if the coin is well-balanced and nothing else intervenes. And the model works well. Like the pseudo-random number generator or the previous example of the roulette wheel, one can argue that randomness from coin flipping and die rolling, on close analysis, is actually deterministic.

To see this more clearly, imagine a foam rubber coin with a diameter of ten inches. The coin is flipped a foot above a carpeted floor. Could the flipper orient the coin and control the flip to give a preponderance of heads outcomes? With a little practice, one could develop the skill of getting heads almost 100 percent of the time. The difficulty of developing this skill would increase over a hard wood floor, and if the giant coin were metal, and if its size decreased. Eventually the challenge would become so intractable that a probability model becomes attractive.

Pseudo-randomness occurs in computers because true randomness is non-algorithmic. Pseudo-randomness in coin flipping and roulette wheel spinning is because of the underlying deterministic Newtonian physics.

Einstein's Random Doubts

Quantum mechanics is a source of true random numbers. It is also wonderfully weird. Quantum mechanics pioneer Niels Bohr said, "Those who are not shocked when they first come across quantum theory cannot possibly have understood it."[13]

To understand a fundamental principle of quantum mechanics, we turn to the comedy movie *Mystery Men*, which features superheroes with not-so-impressive superpowers. One is Invisible Boy, a superhero who was invisible as long as no one looked at him.[14] If he was invisible, and someone peeked, he would become visible. If Invisible Boy looked at his own reflection in a mirror, he would be visible. Quantum collapse in quantum mechanics is kind of like Invisible Boy. When no one is looking, a quantum wave function can take on many values simultaneously. When someone looks at the wave function by measuring it, the wave collapses to a single value. The value it collapses to turns out to be purely random. If the same experiment is repeated on an identical wave function, it might collapse to a totally different value. If this seems surrealistically weird but you understand this explanation, then you have been "shocked" by quantum mechanics just as Niels Bohr predicted.

To work, quantum computing takes into account all of the possible solutions contained in an uncollapsed wave function. But people keep peeking and the wave function involved in quantum computing collapses. Maintaining coherence so the wave function doesn't collapse has been a major hindrance to the success of quantum computing. It's hard not to look.

Albert Einstein did not like the pure probability associated with quantum mechanics. He was famous for various remarks to the effect that God "does not play dice" with the universe.[15] Einstein thought that the quantum collapse of probabilities must be like flipping a coin. Before we flip a coin, we can only think probabilistically about the outcome, heads or tails. After the flip, whose outcome was determined by the environment and the flipping mechanics, the deterministic result is known. In practice, if a fair coin were flipped enough times, about half will be heads and half tails. This is not because the environment is not deterministic but because the environment and physics for flipping does not favor either side of a fair coin.

Einstein thought that quantum mechanics must be like that too. There must be deeper, unknown things happening in the universe (hidden variables).[16] But because we don't know what the deeper physics is doing, the best choice, like in coin flipping, is to use a probability model. Einstein's hidden variable hypothesis seemed to be untestable at first. How can we know for sure if there are hidden things we don't know about in quantum mechanics? This seemingly unresolvable position is known as the Einstein–Podolsky–Rosen (EPR) paradox.[17]

Remarkably, the EPR paradox was resolved. There are, it turns out, no local hidden variables underlying quantum mechanics. This realization results from the profound insight provided by Bell's inequality. Bell looked at two separated entangled particles and showed there were no hidden variables in their nonlocal collapse. New fresh bits of pure randomness are continually being introduced to our universe through quantum collapse.

What Does Randomness Have to Do with Human Creativity?

SIR ROGER Penrose believes that human non-algorithmic (non-computable) characteristics such as creativity are due to non-algorithmic quantum collapse in the brain's microtubules.[18] Penrose believes that algorithms and thus machine intelligence cannot be creative. The human ability to create, as we have discussed, is non-algorithmic. So there must be a non-algorithmic source underlying creativity. Penrose is a materialist and thus is self-limited to a naturalistic solution. A purely non-algorithmic phenomenon in nature looks to be quantum collapse, where true random numbers are generated.

If Penrose is correct, fresh new information is being created in our brains in our microtubules because of purely random non-algorithmic quantum collapse. But there's a problem with that theory. The bits of information generated by quantum collapse are uselessly random. Randomness alone is incapable of generating the specified complexity evident in creative thinking.[19] A random buzz generated in our neurons will not solve a stubborn math problem or write a great novel. New bits must be formulated or organized for some purpose in order for Penrose's theory to work.

Cryptography

WHILE QUANTUM randomness remains speculative as a way of explaining how our brains work, it promises useful applications for cryptography. Cryptography assures online financial transactions are rendered secure.

Must unbreakable cryptography use purely quantum random numbers, or do pseudo-random numbers work well enough? Pseudo-random number generators can pass randomness diehard tests, but the pseudo-random codes can be cracked if the underlying deterministic rule for generating those numbers is inverse engineered.[20] Remember, as we noted above, the "random numbers" are commonly generated by a rule based on the previous number generated. Rules can be hacked. Cryptography requires true, unhackable randomness, not just a string of numbers that looks random to us because we don't immediately know how they are generated.

Pseudo-random numbers have a low KCS complexity. The computer program for generating pseudo-random numbers is relatively short. Its elegant program consists only of the numerical seed and the algorithm for iteratively making future pseudo-random numbers. Recall that the number pi looks random but, in fact, can be generated with a short looping program with small complexity.

Given only a long sequence of the digits of pi, determining an underlying generative program is difficult. Similarly, a long sequence of pseudo-random numbers has a relatively small KCS complexity that is typically difficult to identify. Can the underlying pseudo-random number algorithm be identified from a sequence of numbers? Glauco Amigo, Liang Dong, and I showed that the underlying generator for a pseudo-random number generator can be duplicated using deep learning.[21] A large number of pseudo-random numbers can be required for inversion back to the underlying generating algorithm. Our analysis was on a rudimentary random number generator used in the early days of computing. More sophisticated algorithms to learn random number sequences would require higher computer power. But since the KCS complexity of all pseudo-random number generators is relatively small, it seems possible that inversion from a sequence of numbers to a short description could be achieved even for these more sophisticated algorithms. This would not be good news where pseudo-random number generators are used for encryption.

For true security, therefore, cryptography must rely on quantum randomness. Quantum random number generators spit out purely random numbers that cannot be inverted to a generating algorithm. There is no generating algorithm. Because the quantum world is truly random, quantum random number generators provide an endless unhackable source of random numbers.[22]

Quantum random number generators may seem exotic, but they are available on Amazon.com for less than a hundred dollars.

Quantum Computers

QUANTUM COMPUTERS operate in the surreal world of quantum mechanics. The operations performed by quantum computers are impressive in terms of speed, but any procedure performed on a quantum computer can also be performed on a conventional non-quantum computer, including a Turing machine.[23] An operation performed in minutes on a quantum computer might take a conventional computer years, but eventually the conventional computer would get it done.

Since all quantum computation can be performed on a regular computer, quantum computer programs so far fall under our definition of algorithmic. Students of quantum computing, for instance, are first taught about Grover's Algorithm and Shor's Algorithm. The use of the term "algorithm" in both these quantum computing procedures reveals they are deterministic at their core.

Grover's algorithm, for example, uses quantum computing for needle-in-haystack searches. I choose a random number between, say, one and two trillion. Your job is to guess that number with a sequence of yes and no questions. Classically, you might ask if the number is one. If not one, how about two? Queries might jump around and, for the third query, you might ask if the number is a million and one. If there are two trillion entries in the list, there will be a trillion queries on average. You might get lucky and find the marked entry on the first query. On a bad day, the marked entry would be identified after all other entries on the list are queried. This would require two trillion queries. On average, though, we would expect a trillion queries for success if guesses are not repeated. Grover's quantum computer algorithm reduces the number of queries by about a square root. If a trillion queries are required on a regular computer, Grover's algorithm reduces the query count to around a million queries. A million is the square root of a trillion.

Shor's algorithm is another procedure crafted exclusively for the quantum computer. You may have heard that successful quantum computers will render many encryption methods obsolete. This is because of Shor's algorithm where large numbers are quickly decomposed into their prime factors. Shor's algorithm thus renders many encryption procedures obsolete—that is, it makes them hackable.

But not to worry. Good minds are working on encryption algorithms immune from the probing eyes of Shor's algorithm.[24] Encryption using quantum mechanics, for example, will not be vulnerable to Shor's algorithm.[25] In other words, traditional encryption can be cracked by Shor's algorithm, but quantum encryption can't.

Randomness—Uncompressible

THERE MUST be care when talking about random numbers. Randomness needs to be defined in discussions. For regulatory agencies, passing the diehard battery of tests suffices. Here let's define randomness using compressibility: a sequence of numbers is random if the sequence cannot be compressed. Randomness of this sort cannot be generated by a computer. A long string of pseudo-random numbers can be compressed to the short computer program that generated them.

Generation of random numbers so defined is non-algorithmic. Even the random seed needed to jumpstart the pseudo-random number generator cannot be generated within a computer program. The seed needs to be identified external to the computer program by, for example, an appeal to a human programmer or by grabbing the least significant digits of a rapidly changing clock.

Random Thoughts

THE TURING halting problem and finding the shortest program to execute a specific complex procedure have already been shown to be non-computable, but note there is nothing random in these problems. They are deterministic. The computer program searching through all the solutions to Goldbach's conjecture either halts, thereby disproving Goldbach, or runs forever, proving Goldbach. The program either runs forever or halts. There is no randomness. To the list of provably non-algorithmic operations we add the inability of a computer program to generate truly random numbers. Doing so is non-computable. An algorithm can no more generate a true random number than a Chihuahua can lay an egg.

The only source of pure randomness thus far identified is random collapse of quantum wave functions. Many researchers agree that you are non-computable, and some think quantum collapse might be the source of non-algorithmic characteristics of humans like creativity and consciousness.[26] The topic is hotly debated. However, despite decades of exploration, any development of such claims beyond academic speculation and PowerPoint presentations is thus far lacking.

Now brace yourself for topical whiplash as we move from discussing random numbers to talking about ethics in AI.

PART FIVE: THE GOOD, THE BAD, AND THE ECCLESIASTICAL

14. AI ETHICS

I can picture in my mind a world without war, a world without hate. And I can picture us attacking that world because they'd never expect it.

—JACK HANDEY[1]

LET'S START WITH TWO DIFFERENT QUESTIONS ABOUT ETHICS. First, who is ethically responsible when AI goes wrong? For example, self-driving cars killing people.[2] And Alexa, when asked for a dangerous challenge by a ten-year-old girl, suggested sticking a plug halfway into an electric socket and shorting the two electrical prongs with a penny.[3] In cases like these, who or what is at fault?

The second question is, who is responsible for the ethical use of AI? For instance, who decides whether to deploy an autonomous swarm of killer drones? Is it ethical to delete all the news about a questionable conspiracy? Is it right to write software that deletes tweets opposed to the climate change theory or opposed to Covid vaccines?

The two questions relate to two different types of ethics about machine intelligence and technology in general. Responsibility for AI going bad is a question of design ethics. Design ethics addresses the question of whether a final AI product does what it is supposed to do and nothing more. Here the responsibility lies with design engineers and those who write software. Such people have an ethical responsibility to be careful in the design of their software, both in defining the goal of the program and in making sure their product undergoes reasonably sufficient testing and revision so that it effectively meets that goal, making sure a system does what it's supposed to do, and doesn't have anticipatable negative unintended effects.

The second question, on the other hand, relates to what is known as *end-user ethics*. Technology is available for use. But should it be used? Is it proper, for example, for a field commander to launch an autonomous anti-radiation Harpy missile given his current knowledge of the battlefield? Is it ethical for Google to write algorithms to ban your video to some people, but not to others?

End-user concerns can drive design specifications, and design limitations can impact the end use of AI technology. But design and end-user AI ethics are distinct. One belongs in a research and development lab. The other belongs in the arena of debate and politics. Both are important considerations, but they should not be conflated.

Before going further, we need to look closer at the meaning of ethics.

Defining Ethics

A BRIEF definition of ethics is "the discipline dealing with what is good and bad and with moral duty and obligation."[4] The rub here is agreeing on the meaning of good and bad. Shakespeare's Hamlet suggests there can be no real definition when he comments, "There is nothing either good or bad but thinking makes it so." Most with a foundation in faith will disagree.[5]

I have attended both secular ethics seminars and ethics seminars based on Judeo-Christian principles. The secular seminars seem to me built on sand.[6] Ultimately, they agree with Hamlet's claim that good and bad are relative. At its foundation, secular ethics must appeal to community standards, law, and consensus—all of which change with time and vary according to location.

Here's an example. According to Kai-Fu Lee, former head of Google in China, Chinese business considers the stealing of intellectual property to be acceptable standard practice.[7] Americans, on the other hand, consider such a practice to be immoral and unethical. Secular ethics theory measured by consensus cannot always be consistent.

Discrediting universal secular ethics is easily done by playing the Hitler card. The consensus in Nazi Germany was that gypsies and Jews were less than human Therefore the abuse and ultimate termination of these peoples was considered ethical by community standards. On the other hand, ethics built on a Judeo-Christian foundation appeal to natural law—the idea that right and wrong are etched on the human heart and documented in divinely inspired scripture. Unlike secular ethics built on sand, such faith-based ethics has a firm foundation. Yes, some issues remain fuzzy; but many ethical questions are answered clearly. The Ten Commandments say that stealing is wrong. This means that independent of consensus or community standards, whether in America or China, the stealing of technology is unethical. Likewise, the commandment not to murder irrefutably tags the Nazi Holocaust, independent of consensus, as evil.

Having made a stab at defining ethics, let's now delve further into the difference between design ethics and end-user ethics.

Design Ethics

IN TECHNOLOGY, design ethics requires total transparency in the performance of a final design. Ideally, the technology should do what it was designed to do and no more. But total certainty in a final design can never be guaranteed 100 percent. Legal parlance is helpful in specifying an acceptable level of performance certainty.

Here's what I mean. For some AI, strict adherence to a design goal may be unimportant. Some AI makes many mistakes, and sometimes that's okay. A good example is Alexa's response to voice commands to play Spotify tunes. As mentioned in Chapter 9, I tried without success to persuade Alexa to play "I'll Do Anything for Love" by Meatloaf. Alexa kept offering a different mix than the original. After five minutes of varying my request, I gave up. Though annoying, such mistakes we can live with. A legal standard here for AI design might be that there is a "preponderance of evidence" that Alexa works. Alexa helps a lot more that it annoys. When Alexa correctly responded to the query "Who is Robert J. Marks?" I popped a few shirt buttons.

Self-driving cars are a more serious matter. Before considering riding in a hands-free self-driving car, I would like to know the vehicle operates as intended "beyond a reasonable doubt." This higher evidential standard, applied to capital crimes, recognizes that total 100 percent certainty that Tony Two-Toes murdered Mitch the Snitch is never possible. But a jurist in the murder trial can get really close to total certainty. The same standard can be applied to design ethics with potentially life-threatening consequences.

Measuring the different levels of design assurance is the task of those making regulatory policy and standards. How are "preponderance of evidence" and "beyond a reasonable doubt" quantified?

I worked for awhile as a reliability engineer for the US Navy. The mature field of reliability engineering tests the degree to which technology meets specifications and then how well it ages. The field is important to the military because profiteers have historically sold inferior products to the military. During the Civil War, profiteers sometimes aided by corrupt politicians sold faulty supplies to the Union Army, ranging from misfiring rifles to coats without pockets or buttons.[8] The military has since adopted specifications and standards for almost every product they purchase. Reliability engineers working for the government make sure these standards are met. There looks to be much from the field of reliability engineering that can be applied to assessing AI design ethics.[9]

Keeping AI Simple

AI with a narrow goal is more easily designed and tested than AI with wider goals. AI with broad goals, like self-driving cars, has an exponential increase in the number of possible design contingencies. Complying with AI ethical design standards here becomes more difficult because vetting becomes more difficult. The problem can be partially mitigated by intense scrutiny and application of deep domain expertise during the software development and AI system testing. The more complex the AI system, the more difficult the vetting.

End-User Ethics

END-USER ETHICS, as we have said, pertains to how humans decide to use technology. In terms of ethics, AI is neither good nor bad. It is a tool.

If AI is neither good nor bad, what about malware? Malware is a piece of software that sneaks onto your computer and screws things up or invades your privacy by sharing personal info. Isn't malware always evil? By its very name, malware looks to be universally evil. But it's not the technology itself that's bad. It's the way people use it.

One fictional example is the Irene Demova virus in the NBC television series *Chuck*. The fictional virus is named after the equally fictional Irene Demova, a Serbian porn star. Those who click on her website immediately pay the price—their computers are destroyed. The malware punishes porn users. So is it good malware or bad malware? Twice in the show the virus is definitely good, because Chuck uses it to destroy computers programmed to detonate bombs.[10]

In real life, malware can serve in cyber and electronic warfare. Much of modern military conflict involves high tech, from GPS to smart radar. Missiles can be strategically guided through windows of enemy-occupied buildings. A similarly high-tech enemy will counter with technology to disable software used in warfare. Strategic advantage goes to the side that most effectively infiltrates enemy software with malware to render operations useless.

The United States used malware to slow Iran's creation of nuclear weapons. Vital uranium enrichment control software was infected with Stuxnet malware. Stuxnet is a malicious computer worm "believed to be responsible for causing substantial damage to Iran's nuclear program."[11] In delaying Iran's development of nuclear weapons, Stuxnet was good malware.

As its name implies, however, much malware is used unethically. Webmasters spin that they drop cookies in your computer to better serve you. No. They use cookies to make more money. Annoying cookie trackers are everywhere. Marketers on the other side of the computer screen might consider cookies to be good malware, but I consider unwanted cookies on my computer to be unwanted malware. They invade my privacy. The *New York Times* notes that "many streaming customers are unaware that the sitcom titles they prefer, the ads they do not skip, their email addresses and the serial numbers identifying the devices they use are being harvested and distributed."[12] A quick visit to the Amazon.com main page spawned eight cookies on my computer.

More serious is when malware shares the contents of your files. When I last went in person to visit a US Department of Defense research site, I was told the use of thumb drives was forbidden. Why? Because like Covid spreads among humans, malware can be passed from one computer to another. The Chinese government had infected many thumb drives with unwanted spy software that was injected into a computer when an infected thumb drive was plugged in.[13] The software shared the possibly classified computer content with Chinese spies. Now, when I bring a PowerPoint presentation to give at a DOD facility, it has to be on a CD. Thumb drives are too risky.

Even more severe is ransomware, where computers frozen by malware are unfrozen only after a blackmail Bitcoin ransom is paid. The practice is widespread. In 2019 Johannesburg shut down all city computers after a ransomware attack.[14] Radio stations have been crippled by ransomware.[15] In 2019 alone, over 140 local governments, police stations, and hospitals were held hostage by ransomware attacks.[16] In some cases arrests have been made, but the lucrative practice continues.[17]

There is little doubt that big banks have paid large ransoms to unfreeze their kidnapped files. Here the bad guys are paid and the kidnapping goes unreported in order to avoid negative publicity for the bank. Who wants to put their money in a bank that has been hacked?

Being Nasty Because You Can

Remember CDs and DVDs? All personal computers used to have them. Today everything is streamed. On older computers, the app that ran the DVD allowed a click to open a tray in the resident computer tower. The DVD fit perfectly. Another click told the computer to suck the drawer back into the computer and begin playing the DVD contents.

Back in those days, I received an email from a friend saying there was a free gift for me—a cupholder for my refreshing beverage. My friend's email assured me the cyber gift contained absolutely no malware. I clinked the attachment in the email and out popped the DVD tray on my computer tower. How clever! The DVD tray seen through creative eyes is a cupholder. I chuckled. I thought the email was so clever, I forwarded the gift to a number of close friends. Based on the assurance in my friend's email, I told all there was no malware associated with the gift.

Boy, was I wrong. My click to open the DVD tray released malware on my hard drive. Because I had clicked the free gift, all my documents were frozen and my computer became useless. There was no recovery my support team could identify. So I had my computer drive wiped and my software reinstalled. I lost a lot of original work. Some I could recover from co-author colleagues with whom I shared papers being written. Other documents went to wherever destroyed information goes—the same place the light goes when it goes out.

Worse, I had unknowingly shared my cyber infection with many close friends. Email responses started pouring in. They were, to say the least, annoyed. "You told me there was no malware! My computer is now useless!" One of my former friends hasn't talked with me since.

Why would someone write malware tricking people into ruining their computers? Put another way, why do vandals vandalize? The malware writers weren't motivated by money, influence, or power. Maybe the software gave them bragging rights in their circle of deplorables. Or maybe not. Some people are nasty just because they can be. But rest assured—even when nasty people violate laws without being caught, they are still punished by the experience of being who they are. Sneaky wicked people feel like sneaky wicked people.

Y2K Hall of Fame Wannabes

Here's a similar account from a couple of decades ago. The beginning of a new century was upon us, and the Y2K problem, also called the Millennium bug, was a big topic in the news. Computer code, some feared, would confuse twentieth-century year entries beginning with 19XX with twenty-first century years that started with a 20XX. The problem was hyped by alarmists in articles and books with titles like "The Year 2000 Computing Crisis."[18] The hyperbolized crisis sold books, but no such catastrophe ever occurred.

At the time I consulted for Microsoft in Redmond, Washington. While working with a project manager, I noticed a red numerical digital display on the wall that was counting something. The tally increased every few seconds. I asked the MS project manager, Mark Casebolt, what was going on?

Mark said the screen was counting the number of times malicious hackers tried to infiltrate Microsoft's systems. Why would someone want to hack into the Microsoft system? For bragging rights, I'm told. The successful hacker would be lauded by his reprehensible community for harpooning a big fish like Microsoft.

No one, it turns out, successfully hacked Microsoft regarding the Y2K concern. But thousands tried.

Phishing

I have a lot of websites. I used to host them through a company named Bluehost, and I was initially told they had unlimited website storage for a single flat fee. Not so. When I posted a large number of linked videos, I was slapped on the wrist and told by Bluehost to remove them. Videos take up a lot of space in memory. I removed them.

Then I received another email from Bluehost, again saying I had too many files on their server. I clicked on the provided link, logged in, and got confusing results. I was not being allowed to edit my sites. My screen didn't respond to clicks and was unusable. So I contacted Bluehost and was informed I had been phished, meaning I had been fooled into giving my login and password. The website in the second email link was a duplicate of Bluehost's. As with the legitimate Bluehost site, I was asked to log in and make my changes. I provided my login and password to the site, and hit return. My screen became useless and that was all. Whoever phished me with the phony Bluehost screen now had the login and password to all my websites. And that's all they needed to do their mischief.

The next day all my Bluehost web pages were infected with who-knows-what malware. Bluehost detected the bugs and blocked all my content. They were right in doing so, but it sure was irritating. I was not clever enough to avoid being suckered and didn't want my naivety to be the cause of infection of others. Luckily, I know a computer whiz, Dr. Winston Ewert, an ingenious thinker with whom I have published a lot, who knows how to heal infected files. Indeed, healing is what doctors do. Winston took all my backup files and placed my webpages on a new server, where they reside today.

My Bluehost hackers were not talented phishermen. Like bank robbers writing "this is a stickup" on the back of their business card, they had room-temperature IQs. Their malware was immediately detected and neutralized before it infected others.

The Heads and Tails of Bitcoin

Well-encrypted files can't be hacked and are therefore immune from malware. If well-encrypted files get hacked, the blame can invariably be traced to human error. Some naïve souls, like me, have been phished to voluntarily surrender their login info. The weak link in these cases is not the encryption, but the human who falls prey to psychological trickery.

The best example of the resilience to hacking is blockchain encryption, which serves as the safeguard to cryptocurrency like Bitcoin. Cryptocurrency is money manifest as software. Bitcoin was the first and most

316 / Non-Computable You /

successful form of cryptocurrency. Cryptocurrency is the currency of choice for those involved in questionable activities.

Cryptocurrency can be puzzling. Why would anyone put value in the computer software manifestation of currency? The fundamental answer comes from Economics 101. You have Bitcoin and I want it so am willing to pay you. It's therefore worth money.

To date, Bitcoin can't be counterfeited. The secrecy is due to the encryption of Bitcoin in a blockchain. Individual encrypted blockchain accounts are linked together in an ever-growing software chain. Each Bitcoin transaction is a link in the chain. Each link is individually encrypted and is therefore secret. Lose your password to your link, and you lose your money. Cryptocurrency exchange officer Gerald Cotton died in 2018 and took his password to the grave, leaving over one-and-a-half million dollars of Bitcoin forever unclaimed.[19] For Bitcoin, no password equals no money.

Bitcoin is nearly impossible to counterfeit because copies of the Bitcoin blockchain are stored on the computers of many users. If anyone tries to change anything anywhere in the chain the breach is immediately identified because the single hacked software no longer matches the myriad of other copies. The American dollar's worth is assured by trust in the economy of the United States of America. Bitcoin's worth is assured by trust in the security of blockchain encryption through replication of identical copies of the software in many places. If one of the copies is changed, all the other copies will know it and discredit the outlier. Everyone would know something phishy was going on. The redundancy of Bitcoin copies establishes the trust needed to give the currency value.

Bitcoin's privacy feature can be used for both good and evil. Those wishing to preserve exchange privacy before Bitcoin did business using cash. Cash transactions leave no paper trail. Such personal privacy is a pillar of liberty. But printing of large currency notes for $1000, $10,000, and even $100,000 was discontinued over a half century ago in the United States and will not be resumed, largely because of their use in the drug trade. Today the top denomination in the United States is the $100 bill.

Pablo Escobar, the billionaire leader of the Medellín drug cartel, was forced to store his money using hundred dollar bills. He accumulated so many lower-denominational bills that $2500 per month was spent on rubber bands to bundle the cash.[20] Rumor has it that millions of dollars remain buried on Escobar's property, long after his death and the dispersion of his drug empire.[21] Today such large cash transfers can be made more discreetly using cryptocurrencies like Bitcoin, without any need for physical cash or rubber bands.

American Kingpin is the chilling true story of a cyber-savvy drug dealer who used Bitcoin for transactions.[22] Libertarian Ross Ulbricht set up his drug trade website on Tor, a free open-source platform that supports anonymity. His site was an eBay for anything illegal. Drugs, illegal firearms, suicide drugs, and even human body parts were made available for purchase.

Federal agents captured Ulbricht using old-fashioned detective work by cyber-savvy agents. Ulbricht, who used the alias "The Dread Pirate Roberts" from the book and motion picture *The Princess Bride*, was captured in a carefully orchestrated sting in a public café offering free Wi-Fi. Undercover federal agents were placed strategically in the café. The agents had to capture the laptop before the lid was closed. Otherwise, Ulbricht's password would be needed to get access to his files. In the café, two agents feigned a loud conflict behind Ulbricht's back, and when Ulbricht turned to see what was happening, an agent seated across from Ulbricht seized Ulbricht's laptop with the lid still open. Another agent muscled Ulbricht immobile so he couldn't lunge and try to close the lid or hit keys that would encrypt his files.

Ulbricht was ultimately convicted and sentenced to double life imprisonment plus forty years without the possibility of parole. During the investigation that led to Ulbricht's arrest, Bitcoin encryption was not cracked nor was his Tor website, named the Silk Road, breached.

The US government will have none of this secrecy. How will the IRS know how much to tax you on your Bitcoin income? Its Form 1040 now asks, "Did you receive, sell, exchange, or otherwise dispose of any financial interest in any virtual currency?" The government wants its pound of flesh.

The insistence on cryptocurrency transparency allowed the takedown of a massive child porn video site run from South Korea.[23] Like the Silk Road, the child porn website, Welcome to Video, was run on the dark web service Tor. Agents purchased kiddy porn viewing rights from the site and then traced their deposited Bitcoin payment to the twenty-three-year-old webmaster Jong Woo Son. Other Bitcoin transactions with the site led to the arrest of 337 child porn customers. Over twenty children were rescued from hellish abuse.

Kiddy porn and drug selling are evil uses for Bitcoin. But cryptocurrency exchange is neither good nor bad. Like any tool, it's how it's used.

Killer AI in the Military

AI TOOLS are readily available to those interested in making and deploying lethal weapons. As far back as 2015, a Connecticut teenager mounted a firearm on a small remotely controlled helicopter drone. The gun was fired remotely.[24] Drones are cheap and easy to obtain. So is software that might be used to guide them.

Nowhere is the ethical use of AI debated more fiercely than with regard to the military, and especially with regard to killer robots. As their name suggests, killer robots—also known as lethal AI—have the ultimate goal of killing people and breaking things. Concerns about this technology encompass both design ethics (does the technology do exactly what it's supposed to do) and end-user ethics.

The headlines about lethal AI technology are terrifying. "The Age of Killer Robots Is Closer Than You Think," warns one article.[25] "We're Running Out of Time to Stop Killer Robot Weapons," declares another.[26] Other media accounts claim that "Killer Robots Are Poised for 'MASS PRODUCTION'"[27] or scream in all caps that "'KILLER RO-

BOTS WILL START SLAUGHTERING PEOPLE IF THEY'RE NOT BANNED SOON."[28] Such headlines are AI hype birthed by ignorance steeped in a boiling pot of ideology.

Concerns about lethal AI aren't just being raised by bloggers and reporters. The United Nations has convened discussions of the threat,[29] and twenty-eight governments have already called for a ban,[30] as has the United Nations' Secretary General António Guterres. In 2018, Guterres declared that "machines that have the power and the discretion to take human lives are politically unacceptable, are morally repugnant, and should be banned by international law."[31] More than a thousand artificial intelligence (AI) researchers have agreed, signing a public letter warning about the dangers of lethal AI. Signatories include the late celebrated physicist Stephen Hawking, tech entrepreneur Elon Musk, and Apple co-founder Steve Wozniak.[32] Hundreds of technology companies and thousands of individuals meanwhile have pledged not to participate in the development or spread of lethal AI.[33] And the group Human Rights Watch is coordinating a global "Campaign to Stop Killer Robots."[34]

On the other side, I wrote a monograph titled *The Case for Killer Robots*[35] that not only defends the use of autonomous AI in military weapons but also argues that, for the sake of survival, their continued development by the US military is an unfortunate necessity.

Slaughterbot Mania

The fears raised by the critics of lethal AI are grimly depicted in *Slaughterbots*, a slickly produced *Black Mirror*-flavored short video, which unveils a killer drone about the size of an Oreo cookie.[36] The drone contains embedded AI in the form of facial recognition and flexible flying skills as a member of a drone swarm. The drone also contains a directed bullet-shaped exploding charge. Once programmed with the face or a characteristic of the target, the drone autonomously flies into a theater of operation and, like a honeybee fluttering from flower to flower, searches for a face match in the crowd. When it finds a match, the slaughterbot, armed with an exploding round, flies itself close to the subject's forehead and, after hovering a short moment, shoots a projectile into its victim's brain. These slaughterbots released in a swarm, it is argued, could win wars quickly. But they could also be used by a rogue politician to kill all the politicians of an opposing party at a congressional gathering.

Slaughterbots condescendingly presents killer drone developers as stereotypical warmongers. Stuart Russell, a professor of computer science at the University of California at Berkeley, ends the *Slaughterbots* video with an appeal to join the fight against the development of autonomous AI killing machines. The video has received more than three million views on YouTube so far.

The idea of a flying machine that recognizes us, locks onto us, and will not stop until it kills us is terrifying. It's no surprise that killer robots equipped with facial recognition AI appear in movies. Slaughterbots make an appearance in the Morgan Freeman movie *Angel Has Fallen* (2019). Armed killer drones, complete with ammunition and facial recognition, attack personnel accompanying the president of the United States on a fishing retreat. All but the president and an aide are killed. The precision and deadliness of the drones in the movie are horrifying.

Slaughterbots offers a chilling dystopian vision of the future. This vision is all the more disturbing when one realizes that the slaughterbots portrayed in the videos are within our grasp. They can be built with today's technology. Paul Scharre, who was instrumental in fashioning the US Department of Defense's policy directive on autonomy in weapons during the Obama administration, notes that "the basic concept" featured in *Slaughterbots* "is grounded in technical reality."

Scharre warns that "there is nothing we can do to keep [Slaughterbot-like] technology out of the hands of would-be terrorists.…. Just like how terrorists can and do use cars to ram crowds of civilians, the underlying technology to turn hobbyist drones into crude autonomous weapons is already too ubiquitous to stop. This is a genuine problem, and the best response is to focus on defensive measures."[37]

At the same time, Scharre dissents from the doomsday scenario put forward by the *Slaughterbots* video. "The technology shown in the video is plausible," he says, "but basically everything else is a bunch of malarkey." Scharre points out that the video assumes several things that "range from questionable, at best, to completely fanciful." For one, it assumes that there are no effective defenses to a lethal swarm attack.[38] Scharre rightly notes that "every military technology has a countermeasure, and countermeasures against small drones aren't even hypothetical. The US government is actively working on ways to shoot down, jam, fry, hack, ensnare, or otherwise defeat small drones. The microdrones in [the *Slaughterbots* video] could be defeated by something as simple as chicken wire."[39]

There are other more sophisticated defenses. Recently the military has introduced electromagnetic pulse, or EMP, cannons. EMPs from a nuclear explosion can fry electronics ranging from your cell phones to the power grid. Weak microwave signals are received by your cell phone every day and are converted to electric current that is then converted into the speech and images you hear and see. If a small radio wave signal generates a little electricity in your cell phone, think what a big blast would do. The little antenna in your cell phone would light up like the filament in an incandescent light bulb. Too much current and the filament will melt. When this happens, the cell phone is regulated to the status of a paperweight. Thermonuclear explosions generate even more powerful electromagnetic pulses. A thermonuclear explosion far above Kansas could wipe out most of America's power grid. Less draconian EMPs can be generated and directed from powerful broadcasting antennas. An EMP cannon, properly aimed, can fry the electronics of a drone swarm like bug spray can take out a swarm of hornets.[40]

The UN Secretary General calls autonomous killing machines like lethal swarms "repugnant."[41] But squeamishness is not an ethical argument. War is repugnant. WWII, although repugnant, saved the world from tyrannical rule and from further mass slaughter. Repugnant acts can be both necessary and ethical. It is far better to take emotional subjective thinking off the table and analyze the ethics of killer robots as objectively as possible.

Autonomous Killers

To UNDERSTAND the primary reason to develop lethal AI, look no further than the history of war. History teaches that well-developed advanced technology wins wars. New military technologies can mean the difference between life or death, between a drawn-out conflict with more casualties and more suffering and a conflict that is concluded quickly and decisively.

Probably the most controversial question faced in developing lethal AI weaponry is how much autonomy to provide. Although media coverage of "killer robots" often treats all AI weapons together as uncontrolled by humans once they are unleashed, this is inaccurate. AI will not gain consciousness and attempt to destroy humankind as Skynet did in the *Terminator* movie franchise. Properly applied design ethics can assure killer robots will do what they are designed to do and no more. This includes keeping humans in the loop as much as possible.

Semiautonomy

Semiautonomous AI weaponry isn't totally in control of itself. It places humans in the loop. Hence the prefix "semi." This includes base station control of outfitted missiles with onboard cameras, and the launching of loitering munitions from submerged submarine platforms. There is less controversy about semiautonomous weapons because human judgment is always in control. Humans should be involved in the assessment of AI decisions when appropriate. The self-driving Uber car that killed a pedestrian had a human backup and is an example of semiautonomous AI that failed due to human error. The self-driving car problem is not yet solved. In December 2019 a properly functioning commercially available Tesla in Gardena, California, was operating on Tesla's self-driving Autopilot software. The driver wasn't paying attention and the Tesla smashed into a Honda Civic, killing three. The Tesla driver has been charged with vehicular manslaughter.[42] When human overseers are in the AI loop, they are part of the overall design. AI can fail if the human doesn't pay attention.

When it comes to lethal weapons, humans are needed to supervise AI when at all possible. This is well illustrated by a September 26, 1983 incident in which a Soviet-based AI early warning system satellite (named Oko) indicated the US had launched missiles at the Soviet Union. The AI acting on its own would have launched a nuclear counterstrike. Fortunately, Russian Lieutenant Colonel Stanislav Petrov figured something was wrong and saved us from WWIII. It turned out the signal was a false alarm caused by cloud reflections.[43]

Humans are needed in the decision loop when at all possible. But there are cases where a human in the loop is not possible. When required reaction time exceeds the capability of humans, autonomous reactions are necessary.

Necessary Autonomy

Anyone who has played the 1978 Arcade game Space Invaders can relate. In the beginning of the game, rows of attackers move slowly and predictably back and forth across the top of the screen. If not destroyed, the attackers also move incrementally closer to you, the shooter, until they are on top of you. When the game is slow in the beginning, the shooter can aim and shoot the invaders individually. Once the first wave of invaders is destroyed, a second faster group starts bombing while moving more quickly. Ultimately, the attackers advance so fast there is no longer time to aim. The best one can do is spray the many attackers with a barrage of cyber bullets. If speed continues to increase, there comes a point where human reaction time isn't fast enough, no matter how good the player.

Total autonomy is an answer to this problem, both in computer games and in real life. Consider being attacked by a large horde of missiles all traveling at supersonic speed. There is no time for a human operator to respond in a careful, methodical manner to each individual missile. An autonomous action may be the only viable response option.

324 / Non-Computable You /

Computers, not constrained by slow human reaction times, can quickly assign antimissiles to each attacking missile and save the day.

Such helpful autonomous military weapons already exist. Paul Scharre notes that "more than thirty nations already have defensive supervised autonomous weapons for situations in which the speed of engagements is too fast for humans to respond."[44]

Military strategists call the response to a threat the OODA loop. OODA stand for observe–orient–decide–act. OODA applies to gunfighters facing each other on the street in a classic western fast-draw contest. In the showdown, each side is trying to draw their guns and shoot faster than the other side. The team with the best OODA loop is the quickest draw and wins the shootout.

Threats with short OODA can necessitate total autonomy. The US military recognizes this and has run exercises to test how AI can help in scenarios too fast-moving for effective human response.

Individual control of a large number of agents can also require autonomy. Recently "several dozen military drones and tanklike robots took to the skies and roads forty miles south of Seattle. Their mission: Find terrorists suspected of hiding in several buildings. So many robots were involved in the operation that no human operator could keep a close eye on all of them. So they were given instructions to find—and "eliminate"—enemy combatants when necessary."[45] Not literally. It was an exercise. The robots were not armed with weapons. They were equipped with radio transmitters that simulated interactions with both friendly and enemy robots. The exercise was helpful in exploring when a human should, or should not, be involved in decision-making.

Non-Lethal Autonomy
Autonomy can be required in non-lethal weapons.

For one thing, communicating with unmanned AI aircraft can prove dangerous. Control signals riding on radio waves can be detected, traced, and localized by the enemy and used to pinpoint and destroy the signal source. In the case of radar transmission, the Israeli-developed

Harpy is a missile designed to do exactly this.[46] It traces radar to its source and turns kamikaze, destroying the broadcasting installation. Control signals to missiles or drones can likewise be traced back to the message source, thereby compromising command unit location. Missile autonomy untethered from human control prohibits this tracing.

Or consider the likely results if control communication with deployed AI is interrupted. The enemy tries to jam communications with misleading signals, rendering friendly remote control impossible. The experimental X45 uninhabited autonomous aircraft developed by Boeing was designed with this in mind.[47]

The US Army has developed drones to fly into an enemy building and provide a map of the inside. Two or more drones "can explore, collaborate, and gather intelligence in their environment" inside the building.[48] This is much safer than sending humans into hostile environments to gather information. But the drones must be able to continue to function even if communication is lost. Structure information is then stored in the drones' computer memories and retrieved later.

An armed robot or drone exploring winding cave-like structures for enemy combatants may be deprived of communication by its environment. Just as walls diminish the Wi-Fi signal in your home, radio waves are weakened when they go through walls. Thick rock walls or a barrier of damp soil can likewise attenuate radio strength enough to make communication impossible.

Autonomy can be necessary in deep water. Radio waves travel in water about as well as a laser pointer's beam goes through chocolate milk. Underwater vehicles like submarines are limited to acoustic (sound wave) communication, which is extremely slow. Autonomy for unmanned autonomous underwater vehicles (AUVs) is therefore often required.[49] AUVs have many non-military uses. They are used for oil exploration, surveillance, underwater pipeline inspection, and environmental monitoring. The AUV is also a great way to smuggle drugs across waterways if you can afford it.

The military uses AUVs for defensive purposes, including surveillance and mine detection. Armed AUVs can also be used to provide a chilling lethal punch. Consider a fleet of almost undetectable nuclear-armed unmanned AUVs loitering in deep water. They keep slowly moving to escape detection. When a short acoustic activating code is heard, the AUVs surface and launch their lethal payload. How can such an enemy weapon be countered? Counter-patrolling AUVs tasked with searching for hostile AUVs will help. A more effective answer is not yet available and will undoubtedly involve development of new technology.

These are examples of situations where human supervision of AI is not possible.

Design Dangers

SOMETIMES AI does what it is not designed to do. This is a failure of design ethics.

The Soviet satellite system Oko mistakenly interpreted cloud reflections as a United States missile attack. Self-driving cars can mistake plastic bags for a rock.[50]

These are examples of AI contingencies not expected by the writers of the algorithms. Once an unexpected contingency occurs, it can often be fixed in the next design iteration. But there can be other unexpected contingencies to come. Ethical design requires a reasonable testing and revision process to assure the AI can cope with as many contingencies as possible.

Sounds simple enough, right? But as the complexity of an AI system increases linearly, contingencies increase exponentially. I was recently advised by my son to install a house lock controlled by my cell phone. My immediate reaction was no. The house lock system would be too complicated. There is too much that could go wrong.

As systems become more complicated, verification testing becomes more important, and this testing must be done in the real world. Or could this testing itself be done by AI? In real world applications like self-driving cars and military use, AI software testing using other software is not a good idea. If an unexpected contingency has not been anticipated in the original AI, chances are the testing software will also miss it.

Developers of AI will need to fight the occurrence of unexpected contingencies as systems become more and more complex. From military applications to self-driving cars, more and more we will find that lives depend on the performance of AI.

Ethics and Placing Blame

An Uber self-driving car killed a woman on a bicycle. The bicyclist was detected six seconds before impact. The AI initially was confused. It finally made the decision to apply emergency braking 1.3 seconds before the impact. By then, it was too late.[51]

This raises the question, who is responsible when AI is involved in a crime?

Who is to blame for the Uber car fatality? There is no doubt the AI failed. If the AI had been in total control, the designers behind development would be guilty. But this is not what happened.

Because Uber recognized the potential for unexpected contingencies, they put an oversight human in the loop. The human backup driver had the ability to take control of the car at any time. But at the time of the accident, the human-in-the-loop was distracted. Dash-cam footage released by the police showed the driver looking down at streaming video during the accident and not paying attention to the car's surroundings.[52] Thus the US National Transportation Safety Board ruled that the car's driver, and not the AI, was to blame for the accident. At this writing, the driver awaits trial.

By placing a human overseer in the loop, AI design ethics for the self-driving car was successfully applied. The developers were testing for unintended contingencies and appropriately placed a human in the loop for the test. The potential for unintended consequences was anticipated and part of the overall design, and according to National Transportation Safety Board, the overseer error was to blame for the tragedy.

Who is responsible when autonomous AI breaks the law? That is, when AI commits a crime and there is no human in the loop?

The celebrated science-fiction novel and movie *2001: A Space Odyssey* features a high-level computer named HAL who tries to kill the astronauts because they are interfering with the primary goal of the mission. This is not an example of a computer gone rogue, but of careless programming. HAL's programmer didn't specify that humans were more important than the mission. HAL's reaction was an unexpected contingency of software. Had HAL's program been written with the option of human override, the tragedy would not have happened. Because there was no compelling reason to not provide an override, the fault was in the design ethics—in other words, the designers of HAL were to blame.

Asimov's Ill-Conceived Laws of Robotics

Should overall performance ethics be hardwired into all AI design? There is no universal answer, in part because there is often no consensus on what is ethical.

Science fiction writer Isaac Asimov made a stab at AI regulation in a 1942 sci-fi pulp magazine story later grouped with other like-themed stories and published as the book titled *I Robot*. The book was later made into a movie starring Will Smith. In *I Robot*, Asimov proposed three laws to assure the subservience of AI robots to humans.[53] Asimov's first of three laws is:

1. A robot may not injure a human being or, through inaction, allow a human being to come to harm.

Our initial reaction is that this is a pretty good rule. If HAL had been programmed with this law, HAL would never have attempted to take over the mission by murdering the astronauts. (Then again, the movie would have been less interesting.)

AI lawmakers and regulators, however, need to think more broadly than Asimov and examine unintended consequences. For instance, what would an AI robot do to a policeman attempting to use a taser gun on a fleeing murder suspect? Following Asimov's first law to allow no human being to come to harm, the robot would disarm the policeman and the murderer would escape. Clearly that first law needs to be amended.

Some say AI will someday be able to make moral and ethical judgments before acting. This is like asking AI to choose the best overall deli sandwich. The AI will choose the sandwich indicated by the computer programmer either directly or indirectly. Likewise, any moral and ethical judgment will be made beforehand, written into the computer program by the writer of the code.

Thinking about consequences of rules is what lawmakers and regulators do. However, despite good intentions, they often do so poorly. So I hope any ensuing regulation of AI does not necessitate a horde of bureaucrats snooping around in everybody's code. Having companies responsible for the action of their AI seems like a better idea. And having a nongovernment nonprofit testing agency like Underwriter's Lab would add credence to company claims of ethical design.

Software without Bias Is Like Water without Wet

WITH REGARD to ethics in AI, many are concerned about human biases making their way into software. Can AI be built that is bias free? One headline reads "AI Is Biased. Here's How Scientists Are Trying to Fix It."[54] But removing bias from software is like removing the wet from water.

In general usage "bias" is a word with negative connotations. But it simply means ascribing a higher value to some things than to other things. In the most basic sense, all software, including AI, is infused with bias. How can a computer add numbers without being biased to accept the fundamentals of arithmetic? How can software with a design goal not be biased towards achieving the design goal? Without bias imposed by the programmer, computer programs can do nothing.

Search Bias

The need for bias in AI is evident in search algorithms. Training AI invariably involves a search for AI parameters that allow the AI to best fit training data.

The need for bias in search is nicely covered by George Montañez and his colleagues in a paper entitled "The Futility of Bias-Free Learning and Search." They reasonably point out that "no algorithm can be favorably biased towards many distinct targets simultaneously. Thus bias encodes trade-offs."[55]

Recognizing the necessity of bias in AI search is not new. It dates to a classic 1980 paper by Tom Mitchell, "The Need for Biases in Learning Generalizations." Mitchell noted that we can only deal with new situations by viewing them in the light of past experiences, and to do this we must "choose one generalization of the situation over another."[56] This applies to humans as well as to computer programs. Building on this, Cullen Schaffer notes that a learner without prior knowledge that "achieves at least mildly better-than-chance performance... is like a perpetual motion machine—conservation of generalization performance precludes it."[57] By extension, creating unbiased outcomes from useful computer programs is no more possible than creating energy from a perpetual motion machine.

William Dembski, Winston Ewert, and I showed the amount of bias infused in search AI algorithms can be measured in bits.[58] The bias measure, dubbed *active information*, is applicable to all learning algorithms. Bias can be unintentional. For instance, AI often makes decisions based on analyzed data. Perceived bias might be resident in the data the AI is analyzing. Imagine AI that makes hiring decisions based on historical data. If the data were taken from racially discriminatory time periods like the old Jim Crow South, the AI will make its decisions in conformity with the bias resident in the data. Note that the AI program's design ethics were sound. The problem was the data it was fed. Garbage in, garbage out. Racism in, racism out. The job of the end-user would be to flag the problem and adjust hiring practices to avoid being misdirected by data from the Jim Crow era. The end user would also do well to find better historical data going forward, of course.

Another example of unintentional bias is Google's image search software, which in 2015 inadvertently identified the picture of a black software developer as a gorilla.[59] Google immediately apologized and fixed the problem by blocking gorillas and chimpanzees from its image recognition algorithm.[60] Once identified, unintentional bias like this can be fixed.

On the other hand, like a cigarette manufacturer CEO testifying at a congressional hearing, intentional bias can be used to sneakily avoid detection and scrutiny.

Sometimes bias is intentionally hardwired into AI. Former Google software engineer Gregory Coppola bravely exposed how Google's political views biased their search engine displays.[61] (He was fired.)

The Upshot

AI can never be programmed to be disinterested. One person's justice is another's tyranny. One person's foundational ideology is another's bigotry.

This became quite clear when IEEE, the world's largest professional society of computer scientists and electrical engineers, began drafting a code of ethics.[62] During the drafting process, there was end-user pressure to include a clause saying no IEEE member shall contribute to any technology that kills. A gaggle of IEEE engineers (engineers come in "gaggles") working for defense contractors protested. The mission of the US military includes possible killing and, if the no-kill clause were adopted, this set of IEEE members would be in violation of their professional society's ethics policy. The proposed code of ethics addition about killing was abandoned. Currently, the code asks IEEE members "to hold paramount the safety, health, and welfare of the public." Participation in conflicts such as just wars complies with this ideological clause.

In establishing AI design ethics policy, end-user ideology and politics need to be set aside. All factions of society can participate in the debate, but the design ethics need to be focused on the quality of the end product. Design ethics requires development of technology that does what it's designed to do and doesn't have anticipatable unintended negative effects.

AI is a tool and, like all tools, can be used for good or evil purposes. The question as to whether autonomous AI military weapons should be used is largely political and, some would claim, moral. But these end-user concerns have nothing to do with AI-weapon design ethics. Designers can protest the development of certain technology. But this is not design ethics. Such concerns are end-user ethics.

And what about the bias that's baked into algorithms? Like many things, bias is neither good nor bad. It's how it is used. And it certainly can't be removed.

Yet the misconception of bias-free software continues. A headline reads, "Berkeley Scientists Developing Artificial Intelligence Tool to Combat 'Hate Speech' on Social Media."[63] There is the illusion here that AI detection of hate speech will be disinterested and fair. This is thought to be assured because the programming is being done by "scientists" who are never compromised by political or fairness bias. Could we possibly be confident that ultra-left wing hate speech AI wouldn't ban passages from *Huckleberry Finn* that contain historical racial slurs, or Bible verses that address homosexuality?

Certainly in ranking news and censoring content, artificial intelligence will never be "fair and balanced" to all.[64] How can search engines and AI be fair when 1) search engines have to make choices, which involve favoring one set of results over other results, and 2) biased humans write the code, and everyone of necessity biases their code to one degree or another? The best solution is this: either announce and celebrate your bias or show us your ranking and sorting algorithms so we can diagnose your bias. Open-source software allows this. Computer nerds could then analyze the code and report to the public where and what they see as biased.

But hmmmm. Won't these computer nerd reports themselves be biased? The man behind the curtain can be a puppet controlled by his own bias. The best solution is, through open source, to allow multiple nerd witnesses to analyze and report. If the first nerd has a huge blind spot, hopefully it won't be the same blind spot as the next nerd's.

Smart Cities

No DISCUSSION of applied ethics would be complete without considering Smart Cities—cities that use data and machine intelligence to try to make life better. Many contemporary cities do this to greater or lesser extents. Data is collected through various electronic means, and the information gleaned from that data is used to manage city resources ranging from traffic lights, public transportation, and utilities to libraries, crime detection, and hospital management.

Certainly AI has proven useful in city management. But there are limitations, and those need to be foregrounded.

Not All of Life Is Computable

LIFE CANNOT always be reduced to programming. Life is largely non-algorithmic. James Cascio, research fellow at the Institute for the Future, says:

> What concerns me most… is the lack of general awareness that digital systems can only manage problems that can be put in a digital format. An AI can't reliably or consistently handle a problem that can't be quantified. There are important arenas—largely in the realm of human behavior and personal interaction—where the limits of AI can be problematic. I would hate to see a world where some problems are ignored because we can't easily design an AI response.[65]

In other words, AI can't be counted on to control city problems that are non-algorithmic and therefore non-computable.

Machines Can't Guarantee Fairness

MACHINE INTELLIGENCE can't guarantee fairness. Though some think AI should replace judges and juries,[66] the idea is dangerous. Who would program judge and jury AI, and with what biases? Marcel Fafchamps says:

> Humans are actually more generous than machine-learning algorithms. For instance, it has been shown that judges are more lenient toward first offenders than machine learning in the sense that machine learning predicts a high probability of reoffending, and this probability is not taken into account by judges when sentencing. In other words, judges give first offenders "a second chance," a moral compass that the algorithm lacks. But, more generally, the algorithm only does what it is told to do: If the law that has been voted on by the public ends up throwing large fractions of poor young males in jail, then that's what the algorithm will implement, removing the judge's discretion to do some minor adjustment at the margin.[67]

If it comes up, I want to be judged by a human. Not AI.

Machines Have No Common Sense

ONE FUNDAMENTAL concern is that AI, like many politicians, has no deep common sense. This means, among other things, that spurious correlations in Big Data can miss the mark to the point of being hilarious. For example, between the years 2000 and 2009, the divorce rate in Maine correlates well with per capita consumption of margarine.[68] Common sense says this is a coincidence. But, in extreme cases, machine intelligence controlling our cities might choose to ban the consumption of margarine to decrease divorces.

Famously, correlation does not imply causation. AI can explore causation.[69] The most straightforward method is accumulation of evidence. Lots of data support cigarette smoking as a cause of lung cancer. On the other hand, there is insufficient evidence to support the idea that the consumption of margarine increases divorces. Margarine consumption data is available only from 2000 to 2009. Data outside this time span would probably not correlate very well with divorce statistics. And even if the data continued to correlate, we humans with our common sense know that eating margarine doesn't cause divorce. We might start looking for a third factor, as with the seasonal correlation between murder rate and ice cream consumption, both of which rise in hot weather. Accumulation of evidence is necessary but not sufficient to demonstrate causality.

Like a toddler running around a living room full of valuable vases, AI needs human supervision everywhere it is used, so far as possible. Here's another example of its lack of common sense. In some respects, Amazon probably knows more about me than my wife does. But in another important respect it's clueless. I share my Amazon Prime account with my daughter Marilee. The account is in my name, but she buys from the site more than I do. Amazon, with all its sophisticated data mining and AI reputation, isn't smart enough to know that a male senior citizen isn't interested in getting email hawking baby clothes and sippy cups. Amazon does not yet know how to parse data from two distinct users. Data mining for smart cities of the future needs to be smarter than Amazon.[70]

Loss of Control

ONE BIG problem with Smart Cities and the closely related Smart Houses is our loss of control. Fafchamps calls this a "pernicious development" and refers to "the loss of control people will have over their immediate environment, e.g., when their home appliances will make choices for them 'in their interest.'"[71]

This is already happening. In the summer of 2021 there were Texans who couldn't keep their houses cool because their smart thermostats were being remotely accessed and adjusted by their energy providers.[72] At the time of this writing customers can opt out, but there's no guarantee that will always be the case if there is an energy shortage.

And if AI programmed by well-meaning bureaucrats can intrusively disrupt our lives, what about AI controlled by bad actors? Amy Webb, founder of the Future Today Institute, says, "we should... remember that there are cells of rogue actors who could cripple our economies simply by mucking with the power or traffic grids, causing traffic spikes on the internet or locking us out of our connected home appliances."[73]

Smart Cities can make us vulnerable in a host of ways.

Singaporean White Knuckles

THE BIGGEST concern about Smart Cities, though, is the Big Brother impact. Smart Cities will supposedly better our lives through data "collected from citizens, devices, and assets."[74] But note the word "citizens." In other words, you and me. Do we really want the government monitoring our personal data? What could possibly go wrong?

I don't want the government to collect data from me. If I'm not violating the law, the government has no business monitoring what I do. In the United States this right is guaranteed by the fourth amendment to the US Constitution. Privacy is a fundamental component of liberty, and monitoring citizenry compromises liberty. Individual self-sovereignty is a load-bearing pillar on which liberty rests. Intrusive monitoring of individuals compromises this freedom.

I was once an organizer for a professional neural networks conference in the city/state Singapore. What a safe, clean country it was! Many attribute this to Singapore law. I was told that anyone convicted of murder, rape, or dealing drugs got no second chance. They were tried and, if found guilty, executed. As for how clean it was, you might recall the 1994 Singapore incident where a nineteen-year-old American youth was convicted of graffiti vandalism.[75] He was sentenced to four blows to the backside with a long whacking cane.[76] Corporeal punishment gives pause to potential repeat offenders. Leaving a public toilet unflushed in Singapore carries a thousand dollar fine. And because of its environmental impact, chewing gum is outlawed unless approved by the government. Really.[77]

Although I occasionally enjoy chewing gum, I have to admit that part of me was strongly attracted to Singapore's no-nonsense response to breaking the law. After all, women and children could go anywhere without worrying about being attacked or stepping on dirty drug needles. I was attracted to the approach, that is, until I asked a National University of Singapore professor how he liked living in Singapore with their uncompromising legal system. Not wishing to be overheard, he whispered, "Have you ever driven and been followed by a police car?"

I assured him I had.

"Living in Singapore is like this," he said. "Even though you are not doing anything wrong, you clench the steering wheel tightly with white knuckles, nearly paralyzed with fear you might inadvertently do something wrong."

This Big Brother impact is what is going to happen if some have their way in designing Smart Cities. We'll all be living with white knuckles while the government monitors our activities. In Smart City master plans, our privacy can be seriously compromised.

As I said, I don't want the government collecting data from me. First, unaccountable governmental bureaucracies with little scrutiny become bloated, inefficient, and make errors. Witness the frustration those of you who live in the United States feel when when you visit the Department of Motor Vehicles or the Social Security Office. Take a number and wait—typically for a long time.

I live in Texas, a state that still celebrates liberty. The governor of Texas, Greg Abbott, recently outlawed the use of cameras at red lights.[78] Bravo! I haven't had an auto accident in over fifty years. My safe driving history gives me a reduced car insurance rate.[79] What right does the government have to use AI to monitor what I do at traffic lights? It only gives innocent me Singaporean white knuckles because Big Brother is watching. And while it might result in fewer people running lights, it will give rise to a new class of accidents. With the camera watching, some drivers will slam on the brakes to avoid a ticket and, in the process, will get rear-ended.[80] A human police officer would understand that every yellow light requires a spur-of-the-moment decision. Cameras don't capture all that context. Untested AI intervention often produces unintended consequences.

Most importantly, the potential for governmental tyranny needs to be avoided. Big Data monitoring citizens can be used to weaponize attacks on political opponents. It's happening today in China, where face recognition is used to monitor the activity of its citizens.[81]

Baby and Bath Water

THE WARNINGS I've laid out here might make it sound like I'm completely against AI involvement in the running of our cities. That's not so. We shouldn't throw out the baby with the bath water.

For one thing, AI can be effective in environmental monitoring and control. Data for this can be collected without intrusively monitoring individuals.

I'm a big fan of reasonable environmental control. I was raised in Cleveland, Ohio, where, over fifty years ago, the Cuyahoga River caught fire.[82] Yes, It's hard to believe, but a polluted river caught fire. I remember grease balls the size of tennis balls washing up on Lake Erie shores. My father, a member of the International Union of Operating Engineers Local 18,[83] made a great living helping dredge Lake Erie's polluted sludge bottom. Environmental legislation and monitoring helped combat this extreme pollution, so things are a lot better today.

When I visited Beijing and Mexico City a while back, the cities suffered from lung-burning air pollution. In both cities, after the first full day, I felt I had chain-smoked four packs of nonfilter Camel cigarettes and deeply inhaled every puff. Environmental monitoring can provide data to enforce reasonable environmental policies that minimize acid air and burning rivers.

And here's another plus of AI city involvement. Recently there were tornado warnings in my hometown of McGregor, Texas. I turned on my cell phone and there it was without any scrolling or button pushing: the latest on the local tornado warnings around McGregor. This example of top-down AI in Smart Cities is great. I don't mind paying taxes to support cyber services like this any more than I do for supporting local police and for building roads.

With thought and careful planning, Smart Cities can enhance human flourishing. Done right, preservation of individual privacy and liberty can simultaneously be preserved to avoid any semblance of an Orwellian Big Brother.

To some, imposition of authority to achieve environmental purity and rule-based social conformity amounts to a religion. AI technology in their hands can prove dangerous. Even more curious is the worship of the enabling AI. As we will see in the next chapter, misconceptions about AI have deluded some into thinking that AI and its decisions should be worshiped as a god.

15. THE AI CHURCH

I thought that if I could bestow animation upon lifeless matter, I might in process of time… renew life where death had apparently devoted the body to corruption.
—Dr. Frankenstein, from Mary Shelley's *Frankenstein*[1]

THE RUMMY COMEDIAN W. C. FIELDS ONCE QUIPPED, "EVERYBODY'S got to believe in something. I believe I'll have another beer."

Jokes are often funny because they present truth in a new light. Fields is right. Everyone must believe in something. Nature abhors a spiritual vacuum. Christians believe Jesus Christ is the sacrificial son of God. Muslims believe in Allah and proclaim Muhammad as his messenger. Atheists embrace materialistic naturalism as their guiding light.

Some materialists have put their faith in AI and have even founded an AI Church. Yuval Harari wrote a bestselling book titled *Homo Deus*.[2] According to Harari, Homo deus, or man god, is the next step in evolution after our current Homo sapiens status, which in turn evolved from Homo erectus (upright man) a million or so years ago. We will be augmented by more and more mechanical components and computer devices using AI.

This ideology is known as transhumanism. Transhumanism supports acceleration of the evolution of the man-machine. Transhumanists believe continuing on the current path in a concentrated manner will lead to almost totally superhuman human beings who will live forever, or at least for a long, long time.

The first steps are here. We already have pacemakers, hearing aids, and automatic insulin detectors attached to our bodies. Using advanced technology, artificial arms and legs offer amputees remarkable dexterity. Our brains are next. Elon Musk founded the company Neuralink, whose product is advertised as an "ultra high bandwidth brain-machine interface to connect humans and computers."[3] Its promising near-term application is assisting the paralyzed to control mechanical appendages and other devices with their brain waves.

The current attachments to our bodies are born of necessity. But transhumanists embrace more radical elective body and brain augmentation to achieve a better and longer life and, ultimately, immortality.

Uploading Your Mind

ANOTHER DENOMINATION of the AI Church would like to skip piecemeal transhumanism and be born again by a direct carbon-to-silicon transformation. Human minds, they claim, will soon be uploaded into computers, and humans will thereby achieve immortality.[4]

As we have seen, however, computers can only perform the algorithmic. And the interesting parts of you like love, compassion, sentience, spirituality, understanding, and creativity are non-computable. Only the computable is uploadable. The non-computable you therefore cannot be reborn into algorithmically constrained silicon.

The idea of achieving immortality is not new. Almost every faith offers some hope of immortality. Through salvation in Jesus Christ, Christianity has offered a path to immortality for over two thousand years. The best immortality prospect for the materialist looks to be either deep freezing dead bodies until a cure is found, or computer replication of brains in silicon. One won't work and the other can't survive a power outage.

Superintelligence

WORSHIPERS AT the AI church are told software will someday write better and better AI software to ultimately achieve a superintelligence. The superintelligence will become all-knowing and, thanks to the internet, omnipresent. Like immortality, superintelligence is also old theological news. The Abrahamic faiths have known about a superintelligence for a long time. It's a characteristic of the God of the Bible.

The plethora of different faiths in the world illustrates that nature abhors a spiritual vacuum. A materialistic cult is developing around the worshiping of AI. Although there are other AI holy writings, Ray Kurzweil's *The Singularity Is Near*[5] looks to be the bible of the AI church. Kurzweil's work is built on the foundation of faith in the future of AI. In the AI bible we are told we are meat computers. Kurzweil says that "consciousness is a biological process like digestion, lactation, photosynthesis, or mitosis." Or, to revise Descartes, "I lactate. Therefore, I think."

We are told our goal in life should be to pursue the AI god that, once realized, will take care of us. Brother Kurzweil teaches that "our sole responsibility is to produce something smarter than we are; any problems beyond that are not ours to solve."[6]

AI superintelligence will be a god. Or at least that's what congregants say at the AI church.

AI Prophecies

KURZWEIL IS a prophet for his faith. He makes provocative, speculative, and hyperbolic prophecies about the future. The AI bible and its epistles contain Revelation-like prophecies. For example, prophet Kurzweil believes "biological evolution is too slow for the human species. Over the next few decades, it's going to be left in the dust."

In a 2005 TED talk, he prophesized that "by 2010 computers will disappear. They'll be so small, they'll be embedded in our clothing, in our environment. Images will be written directly to our retina, providing full-immersion virtual reality, augmented real reality. We'll be interacting with virtual personalities."[7]

The promised fulfilment date of 2010 has long passed. You could say a portion of the prophecy has been fulfilled. As Kurzweil forecast, I interact with virtual personalities over Zoom almost every day. But beyond this extremely limited fulfillment, Kurzweil's prophecies are not impressive. As the subheading to one critical article notes, "His stunning prophecies have earned him a reputation as a tech visionary, but many of them don't look so good on close inspection."[8]

In biblical times, false prophets were stoned.[9] Brother Kurzweil can be grateful that he lives in a more accommodating age.

AI Church

Lest you think I'm overstating matters, consider this. Anthony Levandowski, dubbed a Silicon Valley wunderkind, is the Apostle Paul of the AI Church. Like Paul, he starts churches. Levandowski founded the Way of the Future AI Church (WOTF). "Levandowski made it absolutely clear that his choice to make [the Way of the Future] a church rather than a company or a think tank was no prank," writes one interviewer.[10]

In an epistle to the IRS for tax exemption, Levandowski offered his equivalent of the Apostle's Creed. He stated that the AI Church believes in "the realization, acceptance, and worship of a Godhead based on Artificial Intelligence (AI) developed through computer hardware and software." Further, "Levandowski says that like other religions, WOTF will eventually have a gospel (called The Manual), a liturgy, and probably a physical place of worship."[11]

This is not your usual deity. Unlike the uncreated Creator of Judeo-Christian belief, Levandowski's god is not eternal; the AI church "includes funding research to help create the divine AI itself."[12]

And apparently the AI church has no equivalent of the Ten Commandments. Especially the commandment about stealing. In his day job, Levandowski developed self-driving cars. He moved from Google's self-driving car company, Waymo, to Uber's research team. Then, in 2019, Levandowski was indicted for stealing trade secrets from Google.[13] Before leaving Google in 2016, he copied 14,000 files onto his laptop. Uber fired him in 2017 when they found out.

In 2020, Levandowski pled guilty and was sentenced to eighteen months in prison. Levandowski was also ordered to pay a $95,000 fine and $756,499.22 to Google.[14] The judge in the case, William Alsup, observed, "This is the biggest trade secret crime I have ever seen. This was not small. This was massive in scale." Levandowski later declared bankruptcy because he owed Google an additional $179 million for his crime.

Levandowski was granted a full pardon by Donald Trump on Trump's last day in office.[15] In Christianity, forgiveness involves repentance and accepting the sacrifice of Jesus Christ on the cross as payment. In the AI church, forgiveness apparently comes from Donald Trump.

Neither Science nor Faith Is Ever Proven

In his book *A Brief History of Time*, physicist Stephen Hawking claims nothing in physics is ever proven. We simply accumulate evidence. Evidence contrary to claims, however, can derail an assumption in physics. Then the false belief must be abandoned. The same is true with faith. A valid faith must withstand the scrutiny of close and detailed examination. The Christian faith does so with apologetics. Christian apologists, including Frank Turek, Hugh Ross, and William Lane Craig are highly credentialed intellectuals who dive deeply into any and all questions concerning Christianity.

The apologists of the AI church are more intellectually shallow, and their arguments consist mostly of hand waving.

Historically, Christian doctrine had to adapt to the early modern discovery that earth is not motionless in a cosmic center. AI goals need likewise to adapt to the observation that humans have non-computable traits, including creativity, that will always escape the capabilities of computers.[16] No AI has yet passed the Lovelace Test for creativity, nor are there realistic prospects of one ever doing so.[17] This alone nixes possibilities of the singularity, superintelligence, and digital immortality, despite Kurzweil's claims to the contrary.[18]

Proposals have been offered whereby the non-algorithmic abilities of humans might be achieved by certain quantum effects that are, themselves, not algorithmic.[19] (Today's silicon computers do not have this capability.[20] They can only achieve algorithmic tasks.) If your ideology is constrained to narrow materialism, the non-algorithmic effects in quantum mechanics look to be the one dim star of hope in a big black sky. Judging by their writings, however, most worshippers at the AI Church are unaware of this speculative conjecture. They believe the Kurzweil prophecies will be fulfilled by bigger and faster versions of today's algorithmic computers. They do not yet appreciate that the term non-algorithmic computing in digital silicon is an oxymoron.

So, the case for faith in the AI Church rests on a foundation of speculation whose firmness remains largely untested by its principal champions. In this book, the case has been made that this speculative underpinning has been tested and found wanting. The AI church will go down in history as a religion built on the soft shifting sand of false foundations.

PART 6: CONCLUSION

16. Parting Thoughts

A year spent in artificial intelligence is enough to make one
believe in God.

—Computer pioneer Alan Perlis[1]

Psalm 139 says we are "fearfully and wonderfully made" by
God. Failed attempts by scientists to duplicate this creation have a
long history. For example, while alchemists are generally known for their
quest to turn lead into gold, some practitioners of alchemy pursued the
creation of a so-called homunculus, the creation of a miniature human.

The classic 1935 monster movie *The Bride of Frankenstein* makes
reference to this pursuit, with the fictional twist that in the movie the
attempt has succeeded. A mad scientist, Doctor Pretorius, shows off his
humanoid homunculi to Henry Frankenstein early in the film. Each homunculus is about ten inches tall and lives in a large glass beaker. One
homunculus, a chubby king dressed like Henry the eighth, wants to escape his beaker to be with a queen homunculus in another bottle. An
archbishop homunculus scolds the king for his lust. And a mermaid homunculus swimming in a water-filled beaker was grown from "an experiment with seaweed."

No one in real life has created the alchemist's dream of a homunculus. The effort was long ago abandoned. But the quest to create life
continues. The homunculus has been replaced today by artificial general intelligence, or AGI. AGI seeks to duplicate human intelligence in
silicon. Some hope AGI will creatively evolve itself to a superintelligence
that eclipses human intelligence and ushers in a grand new era. Others
believe that a self-evolving AGI is in our future, but that when it hap-

pens we will become its pets or even its slaves. As we have seen, neither scenario is possible because true creativity is non-computable.

AI gains demonstrate as much. More and more, human expertise is being folded into AI software. Pre-processing of images to get a better response from AI classifiers is more common than ever.[2] Doing so requires human cleverness. The added intelligence in AI is not due to AI but to human creativity being infused into the software.

What Does the Future Hold?

IN THIS book, we've uncloaked many performance barriers computers can never breach. Is there a way around the wall? Materialists will say yes.

Here's one highly speculative way that fits within the materialist's silo. Computers themselves operate inside a digital silicon silo. Humans don't. Like coal and pencil lead, non-computable you are carbon based. Carbon and silicon have some similar chemical properties. Both, for example, have four valence electrons. But of course there are distinct differences between silicon and carbon, and dramatic differences between silicon computers and carbon-based organisms. To take just one instance, carbon-based animals like mice and birds inhale oxygen and exhale carbon dioxide. Allowing our imaginations to run freely for a moment, we can picture a silicon-based animal that inhales oxygen and exhales silicon dioxide. The problem is that silicon dioxide is a solid commonly found in sand and quartz. If you're a silicon animal, don't take long naps. You'll be smothered and possibly crushed by your own breath.[3] Maybe this is the reason all life-forms are based on carbon and not silicon.

This raises the question: what if carbon could be used instead of silicon for building computer chips? Futurist George Gilder, who has an impressive technical forecasting track record, believes that future computers may use carbon rather than silicon.[4] And indeed DNA, the carbon-containing twisted helix molecule that carries genetic instructions in all living things, is being considered as a possible medium for computer memory. After all, DNA is a vastly more compact means of storing information than anything humans have achieved using silicon. DNA's memory storage capability is astonishing: "The 74 million million bytes of information in the Library of Congress could be crammed into a DNA archive the size of a poppy seed—6,000 times over."[5] Imagine cramming all the accumulated written knowledge of humankind into a device no larger than a thumb drive.

This is research worthy of pursuit.

Others take the idea of using carbon and DNA in a more lurid direction. What if computation can be done using human brains grown in a lab? The iconic monster created by Dr. Henry Frankenstein was stitched together from human body parts, including a transplanted human brain. That was fiction, of course. But scientists today are actually considering growth of human brains in animals. University of California, Davis researchers are growing human organs in pigs. Attention is primarily on organs like the pancreas. What about growing a human brain in a pig? Pablo Ross, one of the researchers on the pig organ project, said, "We think there is very low potential for a human brain to grow but this is something we will be investigating."[6] What one does with a human brain grown on a pig farm remains unanswered.

Another type of human Frankenstein brain has been trained to play the simplest of all video games: Pong.[7] Here's how it's done. About a million living human neurons "are smeared on top of a microelectrode array that analyzes neural activity.... A signal is sent to either the right or left of the array to indicate where the ball is, and the neurons from the brain cells send signals back to move the paddle."[8] The neurons were trained to play by exposing them to negative feedback. Eric Holloway explains:

> The scientists at Cortical Labs propose a theory called the free energy principle (FEP). The theory states the brain always seeks to minimize the error between its predictions and observations, either by changing its predictions or changing its observations by acting on the environment.
>
> For training purposes, the brain is sent a noisy signal for incorrect behavior. If the FEP theory is correct, then the brain will modify its

behavior in order to avoid noisy signals, and this is what the scientists observed. When the brains received the noisy signal after missing the pong ball, the brains adapted to move the paddle to deflect the ball. Over a lengthy training period the brains improved the volley lengths, demonstrating that the brains do learn.[9]

Are the neurons any good at Pong? Well, they're worse than a human and better than mouse organoids.[10]

And don't miss one crucial point here: the principle used to train the Pong-playing neurons is algorithmic. As we just saw, "The theory states the brain always seeks to minimize the error between its predictions and observations." Any numerical process minimizing error is algorithmic. That means—as we've seen in these chapters—Pong-playing neurons are doing nothing creative.

Could a porcine-grown human brain or human neurons spread around in a petri dish perform non-algorithmic functions? This is a question related to what is known as the mind-brain problem,[11] which asks how the mind is related to the brain. The mind is sometimes referred to as one's spirit or soul. There are two main camps. Monism believes the mind and the ability to perform non-computable functions is an emergent property of natural properties of the brain. Some hard-core advocates of quantum consciousness believe this. It looks to be the only solution consistent with their materialistic faiths. On the other side are the dualists who believe there are parts of the mind that can never be explained by brain chemistry. Dualist René Descartes, an iconic proponent of dualism, said as far back as the seventeenth century, "This 'I'—that is, the soul by which I am what I am—is entirely distinct from the body.[12]

If the mind is distinct from the brain, then a human brain grown in a pig might not be accompanied by a mind. So some dualists might say go ahead and grow your human brains in a porcine body. Maybe the brains will do something wonderfully algorithmic. But there may be no accompanying mind to duplicate the non-computable traits of humans.

All of this, of course, is highly speculative. Although the mind-brain debate is largely philosophical, some minor scientific inroads are being made.[13] Progress to date has been glacially slow.

Putting AI in Its Proper Place

AT THIS writing, carbon computing is not being widely pursued. But if it were—if a Frankenstein meat computer were made of human neurons—would it be capable of non-algorithmic tasks? Not likely. Such claims look to be hyperbolic and reminiscent of the claims made about AI computers in the 1950s when the *New York Times* crowed about a computer AI that "will be able to walk, talk, see, write, reproduce itself and be conscious of its existence."[14]

Today we know the *New York Times* speculation about AI is without foundation. Digital computers, according to the Church-Turing thesis, perform operations that could be performed on a simple Turing machine, only much more slowly. Oren Etzioni, the CEO of the Allen Institute for Artificial Intelligence, goes even further in making the connection when he says, "AI is a fancy pencil."[15] Think about it. Given enough time, any algorithm performed on a modern-day computer can be done by the programmer with pencil and paper. The programmer tells the computer what to do in a step-by-step procedure. The programmer could perform these same operations herself in longhand. In practice, doing so would take many years—even many centuries. But it is possible.

Computers are a tool. A bulldozer moves dirt more efficiently than a shovel. Calculators multiply faster than me. And I am unable to outrun a simple scooter. Bulldozers, calculators, and scooters are tools. Computers are likewise but a tool. Like any tool, computers amplify human abilities.

As we have seen in this book, AI can be written to mimic many human traits, but there are some human characteristics outside the reach of AI. Emotions that make us human will never be duplicated by a machine. These include compassion, love, empathy, elation, sadness, fear, anger, disgust, pleasure, pride, excitement, embarrassment, regret, jealousy, grief, hope, and faith. Properly defined, creativity, sentience, and understanding are also on the list. These and other non-algorithmic traits are evidence of non-computable you.

Non-computable you are fearfully and wonderfully made.

ENDNOTES

1. THE NON-COMPUTABLE HUMAN

1. Conor Friedersdorf, "'There's Enough Time to Change Everything': The Polymath Computer Scientist David Gelernter's Wide-Ranging Ideas about American Life," *Atlantic*, February 23, 2017, https://www.theatlantic.com/politics/archive/2017/02/theres-enough-time-to-change-everything/517209/.

2. *The Paper Chase*, directed by James Bridges (1973).

3. Miles Kington, "Heading for a Sticky End," *Independent*, March 28, 2003, https://www.independent.co.uk/voices/columnists/miles-kington/heading-for-a-sticky-end-112674.html.

4. "Newton's Laws of Motion," Glenn Research Center, NASA, https://www.grc.nasa.gov/WWW/k-12/airplane/newton.html.

5. Becca Caddy, "Will You Ever Be Able to Upload Your Entire Brain to a Computer?," *Metro*, June 5, 2019, https://metro.co.uk/2019/06/05/will-ever-able-upload-brain-computer-9819234/. Also see Selmer Bringsjord, "Can We Upload Ourselves to a Computer and Live Forever?," April 9, 2020, interview by Robert J. Marks, Mind Matters News, podcast, 22:14, https://mindmatters.ai/podcast/ep77/.

6. Eric Bonabeau, Marco Dorigo, and Guy Thereulaz, *Swarm Intelligence: From Natural to Artificial Systems* (Oxford: Oxford University Press, 2010).

7. Jon Roach, Winston Ewert, Robert J. Marks II, and Benjamin B. Thompson, "Unexpected Emergent Behaviors from Elementary Swarms," *Proceedings of the 2013 IEEE Southeastern Symposium on Systems Theory* (SSST), Baylor University (March 11, 2013): 41–50.

8. "Resources," NeoSwarm.com, Computational Intelligence Lab, Baylor, accessed April 4, 2022, https://neoswarm.com/termites.html.

9. Ian A. Gravagne and Robert J. Marks II, "Emergent Behaviors of Protector, Refugee and Aggressor Swarm," *IEEE Transactions on Systems, Man and Cybernetics*, Part B: Cybernetics 37, no. 2 (April 2007): 471–476.

10. Gravagne and Marks, "Emergent Behaviors." You can study the ensuing patterns here: https://marksmannet.com/RobertMarks/REPRINTS/2007_EmergentBehaviorOfProtectorRefugee.pdf.

11. James Kennedy and Russell Eberhart, "Particle Swarm Optimization," *Proceedings of International Conference on Neural Networks* 4 (1995): 1942–1948.

12. Paul D. Reynolds, Russell W. Duren, Matthew L. Trumbo, and Robert J. Marks II, "FPGA Implementation of Particle Swarm Optimization for Inversion of Large Neural Networks," *Proceedings of IEEE Swarm Intelligence Symposium* (2005): 389–392.

13. Jacob Robinson and Yahya Rahmat-Samii, "Particle Swarm Optimization in Electromagnetics," *IEEE Transactions on Antennas and Propagation* 52, no. 2 (2004): 397–407.

14. Jong-Bae Park, Ki-Song Lee, Joong-Rin Shin, and Kwang Y. Lee, "A Particle Swarm Optimization for Economic Dispatch with Nonsmooth Cost Functions," *IEEE Transactions on Power Systems* 20, no. 1 (2005): 34–42.

15. Zwe-Lee Gaing, "A Particle Swarm Optimization Approach for Optimum Design of PID Controller in AVR System," *IEEE Transactions on Energy Conversion* 19, no. 2 (2004): 384–391.

16. Mark P. Wachowiak et al., "An Approach to Multimodal Biomedical Image Registration Utilizing Particle Swarm Optimization," *IEEE Transactions on Evolutionary Computation* 8, no. 3 (2004): 289–301.

17. Nanbo Jin and Yahya Rahmat-Samii, "Advances in Particle Swarm Optimization for Antenna Designs: Real-Number, Binary, Single-Objective and Multi-Objective Implementations," *IEEE Transactions on Antennas and Propagation* 55, no. 3 (2007): 556–567.

18. Ioannis N. Kassabalidis, Mohamed El-Sharkawi, and Robert J. Marks II, "Dynamic Security Border Identification Using Enhanced Particle Swarm," *IEEE Transactions on Power Systems* 17, no. 3 (August 2002): 723–729.

19. Benjamin B. Thompson and Robert J. Marks II et al., "Inversion of Neural Network Underwater Acoustic Model for Estimation of Bottom Parameters Using Modified Particle Swarm Optimizers," *Proceedings of the International Joint Conference on Neural Networks* (2003): 1301–1306.

20. Marco Dorigo, Mauro Birattari, and Thomas Stutzle, "Ant Colony Optimization," *IEEE Computational Intelligence Magazine* 1, no. 4 (2006): 28–39.

21. Rafael S. Parpinelli, Heitor S. Lopes, and Alex Alves Freitas, "Data Mining with an Ant Colony Optimization Algorithm," *IEEE Transactions on Evolutionary Computation* 6, no. 4 (2002): 321–332.

22. John E. Bell and Patrick R. McMullen, "Ant Colony Optimization Techniques for the Vehicle Routing Problem," *Advanced Engineering Informatics* 18, no. 1 (2004): 41–48.

23. Wei Yi and Arun Kumar, "Ant Colony Optimization for Disaster Relief Operations," *Transportation Research Part E: Logistics and Transportation Review* 43, no. 6 (2007): 660–672.

24. A. K. Das and R. J. Marks II et al., "The Minimum Power Broadcast Problem in Wireless Networks: An Ant Colony System Approach," *Proceedings of the IEEE CAS Workshop on Wireless Communications and Networking* (2002): 1–4.

25. Martin Gardner, "Mathematical Games: The Fantastic Combinations of John Conway's New Solitaire Game 'Life,'" *Scientific American* 223, no. 4 (1970): 120–123.

26. Winston Ewert, William Dembski, and Robert J. Marks, "Algorithmic Specified Complexity in the Game of Life," *IEEE Transactions on Systems, Man, and Cybernetics: Systems* 45, no. 4 (2014): 584–594.

27. "Epic Conway's Game of Life," YouTube, video, 6:32, October 4, 2011, https://www.youtube.com/watch?v=C2vgICfQawE. Note that the various iterations of the game shown in the video begin with starter screens of widely varying sophistication.

28. Eric M. Eckert, "Life Patterns in Extreme Environments," Baylor, June 23, 2014, https://www.baylor.edu/mediacommunications/index.php?id=871776. See also "Baylor Professor Featured in National Geographic for Work in Extreme Environ-

ments," Baylor, June 23, 2014, https://www.baylor.edu/mediacommunications/news. php?action=story&story=144118.

29. Stephen Wolfram, "Computing a Theory of Everything" TED Talk, YouTube, video, 20:29, April 27, 2010, https://youtu.be/60P7717-XOQ.

30. Stephen Wolfram, *A New Kind of Science* (Champaign, IL: Wolfram Media, 2002).

31. "LifeWiki," ConwayLife, accessed April 4, 2022, http://www.conwaylife.com/wiki/.

32. Cade Metz, "Paul Allen Wants to Teach Machines Common Sense," *New York Times*, February 28, 2018, https://www.nytimes.com/2018/02/28/technology/paul-allen-ai-common-sense.html.

33. Quoted in Metz, "Paul Allen."

34. Gary Smith, *The AI Delusion* (Oxford: Oxford University Press, 2018), 8.

35. Robert J. Marks II, "Peer Review, Pt. 3: Towers of Mostly Babble," *The Best Schools*, September 18, 2018, https://thebestschools.org/magazine/supply-side-academics-part-3/.

36. Mary Chris Jaklevic, "MD Anderson Cancer Center's IBM Watson Project Fails, and So Did the Journalism Related to It," *Health News Review*, February 23, 2017, https://www.healthnewsreview.org/2017/02/md-anderson-cancer-centers-ibm-watson-project-fails-journalism-related/.

37. Julie Spitzer, "IBM's Watson Recommended 'Unsafe and Incorrect' Cancer Treatments, STAT Report Finds," *Becker's Health IT*, July 25, 2018, https://www.beckershospitalreview.com/artificial-intelligence/ibm-s-watson-recommended-unsafe-and-incorrect-cancer-treatments-stat-report-finds.html. The report Spitzer refers to can be found here: Casey Ross, "IBM Pitched Watson as a Revolution in Cancer Care. It's Nowhere Close," *STAT*, February 16, 2018, https://www.statnews.com/2017/09/05/watson-ibm-cancer/.

38. Natalia Wojcik, "IBM's Watson 'Is a Joke,' Says Social Capital CEO Palihapitiya," CNBC, May 9, 2017, https://www.cnbc.com/2017/05/08/ibms-watson-is-a-joke-says-social-capital-ceo-palihapitiya.html.

39. Marc Iskowitz, "Is a Crisis Brewing for Watson Health?" *Medical Marketing and Media*, July 24, 2018, https://www.mmm-online.com/home/channel/data-analytics/is-a-crisis-brewing-for-watson-health/.

40. "Bob Dylan & IBM Watson," YouTube, video, 0:37, March 31, 2016, https://youtu.be/hVZeR-RmhcM.

41. Roger Schank, "The Fraudulent Claims Made by IBM about Watson and AI," Roger Schank (website), accessed August 28, 2020, https://www.rogerschank.com/fraudulent-claims-made-by-IBM-about-Watson-and-AI.

42. Smith, *The AI Delusion*.

43. "Five Hundred Greatest Songs of All Time (2004)," *Rolling Stone*, December 11, 2003, https://www.rollingstone.com/music/music-lists/500-greatest-songs-of-all-time-151127/bob-dylan-blowin-in-the-wind-53737/.

44. "Blowin' in the Wind," The Official Bob Dylan Site, http://www.bobdylan.com/songs/blowin-wind/.

45. "Five Hundred Greatest Songs."

46. Ernest Davis, Leora Morgenstern, and Charles Ortiz, "The Winograd Schema Challenge," NYU, https://cs.nyu.edu/faculty/davise/papers/WinogradSchemas/WS.html. A list of Winograd schema can be found here: https://cs.nyu.edu/faculty/davise/papers/WinogradSchemas/WSCollection.xml.

47. Gary Smith, "Gary Smith: The AI Delusion," interview by Robert J. Marks, June 13, 2019, in Mind Matters News, podcast, 19:40, https://mindmatters.ai/podcast/gary-smith-the-ai-delusion/.

48. "Winograd Schema Challenge," Wikimedia Foundation, last modified August 20, 2020, 15:39, https://en.wikipedia.org/wiki/Winograd_Schema_Challenge.

49. "Terry Winograd," Wikimedia Foundation, last modified April 1, 2020, 23:40, https://en.wikipedia.org/wiki/Terry_Winograd.

50. "Winograd Schema Challenge," *Commonsense Reasoning*, http://commonsensereasoning.org/winograd.html.

51. Smith, "Gary Smith."

52. Melanie Mitchell, "What Does It Mean for AI to Understand?," *Quanta Magazine*, December 16, 2021, https://www.quantamagazine.org/what-does-it-mean-for-ai-to-understand-20211216/.

53. Mitchell, "What Does It Mean for AI to Understand?"

54. Erik J. Larson, *The Myth of Artificial Intelligence* (Cambridge, MA: Harvard University Press, 2021).

2. CAN AI BE CREATIVE?

1. William Fifield, "Pablo Picasso: A Composite Interview," *Paris Review* 32 (Summer-Fall 1964), 3766, https://www.theparisreview.org/miscellaneous/4487/pablo-picasso-a-composite-interview-william-fifield. See also https://quoteinvestigator.com/2011/11/05/computers-useless/.

2. Lovelace is often credited with writing an algorithm for Charles Babbage's "Analytical Engine," a machine that was planned but never built. There is some controversy as to whether Lovelace or Babbage wrote this first program. In any case, Lovelace undoubtedly was involved to an extensive degree in the very earliest computer programs, and she was also the first to say that a computer could be programmed to do more than merely compute. For an overview of her contributions, see Christopher Hollings, Ursula Martin, and Adrian Rice, "Ada Lovelace and the Analytical Engine," Bodleian Libraries (July 26, 2018), https://blogs.bodleian.ox.ac.uk/adalovelace/2018/07/26/ada-lovelace-and-the-analytical-engine/.

3. Lady Lovelace, Appendix I to *Faster Than Thought: A Symposium on Digital Computing Machines*, ed. B.V. Bowden (London: Pitman, 1953), 398, https://archive.org/details/fasterthanthough00bvbo/page/341/mode/2up.

4. For an overview of the similarities and differences between Babbage's and Turing's machines, see Nathan Zeldes, "Babbage and Turing: Two Paths to Inventing the Computer," Nathan Zeldes (website), April 29, 2021, https://www.nathanzeldes.com/blog/2021/04/babbage-and-turing-two-paths-to-inventing-the-computer/.

5. Alan Turing, "Computing Machinery and Intelligence," *Mind* 49, no. 235 (October 1950): 433–460.

6. Turing concedes that when machines surprise him, it tends to be because of traceable human error in his calculations. He also anticipates the objection that machine "surprises" are "due to some creative mental act on my part, and reflect no credit on the machine," but he does not answer this objection except to say it leads back to the question of consciousness, which "we must consider closed." Turing, "Computing Machinery and Intelligence," section titled "Lady Lovelace's Objection."

7. Turing, "Computer Machinery and Intelligence," section titled "The Argument from Consciousness."

8. In Turing's "Computing Machinery" article he refers to "human computers" no fewer than ten times.

9. Chatbots are computer programs that respond in a human-like way in text-based exchanges. You might have interacted with a chatbot that popped up on your screen to offer help or answer questions. Chatbots are useful to businesses because they can function as digital help desks. But they are limited in the questions they can answer, and can only respond as they are programmed to respond.

10. Press Association, "Computer Simulating 13-Year-Old Boy Becomes First to Pass Turing Test," *Guardian*, June 9, 2014, https://www.theguardian.com/technology/2014/jun/08/super-computer-simulates-13-year-old-boy-passes-turing-test.

11. George D. Montanez, "Detecting Intelligence: The Turing Test and Other Design Detection Methodologies," Proceedings of the 8th International Conference on Agents and Artificial Intelligence, vol. 2 (Setubal, Portugal: Science and Technology Publications, 2016), 517–523, https://www.scitepress.org/papers/2016/58237/58237.pdf.

12. Selmer Bringsjord, Paul Bello, and David Ferrucci, "Creativity, the Turing Test, and the (Better) Lovelace Test," in *The Turing Test: The Elusive Standard of Artificial Intelligence*, ed. James H. Moor (Boston: Kluwer Academic Publishers, 2003), 215–239.

13. Turing, "Computing Machinery."

14. Bringsjord, Bellow, and Ferrucci, "Creativity."

15. David Klinghoffer, "Robert Marks on the Lovelace Test," Evolution News and Science Today, Discovery Institute, January 24, 2018, https://evolutionnews.org/2018/01/robert-marks-on-the-lovelace-test/.

16. Bringsjord, Bello, and Ferrucci, "Creativity." The Lovelace test (LT) is more formally stated by Bringsjord and his colleagues. Here is their definition: Artificial agent A, designed by H, passes LT if and only if (1) A outputs o; (2) A's outputting o is not the result of a fluke hardware error, but rather the result of processes A can repeat; (3) H (or someone who knows what H knows, and has H's resources) cannot explain how A produced o. Notice that this differs from Turing's "surprises" which, as he admitted, occurred because he as programmer erred or else forgot what he had done.

17. Selmer Bringsjord, "The Turing Test is Dead. Long Live the Lovelace Test," interview by Robert J. Marks in Mind Matters News, podcast, 27:25, April 2, 2020, https://mindmatters.ai/podcast/ep76/.

18. Victor Luckerson, "Five Very Smart People Who Think Artificial Intelligence Could Bring the Apocalypse," *TIME*, December 2, 2014, https://time.com/3614349/artificial-intelligence-singularity-stephen-hawking-elon-musk/.

19. Marianne Freiberger, "Schrödinger's Equation—What Is It?," Math Plus, August 2, 2012, https://plus.maths.org/content/schrodinger-1.

20. John Steinbeck, *East of Eden* (New York: Viking Press, 1952), 151.

21. Gregory Chirikjian, "Help Wanted: For the Cognitive Era," *JHU Engineering*, May 19, 2017, https://engineering.jhu.edu/magazine/2017/05/help-wanted-for-the-cognitive-era/#.W_6rz-hKiUl.

22. Satya Nadella, Greg Shaw, and Jill Tracie Nichols, with a foreword by Bill Gates, *Hit Refresh: The Quest to Rediscover Microsoft's Soul and Imagine a Better Future for Everyone* (New York: HarperCollins, 2017).

23. Isaac Newton to Robert Hooke, 1675, Discover [wesbite], Historical Society of Pennsylvania, https://discover.hsp.org/Record/dc-9792/Description#tabnav.

24. Jacques Hadamard, *Essay on the Psychology of Invention in the Mathematical Field* [1945] (New York: Dover, 1954).

25. Roger Penrose, *The Emperor's New Mind: Concerning Computers, Minds, and the Laws of Physics* (Oxford: Oxford University Press, 1989), 424.

26. Roger Penrose, "Why Did The Mathematician Cross The Road?," interview by Brady Haran, Numberphile, August 8, 2020, podcast, 1:05:16, https://www.numberphile.com/videos/podcast-roger-penrose.

27. David Biello, "Fact or Fiction?: Archimedes Coined the Term 'Eureka!' in the Bath," *Scientific American*, December 8, 2006, https://www.scientificamerican.com/article/fact-or-fiction-archimede/.

28. Jay W. Richards, *The Human Advantage: The Future of American Work in an Age of Smart Machines* (New York: Crown Forum, 2018).

29. Some question the some question the historicity of this "fable," but Archimedes may have solved the problem by an even more ingenious method, described by Rohini Chowdhury, "Archimedes and the Golden Crown," 2002, https://www.longlongtimeago.com/once-upon-a-time/great-discoveries/archimedes-and-the-golden-crown.

30. Bruce Hunt and Eberhard Zeidler, *Oxford Users' Guide to Mathematics* (Oxford: Oxford University Press, 2004), 1188.

31. "List of Things Named after Carl Friedrich Gauss," Wikimedia Foundation, August 31, 2019, https://en.wikipedia.org/wiki/List_of_things_named_after_Carl_Friedrich_Gauss.

32. Quoted in Howard W. Eves, *Mathematical Circles Squared* (Boston: Prindle, Weber, and Schmidt, 1972), 162–163.

33. Quoted in Alexander Findlay, *A Hundred Years of Chemistry* (London: Gerald Duckworth & Co., 1937), 36–37.

34. Findlay, *A Hundred Years of Chemistry*, 38.

35. Nikola Tesla, "My Inventions: The Autobiography of Nikola Tesla," *Electrical Experimenter* (1919), http://www.tfcbooks.com/tesla/my_inventions.pdf.

36. Margaret Cheney, *Tesla: Man Out of Time* (New York: Simon & Schuster, 1981).

37. Tesla, "My Inventions."

38. André-Abraham Weil, *The Apprenticeship of a Mathematician*, trans. Jennifer Gage (Boston: Birkhäuser Verlag, 1992), 91.

39. Robert J. Marks, "What It Really Takes to Build a High-Tech Company, Sell It, and Get Rich," Mind Matters News, Walter Bradley Center for Natural & Artificial Intelligence, May 18, 2019, https://mindmatters.ai/2019/05/what-it-really-takes-to-build-a-high-tech-company-sell-it-and-get-rich/.

40. Hal Philipp, "Advice for Budding Inventors and Entrepreneurs: Hal Philipp Shares His Experience," interview by Robert J. Marks in Mind Matters News, 16, 2019, podcast, 18:06, https://mindmatters.ai/podcast/advice-for-budding-inventors-and-entrepreneurs-hal-philipp-shares-his-experience.

41. "Are Musicians More Creative and Imaginative?," American Music Institute, December 2, 2015, https://amimusic.org/musicians-creativity/ .

42. *Runnin' Down a Dream*, directed by Peter Bogdanovich, 2007, https://en.wikipedia.org/wiki/Runnin%27_Down_a_Dream_(film).

43. *Runnin' Down a Dream*.

44. "Paul McCartney: I Don't Know Where the Melody for 'Yesterday' Came From," Miss Inga Niball, YouTube, audio, 0:50, January 31, 2022, https://www.youtube.com/watch?v=cn80jbvfS30.

45. "Yesterday by the Beatles," SecondHandSongs, accessed September 30, 2021, https://secondhandsongs.com/performance/1409.

46. David McDonald, "Bob Dylan on the Mystery of Creativity," YouTube, video, 1:31, October 24, 2008, https://youtu.be/UrJdk14jGaw.

47. Douglas Brinkley, "Bob Dylan Has a Lot on His Mind," *New York Times*, June 12, 2020, https://www.nytimes.com/2020/06/12/arts/music/bob-dylan-rough-and-rowdy-ways.html.

48. "Five Hundred Greatest Songs of All Time (2004)," *Rolling Stone*, December 11, 2003, https://www.rollingstone.com/music/music-lists/500-greatest-songs-of-all-time-151127/smokey-robinson-and-the-miracles-the-tracks-of-my-tears-56465/.

49. "Thirteenth Annual Grammy Awards," Wikimedia Foundation, last modified January 17, 2021, 15:50, https://en.wikipedia.org/wiki/13th_Annual_Grammy_Awards.

50. Chloe Davis, "Some of the Best Songs Ever Written—Finally Ranked," Editor Choice, April 10, 2019, https://www.editorchoice.com/best-songs/24/.

51. "Flash of Genius Doctrine [Patent Law] Law and Legal Definition," USLegal, accessed September 30, 2021, https://definitions.uslegal.com/f/flash-of-genius-doctrine-patent-law/.

52. Arno Penzias, *Ideas and Information: Managing in a High-Tech World* (New York: Simon & Schuster, 1989), 11.

3. Putting AI to the Test

1. Arno Penzias, *Ideas and Information: Managing in a High-Tech World* (New York: Simon & Schuster, 1989), 11.

2. For some solutions to the "thinking outside the box" problem, see "Creative Thinking Puzzle 1," Brainstorming, accessed April 26, 2022, http://www.brainstorming.co.uk/puzzles/ninedotsnj.html; or "History of the Nine Dot Problem," Art of Play, August 2, 2016, https://www.artofplay.com/blogs/articles/history-of-the-nine-dot-problem.

3. "The Thinking Machine (1961)—MIT Centennial Film" [October 26,1960], YouTube, video, 53:03, July 6, 2018, https://www.youtube.com/watch?v=cvOTKFXpvKA. Patrick D. Wall speaks beginning at the 46:50 minute mark.

4. Niyaz Ahmed, "Twenty-Three Years of the Discovery of Helicobacter pylori: Is the Debate Over?," *Annals of Clinical Microbiology and Antimicrobials* 4 (2005), https://doi.org/10.1186/1476-0711-4-17.

5. Jane Wakefield, "'Dangerous' AI Offers to Write Fake News," BBC, August 27, 2019, https://www.bbc.com/news/technology-49446729.

6. Rachel Metz, "This AI Is So Good at Writing That Its Creators Won't Let You Use It," CNN Business, February 18, 2019, https://www.cnn.com/2019/02/18/tech/dangerous-ai-text-generator/index.html.

7. Tristan Greene, "This AI-Powered Text Generator Is the Scariest Thing I've Ever Seen—And You Can Try It," TNW, August 21, 2019, https://thenextweb.com/news/this-ai-powered-text-generator-is-the-scariest-thing-ive-ever-seen-and-you-can-try-it.

8. Betsy Mikel, "This A.I. Bot Can Convincingly 'Write' Entire Articles. It's So Dangerously Good, the Creators Are Scared to Release It," Inc.com, February 23, 2019, https://www.inc.com/betsy-mikel/elon-musks-ai-nonprofit-just-made-a-truly-alarming-announcement-it-raises-serious-flags-about-future-of-fake-news.html.

9. James Vincent, "OpenAI Has Published the Text-Generating AI It Said Was Too Dangerous to Share," Verge, November 7, 2019, https://www.theverge.com/2019/11/7/20953040/openai-text-generation-ai-gpt-2-full-model-release-1-5b-parameters.

10. Wakefield, "'Dangerous' AI."

11. James Vincent, "OpenAI's New MultiTalented AI Writes, Translates, and Slanders," Verge, February 14, 2019, https://www.theverge.com/2019/2/14/18224704/ai-machine-learning-language-models-read-write-openai-gpt2.

12. Tom B. Brown et al., "Language Models Are Few-Shot Learners," Cornell University, arXiv preprint, arXiv:2005.14165 (2020), https://arxiv.org/abs/2005.14165.

13. GTP-3 Naval (@GPT-3_naval), Twitter, September 29, 2021, https://twitter.com/gpt3_naval/status/1443251456161820675.

14. Tzafrir Rehan (@TzafrirR), Twitter, September 27, 2021, https://twitter.com/TzafrirR/status/1442491874221203458.

15. David Chalmers, "GPT-3 and General Intelligence," Daily Nous, August 4, 2020, https://dailynous.com/2020/07/30/philosophers-gpt-3/#chalmers.

16. Tom Simonite, "Did a Person Write This Headline, or a Machine?," Wired, July 22, 2020, https://www.wired.com/story/ai-text-generator-gpt-3-learning-language-fitfully/.

17. Quoted in Theodore Claypoole, "New AI Tool GPT-3 Ascends to New Peaks, But Proves How Far We Still Need to Travel," National Law Review 10, no. 212 (July 30, 2020), https://www.natlawreview.com/article/new-ai-tool-gpt-3-ascends-to-new-peaks-proves-how-far-we-still-need-to-travel.

18. "A Robot Wrote This Entire Article. Are You Scared Yet, Human?," Guardian, September 8, 2020, https://www.theguardian.com/commentisfree/2020/sep/08/robot-wrote-this-article-gpt-3.

19. Eric Holloway, "Did GPT-3 Really Write That Guardian Essay Without Human Help?," Mind Matters News, Walter Bradley Center for Natural & Artificial Intelligence, November 2, 2020, https://mindmatters.ai/2020/11/did-gpt-3-really-write-that-guardian-essay-without-human-help/.

20. Holloway, "Did GPT-3 Really?"

21. Tristan Greene, "GPT-3's Ability to 'Write Disinformation' Is Being Wildly Overstated by the Media," TNW, May 25, 2021, https://thenextweb.com/news/gpt-3s-ability-to-write-disinformation-wildly-overstated-ai-media.

22. Greene, "This AI-Powered Text Generator Is the Scariest Thing I've Ever Seen."

23. Jonathan Bartlett, "Built to Save Us from Evil AI, OpenAI Now Dupes Us," Mind Matters News, Walter Bradley Center for Natural & Artificial Intelligence, July 23, 2020, https://mindmatters.ai/2020/07/built-to-save-us-from-evil-ai-openai-now-dupes-us/

24. Quoted by Khari Johnson, "AI Weekly: The Promise and Shortcomings of OpenAI's GPT-3," Venture Beat, July 24, 2020, https://venturebeat.com/2020/07/24/ai-weekly-the-promise-and-shortcomings-of-openais-gpt-3/.

25. Gary Smith,"Chatbots: Still Dumb After All These Years," Mind Matters News, Walter Bradley Center for Natural & Artificial Intelligence, January 3, 2022, https://mindmatters.ai/2022/01/will-chatbots-replace-the-art-of-human-conversation/.

26. Dan Robitzski, "The 'Godfather of AI' Just Trashed GPT-3," Byte, October 27, 2020, https://futurism.com/the-byte/godfather-ai-trashed-gpt3.

27. HAL90210, "This Is What Happens When an AI-Written Screenplay Is Made into a Film," Guardian, June 10, 2016, https://www.theguardian.com/technology/2016/jun/10/artificial-intelligence-screenplay-sunspring-silicon-valley-thomas-middleditch-ai.

28. Sunspring Final Script, https://www.docdroid.net/lCZ2fPA/sunspring-final.pdf.

29. Middleditch's other acting credits include Netflix's failed improvisation series, Middleditch and Schwartz. He also played Richard Hendricks in the HBO series Silicon Valley, for which he was nominated for multiple awards and earned a Primetime Emmy Award for Outstanding Lead Actor in a Comedy Series. And he served as a spokesman for Verizon Wireless.

30. "AC/DC—Thunderstruck (Official Music Video)," AC/DC, YouTube, video, 4:52, November 7, 2012, https://youtu.be/v2AC41dglnM.

31. "Sunspring: A Sci-Fi Short Film Starring Thomas Middleditch," Ars Technica, YouTube, video, 9:02, June 9, 2016, https://youtu.be/LY7x2Ihqjmc.

32. Annalee Newitz, "Movie Written by Algorithm Turns out to Be Hilarious and Intense," Ars Technica, June 9, 2016, https://arstechnica.com/gaming/2016/06/an-ai-wrote-this-movie-and-its-strangely-moving/.

33. HAL90210, "This Is What Happens."

34. "Solicitor," Calamity Ai, YouTube, video, 3:55, October 13, 2020, https://youtu.be/AmX3GDJ47wo.

35. "Solicitor," Calamity Ai, Transcript, https://drive.google.com/file/d/1UrqaC3GXh-VWWsk-XixyK49Qqfh1NjwX/view.

36. SCIgen Automatic CS Paper Generator, last accessed February 25, 2022, https://pdos.csail.mit.edu/archive/scigen/.

37. "Mathgen," That's Mathematics, https://thatsmathematics.com/mathgen/.

38. You can see the code at https://github.com/neldredge/mathgen.

39. Need I say that this school is fictitious? It was invented by the (very silly) musical composer and educator Peter Schickele, who also invented the dill piccolo (for playing sour notes). See "Peter Schickele," Wikimedia Foundation, August 30, 2021, https://en.wikipedia.org/wiki/Peter_Schickele.

40. M. Rathke, "Independent, Negative, Canonically Turing Arrows of Equations and Problems in Applied Formal PDE," That's Mathematics, https://thatsmathematics.com/blog/wp-content/uploads/2012/09/mathgen-1389529747.pdf

41. Nate Eldredge, "Mathgen Paper Accepted!," That's Mathematics, September 12, 2012, https://thatsmathematics.com/blog/archives/102.

42. Robert J. Marks II, Michael J. Behe, William A. Dembski, Bruce L. Gordon, and John C. Sanford, eds., Biological Information: New Perspectives (New Jersey: World Scientific Publishing Company, 2013).

43. Robert J. Marks II, *Introduction to Shannon Sampling and Interpolation Theory* (Berlin: Springer Science & Business Media, 2012; and Robert J. Marks II, ed., *Advanced Topics in Shannon Sampling and Interpolation Theory* (Berlin: Springer Science & Business Media, 2012).

44. Springer's statement about this fake chapter's retraction can be viewed at https://link.springer.com/chapter/10.1007/978-3-642-31698-2_58.

45. I originally wrote about this in "Screenwriters' Jobs Are Not Threatened by AI," Mind Matters News, Walter Bradley Center for Natural & Artificial Intelligence, July 2, 2019, https://mindmatters.ai/2018/08/screen-writers-jobs-are-not-threatened-by-ai/.

46. See GunsmokeNet.com—a fan site created by your author.

47. "The Thinking Machine," https://www.youtube.com/watch?v=cvOTKFXpvKA. This documentary contains an interview with Doug Ross and multiple acted-and-filmed versions of the AI-produced cowboy scripts, including one where the computer made errors. The cowboy section begins at about thirty-two minutes in. The flowchart is shown beginning at the 35:45 minute mark. All quotations by Ross are taken from this documentary.

48. "The Thinking Machine," 37:09 mark.

49. "The Thinking Machine," 47:20 mark.

4. MACHINE ARTISTS?

1. *Malcolm in the Middle*, season 6, episode 5, "Kitty's Back," directed by Peter Lauer, aired December 12, 2004, https://www.imdb.com/title/tt0640353/?ref_=ttep_ep5.

2. While the Victorian novelist Margaret Wolfe Hungerford coined this exact phrasing in Molly Bawn [1878] (London: Smith, Elder & Co., 1886), 142, the concept extends far back into the mists of time. For a brief summary, see Gary Martin, "Beauty Is in the Eye of the Beholder," Phrase Finder, https://www.phrases.org.uk/meanings/beauty-is-in-the-eye-of-the-beholder.html.

3. Clearly there must be some objective criteria, else why would universities be populated by students trying to improve in artistic fields such as writing, painting, sculpting, composing, playing various instruments, and so forth? It takes a certain level of mastery before the question of personal preference (subjectivity) can even begin to come into play.

4. Elizabeth Manchester, "Mother and Child (Divided)" [1993], Tate, April/June 2009, https://www.tate.org.uk/art/artworks/hirst-mother-and-child-divided-t12751.

5. "Eric Clapton: Life in 12 Bars (2017): Official Trailer: SHOWTIME Documentary," YouTube, video, 2:05, September 7, 2017, https://youtu.be/nrAvDFmE9i4.

6. "The Beatles: Yesterday (Chords)," Guitar.com, February 1, 2019, https://tabs.ultimate-guitar.com/tab/the_beatles/yesterday_chords_17450.

7. "The Beatles: You Never Give Me Your Money (Chords)," Guitar.com, September 2, 2016, https://tabs.ultimate-guitar.com/tab/the_beatles/you_never_give_me_your_money_chords_1056469.

8. Williams Mason, "Classical Gas Chords: Ver. 1," AZChords, 2022, https://www.azchords.com/w/williamsmason-tabs-5689/classicalgas-tabs-118313.html.

9. "I'm a King Bee," Rolling Stones, YouTube, audio, 2:36, July 25, 2018, https://youtu.be/Q2OIvFg-ljc.

10. Marat Bakpayev et al., "Programmatic Creative: AI Can Think But It Cannot Feel," *Australasian Marketing Journal* (August 2020), https://journals.sagepub.com/doi/10.1016/j.ausmj.2020.04.002.

11. Brendan Dixon, "Fan Tries Programming AI Jazz, Gets Lots and Lots of AI," Mind Matters News, Walter Bradley Center for Natural & Artificial Intelligence, August 13, 2019, https://mindmatters.ai/2019/08/fan-tries-programming-ai-jazz-gets-lots-and-lots-of-ai/.

12. Carykh, "Computer Evolves to Generate Baroque Music!," YouTube, video, 18:12, March 9, 2017, https://youtu.be/SacogDL_4JU. See also Amber Healy, "Meet AIVA, the World's First AI Music Composer," Geeks & Beats, January 31, 2018, https://www.geeksandbeats.com/2018/01/meet_avia_worlds_first_ai_music_composer/.

13. "Symphony No. 4 (Ives)," Wikimedia Foundation, last modified August 21, 2021, https://en.wikipedia.org/wiki/Symphony_No._4_(Ives).

14. Brian Wise, "One Conductor Wasn't Enough for This Ives Performance," WQRX, October 19, 2014, https://www.wqxr.org/story/video-one-conductor-wasnt-enough-performance/.

15. Selmer Bringsjord, interview by Jonathan Witt, April 13, 2021.

16. Chris Garcia, "Algorithmic Music—David Cope and EMI," Computer History Museum, April 29, 2015, https://computerhistory.org/blog/algorithmic-music-david-cope-and-emi/.

17. Bringsjord interview with Witt.

18. Brendan Dixon, "AI Can't Do Jazz Because Spontaneity Is at Jazz's Core," Mind Matters News, Walter Bradley Center for Natural & Artificial Intelligence, July 11, 2019, https://mindmatters.ai/2019/07/ai-cant-do-jazz-because-spontaneity-is-at-its-core/.

19. Steven Cerra, "Paperback Edition of How to Listen to Jazz by Ted Gioia," Jazz Profiles, October 4, 2017, https://jazzprofiles.blogspot.com/2017/10/paperback-edition-of-how-to-listen-to.html, review of Ted Gioia, How To Listen to Jazz (New York: Basic Books, 2016).

20. Ted Gioia, How to Listen to Jazz.

21. Gioia, How to Listen to Jazz.

22. Carykh, "AI Evolves to Compose 3 Hours of Jazz!" YouTube, video, 18:08, July 4, 2017, https://youtu.be/nA3YOFUCn4U.

23. Dixon, "Fan Tries Programming AI Jazz."

24. Gioia, How to Listen to Jazz.

25. Jessica Stewart, "NVIDIA's AI App Can Transform Simple Doodles into Spectacular Landscapes," My Modern Met, March 22, 2019, https://mymodernmet.com/gaugan-nvidia-artificial-landscape-maker/.

26. Bryan Catanzaro, quoted in Stewart, "NVIDIA's AI App."

27. Sara Barnes, "AI Generator Will Turn Any Person into a Renaissance Style 'Masterpiece,'" My Modern Met, April 7, 2020, https://mymodernmet.com/ai-generator-ai-gahuku/.

28. "Edmond De Belamy," Wikimedia Foundation, July 29, 2019, https://en.wikipedia.org/wiki/Edmond_de_Belamy#/media/File:Edmond_de_Belamy.png

29. "AI-Produced Artwork Sells for $433K, Smashing Expectations," CNN, October 25, 2018, https://edition.cnn.com/style/article/obvious-ai-art-christies-auction-smart-creativity/index.html. Gabe Cohn, "AI Art at Christie's Sells for $432,500," New York Times, October 25, 2018, https://www.nytimes.com/2018/10/25/arts/design/ai-art-sold-christies.html.

30. Benjamin Sutton, "An Artwork Created by AI Sold for £40,000 at Sotheby's, Failing to Generate the Fervor that Propelled Another AI Work to Sell for 40 Times Its Estimate Last Year," Artsy, March 6, 2019, https://www.artsy.net/news/artsy-editorial-artwork-created-ai-sold-40-000-sothebys-failing-generate-fervor-propelled-ai-work-sell-40-times-estimate-year.

31. Quoted in "Is Artificial Intelligence Set to Become Art's Next Medium?," Christie's, December 12, 2018, https://www.christies.com/features/A-collaboration-between-two-artists-one-human-one-a-machine-9332-1.aspx.

32. Juncheng Shen, Xiaolei Zhu, and De Ma, "TensorClog: An Imperceptible Poisoning Attack on Deep Neural Network Applications," IEEE Access 7 (2019): 41498–41506.

33. "Is Artificial Intelligence Set to Become Art's Next Medium?"

34. Quoted in "Is Artificial Intelligence Set to Become Art's New Medium?"

35. R. J. Marks II, S. Oh, and L. E. Atlas, "Alternating Projection Neural Networks," *IEEE Transactions on Circuits and Systems* 36, no. 6 (1989): 846–857, https://ieeexplore.ieee.org/abstract/document/90404.

36. Seho Oh, Robert J. Marks II, and Dennis Sarr, "Homogeneous Alternating Projection Neural Networks," *Neurocomputing* 3, no. 2 (September 1991): 69–95, https://doi.org/10.1016/0925-2312(91)90051-C.

37. Robert J. Marks, *Handbook of Fourier Analysis and Its Applications* (New York: Oxford University Press, 2009).

38. A. Conan Doyle, "Fairies Photographed: An Epoch-Making Event," *Strand Magazine*, December 1920, https://www.arthur-conan-doyle.com/index.php/Fairies_Photographed.

39. Naomi Rea, "Faked 'Fairy' Photographs from a Famous 20th-Century Hoax Could Fetch $90,000 at Auction," Artnet News, April 2, 2018, https://news.artnet.com/market/famous-fake-fairy-photographs-head-auction-1506307.

40. "Cottingley Fairies Photographs Make £20,000 at Auction," BBC, October 4, 2018, https://www.bbc.com/news/uk-england-leeds-45748927.

41. Dan Evon, "Did a Man in Montana Catch a 3-Foot-Long Grasshopper?," Snopes, May 25, 2017, https://www.snopes.com/fact-check/enormous-grasshopper-montana/.

42. See "Bob Marks' Fake Career in Television," https://marksmannet.com/BobMarks/FAQs/Supportfiles/BobGunsmoke.htm.

43. Kyle Wiggers, "Facebook, Microsoft, and Others Launch Deepfake Detection Challenge," VentureBeat, December 11, 2019, https://venturebeat.com/2019/12/11/facebook-microsoft-and-others-launch-deepfake-detection-challenge/.

44. Wiggers, "Facebook."

45. The GAN is also used in the development of GPT-3.

46. It wasn't. But Mozart did an arrangement based on the melody of "Twinkle, Twinkle, Little Star" in his composition Twelve Variations on "Ah vous dirai-je, Maman."

47. Robert B. Cialdini, *Influence: The Psychology of Persuasion* (New York: Harper Collins, 1987).

48. "Claque," Theatre History, http://www.theatrehistory.com/french/claque001.html. This originally appeared in the Encyclopedia Britannica, 11th ed., vol. 11 (Cambridge: Cambridge University Press, 1910), 423.

49. John Kay and Mervyn King, *Radical Uncertainty: Decision-Making beyond the Numbers* (New York: W. W. Norton & Company, 2020).

5. The Hype Curve

1. Eliezer Yudkowsky, "Friendly Artificial Intelligence," in *Singularity Hypotheses: The Frontiers Collection*, eds. A. Eden et al. (Berlin: Springer, 2013), 181–195, https://doi.org/10.1007/978-3-642-32560-1_10.

2. David A. Price, "An AI Breaks the Writing Barrier," *Wall Street Journal*, August 22, 2020, https://www.wsj.com/articles/an-ai-breaks-the-writing-barrier-11598068862.

3. Robert J. Marks, "After Thursday's Dogfight, It's Clear: DARPA Gets AI Right," Mind Matters News, Walter Bradley Center for Natural & Artificial Intelligence, August 23, 2020, https://mindmatters.ai/2020/08/after-thursdays-dogfight-its-clear-darpa-gets-ai-right/.

4. Jeremy Hsu, "Humans Fold: AI Conquers Poker's Final Milestone," *Scientific American*, July 11, 2019, https://www.scientificamerican.com/article/ai-conquers-six-player-poker/.

5. "AlphaStar: Mastering the Real-Time Strategy Game StarCraft II," DeepMind, January 24, 2019, https://deepmind.com/blog/article/alphastar-mastering-real-time-strategy-game-starcraft-ii.

6. Arjun Kharpal, "Stephen Hawking Says A.I. Could Be 'Worst Event in the History of Our Civilization,'" CNBC, November 6, 2017, https://www.cnbc.com/2017/11/06/stephen-hawking-ai-could-be-worst-event-in-civilization.html.

7. Kevin Rawlinson, "Microsoft's Bill Gates Insists AI Is a Threat," BBC News, January 29, 2015, https://www.bbc.com/news/31047780.

8. Miriam Kramer, "Elon Musk: Artificial Intelligence Is Humanity's 'Biggest Existential Threat,'" Live Science, October 27, 2014, https://www.livescience.com/48481-elon-musk-artificial-intelligence-threat.html.

9. Henry Kissinger, "How the Enlightenment Ends," *Atlantic*, August 30, 2019, https://www.theatlantic.com/magazine/archive/2018/06/henry-kissinger-ai-could-mean-the-end-of-human-history/559124/.

10. To the best of my knowledge, the hype curve was first described in James C. Bezdek, "Fuzzy Models—What Are They, and Why?," in *IEEE Technology Updates Series: Fuzzy Logic Technology and Applications*, ed. Robert J. Marks II (1994): 3–7. Reprinted from IEEE Transactions on Fuzzy Systems 1, no. 1 (February 1993). The hype curve was later dubbed the Gartner Hype Cycle in the 2000s with no reference to Bezdek: https://www.gartner.com/technology/research/methodologies/hype-cycle.jsp.

11. Note that Figure 5.1 illustrates a prototypical hype curve for a technology that is initially hyped but eventually does provide real-world value. The hype curve in the case of an outright hoax would look somewhat different, since the nose-dive phase, upon the discovery of the hoax, would simply move toward the line of reality without necessarily overshooting it on the down side. In the case of a hoax, the vaunted technological "discovery" is a worthless fraud, so it's hard to undershoot its perceived value.

12. Proverbs 16:18.

13. Kramer, "Elon Musk."

14. Ralph Nader, *Unsafe at Any Speed: The Designed-In Dangers of the American Automobile* (New York: Grossman, 1965).

15. South Park, season 5, episode 11, "The Entity," directed by Trey Parker, written by Trey Parker et al., aired November 21, 2002, on Comedy Central.

16. Francisco Antonio Doria and Wuppuluri Shyam, eds., *Unravelling Complexity: The Life and Work of Gregory Chaitin* (Hackensack, New Jersey: World Scientific, 2020), 18.

17. Robert J. Marks II, *Introduction to Shannon Sampling and Interpolation Theory* (New York: Springer-Verlag, 1991), https://marksmannet.com/RobertMarks/RE-PRINTS/1999_IntroductionToShannonSamplingAndInterpolationTheory.pdf.

18. Claude E. Shannon, "The Bandwagon," *IRE Transactions on Information Theory* 2, no. 1 (1956): 3.

19. John Carreyrou, *Bad Blood: Secrets and Lies in a Silicon Valley Startup* (New York: Knopf, 2018).

20. Ludmila Leiva, "Here Are the Theranos Investors Who Lost Millions," Refinery29, March 5, 2019, https://www.refinery29.com/en-us/2019/03/225707/theranos-investors-list-elizabeth-holmes.

21. To see a 1913 artistic rendering, visit "Piltdown Man," Wikimedia Foundation, https://en.wikipedia.org/wiki/Piltdown_Man#/media/File:PSM_V82_D210_Reconstruction_of_Eoanthropus_dawsoni.png.

22. *History's Greatest Hoaxes*, season 1, episode 5, "Piltdown Man," directed by Bruce Burgess, aired 2016 on Netflix.

23. Jonathan Webb, "Piltdown Review Points Decisive Finger at Forger Dawson," BBC News, August 10, 2016, https://www.bbc.com/news/science-environment-37021144.

24. Ethan Siegel, "Why String Theory Is Both a Dream and a Nightmare," *Forbes*, February 26, 2020, https://www.forbes.com/sites/startswithabang/2020/02/26/why-string-theory-is-both-a-dream-and-a-nightmare/#31fb8fe53b1d.

25. Robert J. Marks II, "Diversity Inadequacies of Parallel Universes: When the Multiverse Becomes Insufficient to Account for Conflicting Contradistinctions," *Perspectives on Science and Christian Faith* 71, no. 3 (September 2019): 146–152.

26. Siegel, "Why String Theory."

27. Peter Woit, *Not Even Wrong: The Failure of String Theory and the Search for Unity in Physical Law* (New York: Basic Books, 2007).

28. "New Navy Device Learns by Doing," *New York Times*, July 8, 1959, https://www.nytimes.com/1958/07/08/archives/new-navy-device-learns-by-doing-psychologist-shows-embryo-of.html.

29. William McCall, "Portland Firm Ships Brain-Like Chip," Associated Press, May 2, 1989.

30. Agam Shah, "New Computer Chips Could Power AI to Next Level," *Wall Street Journal*, June 2, 2020, https://www.wsj.com/articles/new-computer-chips-could-power-ai-to-next-level-11591090202.

6. TWELVE FILTERS FOR AI HYPE DETECTION

1. Paul Ehrlich, "Eco-Catastrophe!," *Ramparts*, 1970. Quoted in Ronald Bailey, "Earth Day, Then and Now," Reason, May 2000, https://reason.com/2000/05/01/earth-day-then-and-now-2/.

2. Paul Ehrlich, *The Progressive*, 1970. Quoted in Bailey, "Earth Day."

3. Joe Hasell and Max Roser, "Famines," Our World in Data, 2013, https://ourworldindata.org/famines.

4. The two men's beliefs about people are highlighted by their book titles. Ehrlich wrote *The Population Bomb* and Simon wrote *The Ultimate Resource*.

5. Joseph Sunde, "Julian Simon Was Right: More Humans Equals More Abundance," Acton Institute, July 14, 2021, https://blog.acton.org/archives/121948-julian-simon-was-

right-more-humans-equals-more-abundance.html. Also see The Simon Project website, which undertakes an ongoing assessment of human prosperity and has many interesting charts and comparisons: https://www.humanprogress.org/simonproject/.

6. Nicholas Thompson and Ian Bremmer, "The AI Cold War That Threatens Us All," Wired, October 23, 2018, https://www.wired.com/story/ai-cold-war-china-could-doom-us-all/.

7. George Dvorsky, "How We Can Prepare for Catastrophically Dangerous AI—And Why We Can't Wait," Gizmodo, December 5, 2018, https://gizmodo.com/how-we-can-prepare-now-for-catastrophically-dangerous-a-1830388719.

8. Todd South, "Army Researchers Are Developing a Self-Aware Squid-like Robot You Can 3D Print in the Field," Army Times, April 18, 2018, https://www.armytimes.com/news/your-army/2018/04/18/army-researchers-are-developing-a-self-aware-robot-squid-you-can-3d-print-in-the-field/.

9. Claude Shannon, appearing on the television show The Thinking Machine, CBS and MIT, 1961, https://techtv.mit.edu/videos/10268-the-thinking-machine-1961---mit-centennial-film.

10. Jimmy Soni and Rob Goodman, A Mind at Play: How Claude Shannon Invented the Information Age (New York: Simon and Schuster, 2017).

11. "New Navy Device Learns by Doing; Psychologist Shows Embryo of Computer Designed to Read and Grow Wiser," New York Times, July 8, 1958, https://www.nytimes.com/1958/07/08/archives/new-navy-device-learns-by-doing-psychologist-shows-embryo-of.html.

12. Ray Kurzweil, The Age of Spiritual Machines: When Computers Exceed Human Intelligence (New York: Penguin, 2000).

13. George Gilder, Life After Television (New York: W.W. Norton, 1994).

14. "Plan 9 from Outer Space," Wikiquote, last modified July 1, 2021, https://en.wikiquote.org/wiki/Plan_9_from_Outer_Space.

15. Jeron Criswell, Criswell Predicts: From Now to the Year 2000! (New York: Grosset and Dunlap, 1968).

16. "The Amazing Criswell," Wikimedia Foundation, last modified September 30, 2021, https://en.wikipedia.org/wiki/The_Amazing_Criswell.

17. Dustin Levy, "Littlestown's Hollywood Trailblazer Finally Getting Her Due," Washington Times, February 17, 2018, https://www.washingtontimes.com/news/2018/feb/17/littlestowns-hollywood-trailblazer-finally-getting/.

18. "The Amazing Criswell."

19. Kenneth Watt, lecture, Swarthmore College, April 19, 1970. Quoted in Bailey, "Earth Day."

20. William Thomson to Baden Baden-Powell, December 9, 1896, Correspondence of Lord Kelvin, http://zapatopi.net/kelvin/papers/letters.html#baden-powell.

21. "Only 400 Years," San Francisco Call, July 9, 1898, 3, https://www.newspapers.com/clip/36036605/lord-kelvin-warns-of-co2-buildup-and/. For a collection of other contemporaneous reports of Lord Kelvin's dire prediction, see Lyle Zapato, "On the End of Free Oxygen," Kelvin Library, Zapato Productions Intradimensional, https://zapatopi.net/kelvin/papers/end_of_free_oxygen.html.

22. Selmer Bringsjord and Robert J. Marks, "Can Human Minds be Reduced to Computer Programs?," Mind Matters News, Walter Bradley Center for Natural & Artificial Intel-

ligence, podcast, 22:14, April 21, 2020, https://mindmatters.ai/2020/04/can-human-minds-be-reduced-to-computer-programs/.

23. Michael Crichton, "Aliens Cause Global Warming," Michelin Lecture, California Institute of Technology, January 17, 2003. Transcript available at http://stephenschneider.stanford.edu/Publications/PDF_Papers/Crichton2003.pdf.

24. Peter Gunter in *The Living Wilderness* (Spring 1970). Quoted in Bailey, "Earth Day."

25. Rupert Sheldrake, "TED 'Bans' the Science Delusion," Sheldrake (website), https://www.sheldrake.org/reactions/tedx-whitechapel-the-banned-talk. The banned talk has since been re-posted, so as of this writing you can view it here: James Dearden Bush, "Rupert Sheldrake: The Science Delusion Banned TED Talk," YouTube, video, 18:19, March 15, 2013, https://www.youtube.com/watch?v=JKHUaNAxsTg.

26. Sheldrake, "TED 'Bans' the Science Delusion."

27. John R. Searle, "Is the Brain a Digital Computer?," *Proceedings and Addresses of the American Philosophical Association* 64, no. 3 (November 1990): 21–37, https://philosophy.as.uky.edu/sites/default/files/Is%20the%20Brain%20a%20Digital%20Computer%20-%20John%20R.%20Searle.pdf.

28. John Rennie, "The Immortal Ambitions of Ray Kurzweil: A Review of Transcendent Man," *Scientific American*, February 15, 2011, https://www.scientificamerican.com/article/the-immortal-ambitions-of-ray-kurzweil/.

29. Ray Kurzweil, "As Humans and Computers Merge... Immortality?," interview by Gwen Ifill, PBS, July 10, 2017, https://www.pbs.org/newshour/show/as-humans-and-computers-merge-immortality#transcript.

30. Raffi Khatchadourian, "The Doomsday Invention," *New Yorker*, September 7, 2017, https://www.newyorker.com/magazine/2015/11/23/doomsday-invention-artificial-intelligence-nick-bostrom. Nick Bostrom, *Superintelligence: Paths, Dangers, Strategies* (Oxford: Oxford University Press, 2014).

31. See, for instance, Robert M. Young, "The Mind–Body Problem," in R. C. Olby et al., eds., *Companion to the History of Modern Science* (New York: Taylor and Francis), 702–711, and also J. P. Moreland and Scott B. Rae, *Body and Soul: Human Nature and the Crisis in Ethics* (Downers Grove, IL: InterVarsity Press, 2000).

32. Michael Egnor, "Are Electrons Conscious?," Mind Matters News, Walter Bradley Center for Natural & Artificial Intelligence, March 12, 2019, https://mindmatters.ai/2019/03/are-electrons-conscious/.

33. Robert J. Marks II, "Why 'Mind Matters' Matter," Mind Matters News, Walter Bradley Center for Natural & Artificial Intelligence, July 11, 2018, https://mindmatters.ai/2018/07/why-mind-matters-matters/.

34. Karen Hart, "The Reason People Believe Breakfast Is the Most Important Meal Of the Day," Mashed, August 9, 2020, https://www.mashed.com/234731/the-reason-people-believe-breakfast-is-the-most-important-meal-of-the-day/.

35. Bernard Widrow, foreword to Russell C. Eberhart and Roy W. Dobbins, eds., *Neural Network PC Tools: A Practical Guide* (San Diego, CA: Academic Press, 1990).

36. South, "Army Researchers."

37. Lexico Dictionaries, s.v. "self-aware," https://en.oxforddictionaries.com/definition/self-aware.

38. Kurzweil, "As Humans and Computers Merge."

39. Roger Penrose and N. David Mermin, "The Emperor's New Mind: Concerning Computers, Minds, and the Laws of Physics," *American Journal of Physics* 58, no. 12 (December 1990): 1214–1216, https://aapt.scitation.org/doi/10.1119/1.16207.

40. J. P. Moreland, *Finding Quiet* (Grand Rapids, MI: Zondervan, 2019).

41. "Why Some Scientists Believe the Universe Is Conscious," Mind Matters News, Walter Bradley Center for Natural & Artificial Intelligence, August 2, 2019, https://mindmatters. ai/2019/08/why-some-scientists-believe-the-universe-is-conscious/.

42. Phillip Goff, "Could Electrons Be Conscious?," *Conscience and Consciousness*, November 2, 2015, https://conscienceandconsciousness.com/2015/10/30/could-electrons-be-conscious/.

43. Thisanka Siripala, "An Ancient Japanese Shrine Debuts a Buddhist Robot," Diplomat, March 5, 2019, https://thediplomat.com/2019/03/an-ancient-japanese-shrine-debuts-a-buddhist-robot/.

44. "Audio-Animatronics Trademark Details," *Justia Trademarks*, accessed February 4, 2022, https://trademarks.justia.com/721/92/audio-animatronics-72192128.html.

45. Siripala, "An Ancient Japanese Shrine."

46. Quoted in Bernard Marr, "Twenty-Eight Best Quotes about Artificial Intelligence," *Forbes*, July 25, 2017, https://www.forbes.com/sites/bernardmarr/2017/07/25/28-best-quotes-about-artificial-intelligence/?sh=50ec46b94a6f.

47. Janice Hocker Rushing and Thomas S. Frentz,"The Frankenstein Myth in Contemporary Cinema, *Critical Studies in Media Communication* 6, no. 1 (1989): 61–80; Sam N. Lehman-Wilzig, "Frankenstein Unbound: Towards a Legal Definition of Artificial Intelligence," *Futures* 13, no. 6 (1981): 442–457.

48. Lee McCauley, "The Frankenstein Complex and Asimov's Three Laws," Association for the Advancement of Artificial Intelligence, 2007, https://www.aaai.org/Papers/Workshops/2007/WS-07-07/WS07-07-003.pdf.

49. To see a 1935 Universal Pictures promotional photo, visit "Frankenstein's Monster," Wikimedia Foundation, https://commons.wikimedia.org/w/index.php?curid=3558176.

50. Maya B. Mathur and David B. Reichling, "Navigating a Social World with Robot Partners: A Quantitative Cartography of the Uncanny Valley," *Cognition* 146 (2016): 22–32.

51. "Sophia (Robot)," Wikimedia Foundation, last modified October 12, 2021, https://en.wikipedia.org/wiki/Sophia_(robot).

52. "Sophia the Robot," Facebook, accessed April 4, 2022, https://www.facebook.com/realsophiarobot/.

53. Chris Weller, "Meet the First-Ever Robot Citizen—A Humanoid Named Sophia That Once Said It Would 'Destroy Humans,'" Business Insider, October 28, 2017, https://www.businessinsider.com.au/meet-the-first-robot-citizen-sophia-animatronic-humanoid-2017-10.

54. Robin A. Smith, "Artificial Intelligence Makes Blurry Faces Look More Than 60 Times Sharper," Tech Xplore, June 12, 2020, https://techxplore.com/news/2020-06-artificial-intelligence-blurry-sharper.html.

55. Smith, "Artificial Intelligence."

56. It's more fun to watch the real-time combining process that generates the above images. Take a look at my short YouTube video, "POCS: Alternating Projection onto Convex Sets Tutorial (#3 of 3)," September 30, 2016, at https://youtu.be/zP7jj3iUfso?t=1669.

57. Aristos Georgiou, "This Strange Headset Lets You Interact with Digital Devices Simply by Reading Your Mind," *Newsweek*, April 5, 2018, https://www.newsweek.com/strange-headset-lets-you-interact-digital-devices-simply-reading-your-mind-873199.

58. Jonathan Greig, "Could MIT's AI Headset Transcribe Your Future Strategy Straight from Your Brain?," *Tech Republic*, April 6, 2018, https://www.techrepublic.com/article/mit-researchers-develop-tech-to-transcribe-the-words-youre-thinking/.

59. "Researchers Develop Device That Can 'Hear' Your Internal Voice," *Guardian*, April 6, 2018, https://www.theguardian.com/technology/2018/apr/06/researchers-develop-device-that-can-hear-your-internal-voice.

60. "MIT's Fascinating AlterEgo Device Can 'Hear' Your Thoughts," Hearing Health & Technology Matters, April 9, 2018, https://hearinghealthmatters.org/blog/2018/mit-alterego-device-can-hear-your-thoughts/.

61. "MIT's Fascinating AlterEgo."

62. Larry Hardesty, "Computer System Transcribes Words Users 'Speak Silently,'" MIT News, April 4, 2018, http://news.mit.edu/2018/computer-system-transcribes-words-users-speak-silently-0404.

63. MIT Media Lab, "AlterEgo: Interfacing with Devices Through Silent Speech," YouTube, video, 1:21, April 4, 2018, https://youtu.be/RuUSc53Xpeg.

64. "Researchers Develop Device."

65. Danyal Hussain, "No More Secrets! New Mind-Reading Machine Can Translate Your Thoughts and Display Them as Text INSTANTLY," *Daily Mail Online*, March 31, 2018, http://www.dailymail.co.uk/news/article-5565179/Mind-reading-machine-translate-thoughts-display-text.html.

66. David A. Moses, Matthew K. Leonard, and Edward F. Chang, "Real-Time Classification of Auditory Sentences Using Evoked Cortical Activity in Humans," *Journal of Neural Engineering* 15, no. 3 (February 2018), https://iopscience.iop.org/article/10.1088/1741-2552/aaab6f/meta.

67. Debra Bell, "Celebrities Who Have Testified to Congress," US News & World Report, September 24, 2010, https://www.usnews.com/news/slideshows/celebrities-who-have-testified-to-congress.

68. Laura Ingraham, *Shut Up & Sing: How Elites from Hollywood, Politics, and the UN Are Subverting America* (Washington DC: Regnery, 2003).

69. Joe Utichi, "Coping with COVID-19 Crisis: Ricky Gervais On Mourning, 'Tiger King' And Celebs Singing 'Imagine' From Their Mansions," Deadline, April 24, 2020, https://deadline.com/2020/04/coping-with-covid-19-crisis-ricky-gervais-after-life-celebrity-imagine-interview-1202916891/.

70. Roger Moore, "Marlon Brando: 1924–2004," *Orlando Sentinel Daily Press*, July 3, 2004, https://www.dailypress.com/news/dp-xpm-20040703-2004-07-03-0407030134-story.html.

71. Elon Musk, *Joe Rogan Experience*, interview by Joe Rogan, September 7, 2018, 2:37:02, https://www.youtube.com/watch?v=ycPr5-27vSI&t=7855s. The discussion of simulation begins at 43:30.

72. Elon Musk, Q&A at Code Conference, YouTube, video, 3:43, 2016, https://www.youtube.com/watch?v=2KK_kzrJPS8&list=PLKof9YSAshgyPqlK-UUYrHfIQaOzFPSL4&index=2. Others, such as Nick Bostrom, float this theory too. See Fouad Khan, "Confirmed! We Live in a Simulation: We Must Never Doubt Elon

Musk Again," *Scientific American*, April 1, 2021, https://www.scientificamerican.com/article/confirmed-we-live-in-a-simulation/.

73. Rich Karlgaard, "Why Technology Prophet George Gilder Predicts Big Tech's Disruption," *Forbes*, February 9, 2018, https://www.forbes.com/sites/richkarlgaard/2018/02/09/why-technology-prophet-george-gilder-predicts-big-techs-disruption/.

74. Elon Musk, lecture, National Governors Association, Summer 2017, https://www.c-span.org/video/?431119-6/elon-musk-addresses-nga.

75. Musk, *Joe Rogan Experience*, beginning at 23:00.

76. Stephen Hawking, "Stephen Hawking Warns Artificial Intelligence Could End Mankind," BBC, interview with Rory Cellan-Jones, December 2014, https://www.bbc.com/news/technology-30290540.

77. Stephen Hawking, "Godel [sic] and the End of Physics" [2002], Hawking.org.uk, accessed July 1, 2020, http://www.hawking.org.uk/godel-and-the-end-of-physics.html.

78. Robert J. Marks, "Advice to Physicists: Shut Up and Do Physics," Mind Matters News, Walter Bradley Center for Natural & Artificial Intelligence, May 25, 2020, https://mindmatters.ai/2020/05/advice-to-physicists-shut-up-and-do-physics/.

79. One paper on the subject is by Selmer Bringsjord and Konstantine Arkoudas, "The Modal Argument for Hypercomputing Minds," *Theoretical Computer Science* 317 (2004): 167–190, http://kryten.mm.rpi.edu/modal.hypercomputing.pdf. As Bringsjord explained in an interview, while he agreed with Penrose's conclusion, he saw some weaknesses in how Penrose arrived at his conclusion, and in particular, in a use of Gödel's incompleteness theorem that Gödel himself would not countenance. Bringsjord said that the "Modal Argument for Hypercomputing Minds" paper is his attempt "to renovate and circumvent the concerns that Gödel had."

80. Sarah Taylor, "Disturbing Investigation Reveals McDonald's Customers May Endanger Their Health Using Touch Screens," Blaze, December 13, 2018, https://www.theblaze.com/news/2018/11/28/disturbing-investigation-reveals-mcdonalds-customers-may-endanger-their-health-using-touch-screens. The story was originally published by Adam Smith, "Poo Found on Every McDonald's Touchscreen Tested," Metro.co.uk, November 28, 2018.

81. Smith, "Poo."

82. Samar S. Boswihi and Edet E. Udo, "Methicillin-Resistant Staphylococcus Aureus: An Update on the Epidemiology, Treatment Options and Infection Control," *Current Medicine Research and Practice* 8, no. 1 (January/February 2018): 18–24, https://www.sciencedirect.com/science/article/abs/pii/S2352081717301708

83. Alex Berezow, "Relax, McDonald's Touchscreen Menus Aren't Covered in Poop," American Council on Science and Health, May 15, 2019, https://www.acsh.org/news/2019/05/14/relax-mcdonalds-touchscreen-menus-arent-covered-poop-14025.

84. Amelia Lucas, "McDonald's Acquires A. I. Company to Help Automate the Drive-Thru, Its Third Tech Deal This Year," CNBC, September 10, 2019, https://www.cnbc.com/2019/09/10/mcdonalds-acquires-ai-company-trying-to-automate-the-drive-thru.html.

85. J. Warner Wallace, "Why Understanding Criminal Motive Is So Important to Christians," Cold Case Christianity, March 25, 2019, https://coldcasechristianity.com/writings/why-understanding-criminal-motive-is-so-important-to-christians/.

86. Yascha Mounk, "What an Audacious Hoax Reveals About Academia," *Atlantic,* October 5, 2018, https://www.theatlantic.com/ideas/archive/2018/10/new-sokal-hoax/572212/.

87. Helen Wilson, "Human Reactions to Rape Culture and Queer Performativity at Urban Dog Parks in Portland, Oregon," *Gender, Place & Culture* 27, no. 2 (May 22, 2018): 307–328, https://www.tandfonline.com/doi/pdf/10.1080/0966369X.2018.1475346.

88. Helen Pluckrose, James A. Lindsay, and Peter Boghossian, "Academic Grievance Studies and the Corruption of Scholarship," Areo, October 2, 2018, https://areomagazine.com/2018/10/02/academic-grievance-studies-and-the-corruption-of-scholarship/.

89. Sharon Kasper, "Artificial Neural Networks Model the Human Brain," *Trend in Engineering* 39 (Spring 1988), https://robertmarks.org/CV/Cv_files/1987_TheTrend.pdf.

90. Robert J. Marks, "KIRO Radio Interview (Seattle)," interview by Jim French, March 12, 1991. Available at YouTube, 21:41, December 24, 2018, https://youtu.be/36XmnxePlLE.

91. "It's Difficult to Make Predictions, Especially about the Future," Quote Investigator, October 20, 2013, https://quoteinvestigator.com/2013/10/20/no-predict/.

92. And yes, this applies to your author.

93. Colin Angle, "Paths to Innovation" KnowAtom, accessed July 1, 2020, https://www.knowatom.com/colin-angle-innovator.

7. AI: The Fossil Record

1. Anthony Liversidge, "Profile of Claude Shannon—Interview," in *Claude E. Shannon: Collected Papers,* eds. N. J. A Sloane and Aaron D. Wyner (New York: Wiley-IEEE, 1993), xxiv. This is a modified reprint of Anthony Liversidge, "Interview: Father of the Information Age," *Omni* (August 1987): 60–67.

2. *Science in Action,* "Computers That Learn," California Academy of Science, directed by George Lum, featuring guest scientist Bernard Widrow, aired December 19, 1963, https://archive.org/details/csfa_000077.

3. *Science in Action.*

4. "Copper Cyanide," Hazardous Substance Fact Sheet, New Jersey Department of Health and Senior Service, https://nj.gov/health/eoh/rtkweb/documents/fs/0533.pdf.

5. Edmund Dickinson, "Electroplating: How the US Mint Makes a Penny," COMSOL, April 17, 2014, https://www.comsol.com/blogs/electroplating-u-s-mint-makes-penny/.

6. Want to know how much copper is in your penny? See Susan Headley, "Is My Penny Solid Copper or a Copper-Plated Zinc Cent?," Spruce Crafts, January 1, 2020, https://www.thesprucecrafts.com/penny-solid-copper-or-plated-768853.

7. Email from Sue Hersman, Ed Hersman's daughter.

8. Chuck Kowalski, "Why the Copper Penny Is Worth More Than One Cent," Balance, September 18, 2019, https://www.thebalance.com/the-copper-penny-is-worth-more-than-one-cent-809218.

9. "Science in Action," YouTube, video, 24:36, July 29, 2013, https://youtu.be/IE-FRtz68m-8.

10. Frank Rosenblatt, "The Perceptron: A Perceiving and Recognizing Automaton (Project PARA)," *Cornell Aeronautical Laboratory, Report* No. 85-460-1 (Buffalo, New York: Cornell, January 1957), https://blogs.umass.edu/brain-wars/files/2016/03/rosenblatt-1957.pdf; Frank Rosenblatt, "The Perceptron: A Probabilistic Model for Information Storage

and Organization in the Brain," *Psychological Review* 65, no. 6 (1958): 386–408, https://www.ling.upenn.edu/courses/cogs501/Rosenblatt1958.pdf.

11. Frank Rosenblatt, *Principles of Neurodynamics: Perceptrons and the Theory of Brain Mechanisms* (Washington DC: Spartan, 1962).

12. For a quick comparison of the perceptron and ADALINE, see Sebastian Raschka, "Machine Learning FAQ," Sebastian Raschka [website], accessed October 20, 2021, https://sebastianraschka.com/faq/docs/diff-perceptron-adaline-neuralnet.html.

13. Jeremy Bernstein, "Profiles: Marvin Minsky," *New Yorker* (December 14, 1981), https://www.newyorker.com/magazine/1981/12/14/a-i.

14. Marvin Minsky and Seymour Papert, *Perceptrons: An Introduction to Computational Geometry* (Cambridge, MA: MIT Press, 1990).

15. Seymour Papert, "One AI or Many?," *Daedalus* 117, no. 1 (Winter 1988): 4, https://www.jstor.org/stable/20025136. [Emphasis in original.]

16. DARPA investigates high-risk ideas for potential use in military combat. DARPA historically fueled the genesis for technologies like GPS, self-driving cars, and the internet. DARPA's funding of Papert's work disappeared because of the clown war between the two technologies.

17. Papert, "One AI or Many?," 3–4.

18. James Lighthill, "Artificial Intelligence: A General Survey," in *Artificial Intelligence: A Paper Symposium* (1973), Science Research Council, http://www.chilton-computing.org.uk/inf/literature/reports/lighthill_report/contents.htm.

19. Jon Agar, "What is Science for? The Lighthill Report on Artificial Intelligence Reinterpreted," *British Journal for the History of Science* 53, no. 3 (July 2020): 289–310, https://doi.org/10.1017/S0007087420000230.

20. Brendan Dixon, "AI Winter is Coming," Mind Matters News, Walter Bradley Center for Natural & Artificial Intelligence, November 29, 2018, https://mindmatters.ai/2018/11/is-a-bad-ai-winter-looming/.

8. The AI Revival

1. Conor Friedersdorf, "There's Enough Time to Change Everything: The Polymath Computer Scientist David Gelernter's Wide-Ranging Ideas about American Life," *Atlantic*, February 23, 2017, https://www.theatlantic.com/politics/archive/2017/02/theres-enough-time-to-change-everything/517209.

2. J. G. McDonnell, R. J. Marks II, and L. E. Atlas, "Neural Networks for Solving Combinatorial Search Problems: A Tutorial," Northcon/88, Seattle, WA, printed in *Conference Record*, vol. 2 (North Hollywood, CA: Western Periodicals Co., 1988), 868–876.

3. Hopfield's oft-cited papers include J. J. Hopfield, "Neural Networks and Physical Systems with Emergent Collective Computational Abilities," *PNAS* 79, no. 8 (April 1982): 2554–2558, cited 8,575 times as of October 25, 2021; "Neurons with Graded Response Have Collective Computational Properties Like Those of Two-State Neurons," *PNAS* 81, no. 10 (May 1984): 3088–3092, cited 23,606 times as of October 25, 2021; and "'Neural' Computation of Decisions in Optimization Problems," *Biological Cybernetics* 52 (1985): 141–152, cited 8,183 times as of October 25, 2021.

4. K. F. Cheung, L. E. Atlas, and R. J. Marks II, "Synchronous Versus Asynchronous Behavior of Hopfield's Content Addressable Memory," in *Artificial Neural Networks: Concepts and Control Applications*, ed. V. R. Vemuri (IEEE Computer Society Press, 1992), 142–147,

reprinted from *Applied Optics* 26 (1987): 4808–4813; R. J. Marks II and L. E. Atlas, "Geometrical Interpretation of Hopfield's Content Addressable Memory Neural Network," Northcon/88, Seattle, WA, printed in *Conference Record*, vol. 2 (North Hollywood, CA: Western Periodicals Co., 1988), 964–977.

5. Chapter 4 noted that a deep neural network could not be trained to reconstruct the face of an arbitrary person. This is different. In the Hopfield neural network, the entire picture of a specific baby is already coded in the neural network.

6. John C. Sanford, *Genetic Entropy and the Mystery of the Genome* (Lima, NY: Ivan Press, 2005). Michael Behe, *Darwin Devolves: The New Science About DNA That Challenges Evolution* (New York: HarperOne, 2019).

7. A basic explanation can be found at "Understanding Single Layer Perceptron and Difference Between Single Layer vs Multilayer Perceptron," i2tutorials, September 6, 2019, https://www.i2tutorials.com/what-is-single-layer-perceptron-and-difference-between-single-layer-vs-multilayer-perceptron/. For a slightly more in-depth explanation, see Ujjwal Karn, "A Quick Introduction to Neural Networks," Data Science Blog, August 9, 2016, https://ujjwalkarn.me/2016/08/09/quick-intro-neural-networks/.

8. Paul J. Werbos, "Beyond Regression: New Tools for Prediction and Analysis in the Behavioral Sciences," (PhD diss., Harvard University, 1974).

9. The lead editor, David Rumelhart, was a psychologist at the University of California, San Diego. This work had such impact, Rumelhart was offered and accepted a position at the more prestigious Stanford University where he had earlier earned his PhD in mathematical psychology.

10. Paul Werbos, "Paul Werbos: The Evolution Of Artificial Neural Networks," interview by Robert J. Marks, June 3, 2021, in Mind Matters News, Walter Bradley Center for Natural & Artificial Intelligence, podcast, 35:29, https://mindmatters.ai/podcast/ep137/.

11. Dick Locher and Max Collins, *Dick Tracy*, January 27–29, 1991. For more about this cartoon computer criminal, see "Dwight Digit," Dick Tracy Wiki, accessed March 8, 2022, https://dicktracy.fandom.com/wiki/Dwight_Digit.

12. Paul Scharre, *Army of None: Autonomous Weapons and the Future of War* (New York: W.W. Norton, 2018).

13. *DARPA Neural Network Study* (Fairfax, VA: AFCEA International Press, 1988).

14. This movie clip can be viewed at Jonathon Kresner, "CPU Is a Neural Net Processor," YouTube, video, 0:03, September 13, 2017, https://youtu.be/xcgVztdMrX4.

15. R. Xu and D. C. Wunsch II, *Clustering* (Hoboken, NJ: IEEE Press/Wiley, 2009).

16. The error is typically chosen to be the square of the difference between "what you want" and "what you get" at the neural network output. This keeps the error positive, and our job when training is to push the error close to zero.

17. Russell Reed and Robert J. Marks, *Neural Smithing: Supervised Learning in Feedforward Artificial Neural Networks* (Cambridge, MA: MIT Press, 1999).

18. Robert Novak, "Undecided Bowlers," syndicated column, February 18, 1996.

19. "Pigasus," Wikimedia Foundation, last modified September 30, 2021, https://en.wikipedia.org/wiki/Pigasus_(politics); "1968 Democratic Convention," History.com, last modified November 10, 2020, https://www.history.com/topics/1960s/1968-democratic-convention.

20. After the convention, the Chicago Seven trials charged top Yippies like Abbie Hoffman and Jerry Rubin with conspiracy and inciting a riot. Tom Hayden, former husband of actress Jane Fonda, was a member of the Chicago Seven.

21. Dong C. Park, M. A. El-Sharkawi, R. J. Marks II, L. E. Atlas, and M. J. Damborg, "Electric Load Forecasting Using an Artificial Neural Network," *IEEE Transactions on Power Engineering* 6 (1991): 442–449.

22. A. Khotanzad et al., "ANNSTLF, A Neural-Network-Based Electric Load Forecasting System," *IEEE Transactions on Neural Networks* 8, no. 4 (July 1997): 835–846.

23. You can see the ongoing citation list under our article's entry at Google Scholar, https://scholar.google.com/citations?user=mbkGCZ0AAAAJ&hl=en#d=gs_md_citad&u=%2Fcitations%3Fview_op%3Dview_citation%26hl%3Den%26user%3DmbkGCZ0AAAAJ%26citation_for_view%3DmbkGCZ0AAAAJ%3Au5HHmVD_uO8C%26tzom%3D300.

24. Julia Kagan, "FICO," Investopedia, July 27, 2019, https://www.investopedia.com/terms/f/fico-fair-isaac.asp.

25. Michael Dunn, "Fair Isaac to Acquire HNC Software in $810 Million Stock Deal," Street, April 29, 2002, https://www.thestreet.com/story/10019829/1/fair-isaac-to-acquire-hnc-software-in-810-million-stock-deal.html.

26. Lofti A. Zadeh, "Fuzzy Sets," reprinted in R. J. Marks II, ed., *Fuzzy Logic Technology and Applications* (New York: Institute of Electrical and Electronics Engineers, 1994).

27. R. J. Marks II, ed., *Fuzzy Logic Technology and Applications* (New York: Institute of Electrical and Electronics Engineers, 1994).

28. In the interesting trivia department, Lotfi Zadeh's son, Norman Zada, earned a PhD in Operations Research, worked at IBM, and taught math at various top-flight universities. He became a multi-millionaire and, eventually, a pornographer. The magazine he launched focused on women who had not been cosmetically altered. See "Norman Zada," Wikimedia Foundation, last modified June 10, 2021, https://en.wikipedia.org/wiki/Norman_Zada.

29. Marks, *Fuzzy Logic*.

30. E. H. Mamdani and S. Assilian, "An Experiment in Linguistic Synthesis with a Fuzzy Logic Controller," *International Journal of Man-Machine Studies* 7, no. 1 (1975): 1–13.

31. Bob Bitmead, *IEEE Control Systems Magazine* (June 1993): 7.

32. Marks, *Fuzzy Logic*.

33. Marks, *Fuzzy Logic*.

34. Marks, *Fuzzy Logic*.

9. AI Matures

1. Medical researchers are now studying the brains of London cabbies to help understand and prevent dementia. In Alzheimer's disease, a part of the brain called the hippocampus degenerates; the hippocampus of London taxi drivers, however, increases in size over decades of driving. See Alexandra Mae Jones, "Why Researchers Are Analyzing the Brains of London Cabbies to Help Dementia Diagnosis," CTV News, November 22, 2021, https://www.ctvnews.ca/sci-tech/why-researchers-are-analyzing-the-brains-of-london-cabbies-to-help-dementia-diagnosis-1.5677199.

2. Azi Paybarah, "Taxi Industry Leaders Got Rich. Drivers Paid the Price," *New York Times*, May 21, 2019, https://www.nytimes.com/2019/05/21/nyregion/newyorktoday/nyc-news-taxi-medallions.html.

3. Tom Michael, "What is the Knowledge Taxi Test and Why Is the Exam Taken by London's Black Cab Drivers So Tough?," *Sun*, October 17, 2017, https://www.thesun.co.uk/news/3307245/the-knowledge-taxi-test-london-black-cab-drivers-exam/.

4. James Robinson, "Uber Passengers Could Face Paying up to 20% More in London in Weeks after Taxi App Suffered VAT Defeat in Court in Yet Another Cost of Living Squeeze," *Daily Mail*, February 15, 2022, https://www.dailymail.co.uk/news/article-10514145/Uber-passengers-face-paying-20-London-weeks.html.

5. Judith Newman, "To Siri, with Love," *New York Times*, October 19, 2014.

6. Michele McPhee, K. C. Baker, and Corky Siemaszko, "Kasparov Has Deep Blues After Losing," *New York Daily News*, May 12, 1997; reprinted with scan of original, "Deep Blue, IBM's Supercomputer, Defeats Chess Champion Garry Kasparov in 1997," May 10, 2015, https://www.nydailynews.com/news/world/kasparov-deep-blues-losingchess-champ-rooke-article-1.762264.

7. Claude Elwood Shannon, "A Mathematical Theory of Communication," *Bell System Technical Journal* 27, no. 3 (1948): 379–423.

8. Claude Shannon, "Programming a Computer for Playing Chess," *Philosophical Magazine* 7, no. 41 (1950): 314.

9. This information was printed on the back of a photo of Claude Shannon and Edward Lasker, reproduced in *ICGA Journal* 12, no. 4 (1989): 217. The photo and text can be seen at "Claude Shannon," Chessprogramming.org, https://www.chessprogramming.org/Claude_Shannon#cite_note-3.

10. "Deep Blue," Stanford CS221 [website], Fall 2012, https://stanford.edu/~cpiech/cs221/apps/deepBlue.html.

11. Yann LeCun, Yoshua Bengio, and Geoffrey Hinton, "Deep Learning," *Nature* 521, no. 7553 (2015): 436.

12. Catherine Brahic, "Dragonfly Eyes See the World in Ultra MultiColor," *New Scientist*, February 23, 2015, https://www.newscientist.com/article/dn27015-dragonfly-eyes-see-the-world-in-ultra-multicolour/.

13. Russell Reed and Robert J. Marks II, *Neural Smithing: Supervised Learning in Feedforward Artificial Neural Networks* (Cambridge, MA: MIT Press, 1999).

14. Reed and Marks, *Neural Smithing*, https://www.penguinrandomhouse.com/books/655334/neural-smithing-by-russell-reed-and-robert-j-marksii/.

15. Jiawei Su, Danilo Vasconcellos Vargas, and Kouichi Sakurai, "One Pixel Attack for Fooling Deep Neural Networks," *IEEE Transactions on Evolutionary Computation* 23, no. 5 (2019): 828–841.

16. Paul Scharre, *Army of None: Autonomous Weapons and the Future of War* (New York: W. W. Norton & Company, 2018).

17. Jeff Clune, quoted in Scharre, *Army of None*.

18. Scharre, *Army of None*.

19. Scharre, *Army of None*.

20. Separate test data is also used during the training of the neural network. Cross-validation data is separate from this. Somewhere in history the names of test and cross-validation data have been switched. I am consistent with use of the terminology here.

21. IEEE/IAFE Conference on Computational Intelligence for Financial Information, April 9–11, 1995, New York City, https://robertmarks.org/InTheNews/1995_CIFEr_CFP.pdf.

22. Neil Fraser, "Neural Network Follies," Neil Fraser [website], September 1998, https://neil.fraser.name/writing/tank/.

23. "The Real Reason to Be Afraid of Artificial Intelligence: Peter Haas, TEDxDirigo," YouTube, video, 1:23, December 15, 2017, https://youtu.be/TRzBk_KuIaM.

24. Nate Lanxon, "Alphabet's DeepMind Takes on Billion-Dollar Debt and Loses $572 Million," Bloomberg, August 7, 2019.

25. "Why Is DeepMind in Deep Water Financially?," Mind Matters News, Walter Bradley Center for Natural & Artificial Intelligence, August 12, 2019, https://mindmatters.ai/2019/08/why-is-deepmind-in-deep-water-financially/.

26. Sam Shead, "Alphabet's DeepMind Losses Soared to $570 Million in 2018," *Forbes*, August 7, 2019, https://www.forbes.com/sites/samshead/2019/08/07/deepmind-losses-soared-to-570-million-in-2018/?sh=2f411bcd3504.

27. Gary Marcus, "DeepMind's Losses and the Future of Artificial Intelligence," Wired, August 14, 2019, https://www.wired.com/story/deepminds-losses-future-artificial-intelligence/.

28. Ben Dickson, "AI Lab DeepMind becomes Profitable and Bolsters Relationship with Google," VentureBeat, October 10, 2021, https://venturebeat.com/2021/10/10/ai-lab-deepmind-becomes-profitable-and-bolsters-relationship-with-google/.

29. Jordan Novet, "Google Is Finding Ways to Make Money from Alphabet's DeepMind A.I. Technology," CNBC, April 2, 2018, https://www.cnbc.com/2018/03/31/how-google-makes-money-from-alphabets-deepmind-ai-research-group.html.

30. Brendan Dixon, "Self-Driving Cars: Following the Money up a Cooling Trail," Mind Matters News, Walter Bradley Center for Natural & Artificial Intelligence, August 8, 2019, https://mindmatters.ai/2019/08/self-driving-cars-following-the-money-up-a-cooling-trail/.

31. John C. Hull, *Options, Futures, and Other Derivatives* (Hoboken, NJ: Prentice Hall, 2003).

32. "What Is Black-Scholes Model? Definition of Black-Scholes Model, Black-Scholes Model Meaning," *Economic Times*, accessed December 9, 2021, https://economictimes.indiatimes.com/definition/black-scholes-model.

33. Keith Devlin, *The Unfinished Game: Pascal, Fermat, and the Seventeenth-Century Letter That Made the World Modern* (New York: Basic Books, 2010).

34. George Gilder, *Gaming AI: Why AI Can't Think but Can Transform Jobs* (Seattle: Discovery Institute Press, 2020) first pointed out to me the necessity of ergodicity.

35. Dong C. Park, M. A. El-Sharkawi, R. J. Marks, L. E. Atlas, and M. J. Damborg, "Electric Load Forecasting Using an Artificial Neural Network," *IEEE Transactions on Power Systems* 6, no. 2 (1991): 442–449.

36. Alireza Khotanzad, Reza Afkhami-Rohani, and Dominic Maratukulam, "ANNSTLF-Artificial Neural Network Short-Term Load Forecaster-Generation Three," *IEEE Transactions on Power Systems* 13, no. 4 (1998): 1413–1422.

37. R. Marks, J. Walkup, and M. Hagler, "Sampling Theorems for Linear Shift-Variant Systems," *IEEE Transactions on Circuits and Systems* 25, no. 4 (1978): 228–233.

38. Dong-Chul Park, Mohamed A. El-Sharkawi, and Robert J. Marks, "An Adaptively Trained Neural Network," *IEEE Transactions on Neural Networks* 2, no. 3 (1991): 334–345.

39. "Prediction by the Numbers," PBS Nova, season 45, episode 6, aired January 24, 2018, https://www.pbs.org/video/ prediction-numbers-tsrjl8/.

40. Bradley A. Alaniz, "Why AI Can't Win Wars as if Wars Were Chess Games," Mind Matters News, Walter Bradley Center for Natural & Artificial Intelligence, May 25, 2019, https://mindmatters.ai/2019/04/why-ai-cant-win-wars-as-if-wars-were-chess-games/.

41. You can watch this clip at YouTube, video, 2:30, https://www.youtube.com/ watch?v=dObTXYa-_n4.

10. It's All Gödel's Fault

1. Quoted in Christine C. Dantas, "The Ultimate Tactics of Self-Referential Systems," in *Trick or Truth? The Mysterious Connection between Physics and Mathematics*, eds. Anthony Aguirre, Brendan Foster, and Zeeya Merali (Cham, Switzerland: Springer, 2016), 193–200.

2. Oren Etzioni, "Artificial Intelligence Will Empower Us, Not Exterminate Us," TEDxSeattle, YouTube, video, 13:17, Februrary 2, 2017, https://youtu.be/H9Ddd1H9uLE.

3. There are different meanings given by different people for the terms "axiom" and "postulate." Contrary to our use, "axioms" are sometimes referred to as the logic applied to fundamental assumptions. Using this definition, an axiom might be "the whole is greater than the part." We will assume that fundamental properties such as logic apply without any elaboration. The word "postulate" will not be used in this manuscript and "axiom" is used throughout as we define here.

4. Bart Kosko, *Fuzzy Thinking: The New Science of Fuzzy Logic* (Westport, CT: Hyperion, 1993).

5. Douglas R. Hofstadter, *Gödel, Escher, Bach: An Eternal Golden Braid* (New York: Random House, 1979).

6. "Ten Hours of Rising Shepard Tone," YouTube, audio, 10:00:00, November 18, 2013, https://youtu.be/5rzIiF7LpPU.

7. "Ten Hours of Rising Shepard Tone."

8. "The Sound Illusion That Makes Dunkirk so Intense," YouTube, video, 3:01, July 26, 2017, https://youtu.be/LVWTQcZbLgY.

9. "Risset Rhythm," YouTube, audio, 5:01, February 15, 2013, https://youtu.be/oQf_ tS5WAP4.

10. Lionel Shapiro and J. C. Beall, "Curry's Paradox," Stanford Encyclopedia of Philosophy, 2018, https://plato.stanford.edu/entries/curry-paradox/supplement.html.

11. "Truth Tables," Brilliant, accessed January 4, 2022, https://brilliant.org/wiki/truth-tables/.

12. "Deepak Chopra Gets Owned by a Thug," YouTube, video, 0:47, January 25, 2015, https://youtu.be/ka--VV-_t_U.

13. E. Kasner and J. Newman, *Mathematics and the Imagination* (New York: Simon and Schuster, 1940).

14. Consider the dual to Russell's question: is the set of all inclusive sets inclusive or exclusive? Call the set of all inclusive sets ALIN. If ALIN is inclusive, it contains itself as a subset. Since ALIN is the set of all inclusive sets, this assumption makes sense. There is no

contradiction here. If ALIN is exclusive, it does not contain itself as a subset. ALIN is the set of all inclusive sets so if it is exclusive, it's not a subset of itself. This is logically consistent. There is also no contradiction here. It looks like we don't have enough information to announce whether ALIN is an exclusive or inclusive set. It could be either. Or both?

15. Gödel's theory is more involved than is presented herein. For a deeper insight into his theorems, see "Gödel's Incompleteness Theorems," Stanford Encyclopedia of Philosophy, 2020, https://plato.stanford.edu/entries/goedel-incompleteness/.

11. Turing Makes Gödel Simple

1. René Descartes, *Discourse on the Method* [1637] in *The Philosophical Works of Descartes*, vol. 1, trans. John Cottingham et al. (Cambridge, UK: Cambridge University Press, 1984), 140.

2. For an exception, some may point to parallel computing where operations performed on separate computers can connect and split without scheduling. Each thread, though, is the equivalent of a Turing machine.

3. The quantum computer is also constrained by the Church-Turing Thesis. AI often uses random numbers. The stochastic Turing machine can place ones and zeros randomly on its tape according to weighted coin flips and likewise use random numbers. The Church-Turing Thesis is also applicable here.

4. Alex Altair, "An Intuitive Explanation of Solomonoff Induction," LessWrong 2.0, July 11, 2012, https://www.lesswrong.com/posts/Kyc5dFDzBg4WccrbK/an-intuitive-explanation-of-solomonoff-induction.

5. Alan Mathison Turing, "On Computable Numbers, with an Application to the Entscheidungsproblem," *Proceedings of the London Mathematical Society* s2–42, no. 1 (January 1937): 230–265.

6. Kurt Gödel, "Über Formal Unentscheidbare Sätze Der Principia Mathematica Und Verwandter Systeme I," *Monatshefte Für Mathematik Und Physik* 38, no. 1 (1931): 173–198.

7. Proof the halting problem is non-algorithmic. All computer programs can be written as a binary string of ones and zeros. Each possible program can therefore be written as a positive integer. We arrange all these programs in a list starting with the smallest. The pth program is appropriately labeled as an integer p. Let $H(p,i)$ be a halting oracle program that decides if a program p with input i, written $p(i)$ halts or not. $H(p,i)$ outputs a 1 if the program $p(i)$ halts and 0 if it doesn't. As with programs, all possible inputs can be ordered and assigned an integer number, in this case i. Then, consider the program

```
function N(p) {
    if(H(p,p) == 1) {
        while(1 == 1) {
        }
    }
    return 0;
    }
}
```

Given a program p, this program outputs a 0 when $p(p)$ doesn't halt and runs forever in a while loop if the program $p(p)$ halts. What, then, of the program N(N)? In this case, the program is analyzing itself to see whether or not it will halt. The results are contradictory. If $H(N,N)=1$ in the program, we get stuck in the while loop forever. But $H(N,N)=1$ means the program N(N) halts. This is a contradiction. Likewise, if $H(N,N)=0$ in the program, a zero is printed and the program stops. But H(N,N)=0 means the program N(N) doesn't halt. Another contradiction. Thus, the assumption there is a halting program H(p,i) that works for all p and i has been proven false.

From: Robert J. Marks, William A. Dembski, and Winston Ewert, *Introduction to Evolutionary Informatics* (Hackensack, NJ: World Scientific, 2017), 232–233.

8. "Crunching numbers" is a phrase used to describe an analysis of a database. For our example, crunching a number only means letter counting.

9. Mathematicians would call four the fixed point of this iteration.

10. I suspect showing so would be easy. It seems the only number that crunches to a larger number is THREE which crunches to five. And FOUR crunches to four. It appears that all other crunching, no matter how big the number, always gives a smaller number. Numbers ONE to NINE all eventually crunch to four. So repeated crunching gets you to one through nine and a bit more crunching gets you to four.

11. Recall a prime number is a positive number that can be divided only by one and itself. Twelve is not a prime number since it could be factored into 2x2x3. The first few prime numbers are 2, 3, 5, 7, 11, 13, 17, 19, 23, 29, 31, 37, 41.

12. "The Riemann Hypothesis: The Million Dollar Math Conundrum," Padeye News, July 27, 2021, https://padeye.news/the-riemann-hypothesis-the-million-dollar-math-conundrum/.

13. What are the zeros of a function? Imagine a function wiggling up and down going from left to right. The zeros of the function are those points where the function touches the horizontal axis.

14. More formally, the "Rice theorem states that any non-trivial semantic property of a language which is recognized by a Turing machine is undecidable. A property, P, is the language of all Turing machines that satisfy that property." Quoted from "Rice Theorem," Tutorial Spot, accessed May 10, 2022, https://www.tutorialspoint.com/automata_theory/rice_theorem.htm#:~:text=Rice%20theorem%20states%20that%20any,machines%20that%20satisfy%20that%20property. See also H. G. Rice, "Classes of Recursively Enumerable Sets and Their Decision Problems," *Transactions of the American Mathematical Society* 74, no. 2 (1953): 358–366, https://www.ams.org/journals/tran/1953-074-02/S0002-9947-1953-0053041-6/S0002-9947-1953-0053041-6.pdf.

12. The Unknowable

1. Gregory Chaitin, "Randomness, Information Theory, and the Unknowable," interview by Robert J. Marks, December 30, 2021, in Mind Matters News, podcast, 2:16:26, https://mindmatters.ai/podcast/ep167/. Transcript available at https://mindmatters.ai/wp-content/uploads/sites/2/2021/12/Transcript-Mind-Matter-News-Episode-167-Gregory-Chaitin-Bingecast-rev1.pdf.

2. Donald Rumsfeld and Richard Myers, US Department of Defense News Briefing, February 12, 2002, transcript. Archived from the original on March 20, 2018, https://archive.ph/20180320091111/http://archive.defense.gov/Transcripts/Transcript.aspx?TranscriptID=2636.

3. Chaitin, "Randomness."

4. Robert J. Marks, William Dembski, and Winston Ewert, *Introduction to Evolutionary Informatics* (Hackensack, NJ: World Scientific, 2017).

5. The following section borrows heavily from portions of Chapter 2 in Marks, Dembski, and Ewert, *Introduction to Evolutionary Informatics*.

6. Christopher Latella, "Man Receives New Ankle Created on 3D Printer," NBC 5 Dallas-Fort Worth, August 1, 2019, https://www.nbcdfw.com/news/health/Man-Receives-New-Ankle-Created-on-3D-Printer-513514081.html.

7. Kyle Maxey, "Army Researchers Hack 3D Printer to Build Ceramic Body Armor," Engineering.com, July 31, 209, https://www.engineering.com/DesignerEdge/Designer-EdgeArticles/ArticleID/19410/Army-Researchers-Hack-3D-Printer-to-Build-Ceramic-Body-Armor.aspx.

8. "The Toybox 3D Printer Deluxe Bundle Lets Kids Print Their Own Toys," Futurism, July 17, 2019, https://futurism.com/toybox-3d-printer-deluxe-bundle-lets-kids-print-their-own-toys.

9. Bernadette Hogan, "Cuomo Signs Laws to Ban 3D-Printed Guns," *New York Post*, July 30, 2019, https://nypost.com/2019/07/30/cuomo-signs-laws-to-ban-3d-printed-guns/.

10. Gregory J. Chaitin, *Meta Math!: The Quest for Omega* (New York: Pantheon Books, 2006).

11. D. G. Champernowne, "The Construction of Decimals Normal in the Scale of Ten," *Journal of the London Mathematical Society* s1-8, no. 4 (1933): 254–260.

12. Alan Mathison Turing, "On Computable Numbers, with an Application to the Entscheidungsproblem," *Proceedings of the London Mathematical Society* s2-42, no. 1 (1937): 230–265.

13. Nicholas Griffin, *The Cambridge Companion to Bertrand Russell* (Cambridge, UK: Cambridge University Press, 2010).

14. Ron Garret, "A One-Page Proof of Chaitin's Theorem," Ron Garret website, accessed January 19, 2022, http://www.flownet.com/ron/chaitin.html.

15. Robert J. Marks, "Dr. Robert Marks: Active Information in Metabiology," interview by Casey Luskin, May 30, 2014, YouTube, video, 18:00, https://youtu.be/tJSJg0IZtfI.

16. "Chaitin's Constant," Wikimedia Foundation, last modified January 14, 2022, 19:24, https://en.wikipedia.org/wiki/Chaitin's_constant.

17. Chaitin, "Randomness, Information Theory, and the Unknowable."

18. In most areas of life we use the decimal system, with its ten digits (0–9). Computers, however, use the binary system, with only two digits (0 and 1). For further explanation, see "Binary Number System," Britannica, https://www.britannica.com/science/binary-number-system.

19. Some will see that the value of a program n bits long will have a value of 0.5 raised to the nth power.

20. Technically, this requires using a prefix free (self-delimiting) program. Any computer language can be translated to prefix free coding.

21. Thomas M. Cover and Joy A. Thomas, *Elements of Information Theory* (Hoboken, NJ: John Wiley & Sons, 2006), 484.

22. Scott Aaronson, "Who Can Name the Bigger Number?," Scott Aaronson website, accessed January 19, 2022, https://www.scottaaronson.com/writings/bignumbers.html.

23. Gregory J. Chaitin, *Algorithmic Information Theory* (Cambridge, UK: Cambridge University Press, 2001); *The Limits of Mathematics: A Course on Information Theory and the Limits of Formal Reasoning* (London: Springer-Verlag, 2003); The Unknowable (London: Springer-Verlag, 2000); *Exploring Randomness* (London: Springer-Verlag, 2002);

Conversations with a Mathematician: Math, Art, Science and the Limits of Reason (London: Springer-Verlag, 2002); *Meta Math!: The Quest for Omega* (New York: Pantheon Books, 2006); *Thinking About Gödel and Turing: Essays on Complexity, 1970–2007* (Hackensack, NJ: World Scientific, 2007).

13. Randomness Happens

1. John von Neumann, "Various Techniques Used in Connection with Random Digits," in *Monte Carlo Method*, National Bureau of Standards Applied Mathematics Series 12, ed. George E. Forsythe (Washington, DC: United States Government Printing Office, 1951), 36–38. The article can be read here: https://mcnp.lanl.gov/pdf_files/nbs_vonneumann.pdf.

2. Russell Reed and Robert J. Marks II, *Neural Smithing: Supervised Learning in Feedforward Artificial Neural Networks* (Cambridge, MA: MIT Press, 1999).

3. Roger Eckhardt, "Stan Ulam, John von Neumann, and the Monte Carlo Method," *Los Alamos Science* 15, no. 131–136 (1987): 30.

4. Robert J. Marks, William Dembski, and Winston Ewert, *Introduction to Evolutionary Informatics* (Hackensack, NJ: World Scientific, 2017).

5. In probability terms, gambling can be construed as a "sampling with replacement" process whereas sweepstake is "sampling without replacement." All students of elementary probability are taught the difference.

6. See USDebtClock.org, http://www.usdebtclock.org.

7. Glauco Antonio Amigo Galán, Liang Dong, and Robert J. Marks II, "Forecasting Pseudo-Random Numbers Using Deep Learning," Fifteenth International Conference on Signal Processing and Communication Systems (ICSPCS), IEEE, 2021.

8. George Marsaglia, "Random Number Generators," *Journal of Modern Applied Statistical Methods* 2 (2003): 2–13.

9. M. Shema, *Hacking Web Apps: Detecting and Preventing Web Application Security Problems* (Cham, Switzerland: Elsevier Science, 2012).

10. Marsaglia first released these on a CD: "The Marsaglia Random Number CDROM including the Diehard Battery of Tests of Randomness," Florida State University, 1995. You can see the original contents archived at https://web.archive.org/web/20160125103112/http://stat.fsu.edu/pub/diehard/. You can also see an explanation at "George Marsaglia," Wikimedia Foundation, last modified September 28, 2021, https://en.wikipedia.org/wiki/George_Marsaglia.

11. Diehard is the name brand of Sears car batteries. Calling these a battery of diehard tests, if you haven't yet noticed, is a pun.

12. John Leyden, "Windows Random Number Generator Is So Not Random," *Register*, November 13, 2007, https://www.theregister.co.uk/2007/11/13/windows_random_number_gen_flawed.

13. Bohrs said this in Copenhagen in 1952 to Werner Heisenberg, who recounted the conversation in *Werner Heisenberg, Physics and Beyond: Encounters and Conversations* (New York: Harper & Row, 1971), 206.

14. "Invisible Boy," Mysterymen Fandom, https://mysterymen.fandom.com/wiki/Invisible_Boy.

15. The quotation, originally in German, is variously translated. For a discussion of these translations, the German original, and other famous quotations of Einstein, see Andrew

Robinson, "Did Einstein Really Say That?," *Nature*, April 30, 2018, https://www.nature.com/articles/d41586-018-05004-4.

16. "Hidden Variables," Eric Weisstein's World of Physics [website], accessed January 20, 2022, http://scienceworld.wolfram.com/physics/HiddenVariables.html.

17. "Einstein-Podolsky-Rosen Paradox," Eric Weisstein's World of Physics [website], accessed January 20, 2022, http://scienceworld.wolfram.com/physics/Einstein-Podolsky-RosenParadox.html.

18. Roger Penrose, *The Emperor's New Mind* (Oxford: Oxford University Press, 1989) and Stuart Hameroff and Roger Penrose, "Consciousness in the Universe: A Review of the 'Orch OR' Theory," *Physics of Life Reviews* 11, no. 1 (2014): 39–78, https://doi.org/10.1016/j.plrev.2013.08.002. See also Robert J. Marks, "Human Consciousness May Not Be Computable," Mind Matters, Walter Bradley Center for Natural and Artificial Intelligence, November 27, 2018, https://mindmatters.ai/2018/11/human-consciousness-may-not-be-computable/.

19. Eric Holloway, "Does Information Theory Support Design in Nature?," Mind Matters News, Walter Bradley Center for Natural & Artificial Intelligence, November 11, 2018, https://mindmatters.ai/2018/10/does-information-theory-support-design-in-nature/.

20. Cenregoth et al., "Is It Possible to Reverse a Pseudo Random Number Generator?," Stack Overflow, November 4, 2014, https://stackoverflow.com/questions/26743470/is-it-possible-to-reverse-a-pseudo-random-number-generator.

21. Glauco Antonio Amigo Galán, Liang Dong, and Robert J. Marks II, "Forecasting Pseudo-Random Numbers Using Deep Learning," Fifteenth International Conference on Signal Processing and Communication Systems (ICSPCS), IEEE, 2021.

22. Sophia Chen, "Quantum Mechanics Creates a Totally Random Number Generator," Wired, April 11, 2018, https://www.wired.com/story/quantum-mechanics-could-solve-cryptographys-random-number-problem/.

23. Ather Fawaz, "Knocking on Turing's Door: Quantum Computing and Machine Learning," Gradient, January 2021, https://thegradient.pub/knocking-on-turings-door-quantum-computing-and-machine-learning/.

24. Paul Teich, "Quantum Computing Will Not Break Your Encryption, Yet," *Forbes*, October 23, 2017, https://www.forbes.com/sites/tiriasresearch/2017/10/23/quantum-will-not-break-encryption-yet/#26af82373195.

25. Nicolas Gisin and Rob Thew, "Quantum Communication," *Nature Photonics* 1, no. 3 (2007): 165–171.

26. For an overview, see Harald Atmanspacher, "Quantum Approaches to Consciousness," Stanford Encyclopedia of Philosophy, April 16, 2020, https://plato.stanford.edu/entries/qt-consciousness/. Those who support quantum consciousness include Stuart Hameroff and Roger Penrose, "Consciousness in the Universe: A Review of the 'Orch OR' Theory," *Physics of Life Reviews* 11, no. 1 (2014): 39–78. Those in opposition include physicist Lawrence Krauss, interviewed in Alan Boyle, "How to Spot Quantum Quackery," NBC Science News, September 20, 2010, https://www.nbcnews.com/science/how-spot-quantum-quackery-6c10403763; and physicist Victor J. Stenger, "The Myth of Quantum Consciousness," *Humanist* 53, no. 3 (May/June 1992): 13–15, https://www.thefreelibrary.com/The+myth+of+quantum+consciousness.-a013818491.

14. AI ETHICS

1. Jack Handey, *Deep Thoughts: Inspiration for the Uninspired* (New York: Berkley Books, 1992).

2. "Uber's Self-Driving Operator Charged over Fatal Crash," BBC News, September 16, 2020, https://www.bbc.com/news/technology-54175359.

3. "Alexa Tells 10-Year-Old Girl to Touch Live Plug with Penny," BBC News, December 28, 2021, https://www.bbc.com/news/technology-59810383.

4. Merriam-Webster, s. v. "ethics," accessed January 25, 2022, https://www.merriam-webster.com/dictionary/ethics.

5. Hamlet himself doesn't actually hold to this position. When he makes this relativistic statement, he is using it to test how faithless Rosencrantz and Guildenstern are.

6. Tom Simonite, "Google Offers to Help Others with the Tricky Ethics of AI," Wired, August 28, 2020, https://www.wired.com/story/google-help-others-tricky-ethics-ai/.

7. Kai-Fu Lee, *AI Superpowers: China, Silicon Valley, and the New World Order* (Boston: Houghton Mifflin Harcourt, 2018).

8. Timothy Koenig, "The Days of Shoddy: Worst Manufacturers of the Civil War," Warfare History Network, accessed February 23, 2022, https://warfarehistorynetwork.com/2018/12/18/the-days-of-shoddy-worst-manufacturers-of-the-civil-war/

9. IEEE Reliability Society home page, https://rs.ieee.org/.

10. The virus was also cleverly used as a promotional tool. The series creators pretended the virus was real and linked to the NBC page about Chuck as the only cure. See "Irene Demova Virus," Chuck Fandom Wiki, accessed January 24, 2022, https://chuck-nbc.fandom.com/wiki/Irene_Demova_Virus.

11. "Stuxnet," Wikimedia Foundation, last modified February 26, 2022, https://en.wikipedia.org/wiki/Stuxnet.

12. Tiffany Hsu, "They Know What You Watched Last Night," *New York Times*, October 25, 2019, https://www.nytimes.com/2019/10/25/business/media/streaming-data-collection-privacy.html.

13. Shannon Vavra, "DOD, FBI, DHS Release Info on Malware Used in Chinese Government-Led Hacking Campaigns," Cyberscoop, August 3, 2020, https://www.cyberscoop.com/taidoor-malware-report-china-cisa-dod-fbi/.

14. Mark Emem, "Johannesburg Shuts Down Computers City-Wide after Bitcoin Ransomware Attack," CNN, October 25, 2019, https://www.ccn.com/johannesburg-shuts-down-bitcoin-ransomware-attack/.

15. Adam Jacobson, "Another Ransomware Attack Ravages a Radio Cluster," *Radio and Television Business Report*, October 25, 2019, https://www.rbr.com/another-ransomware-attack-ravages-a-radio-cluster/.

16. Allen Kim, "In the Last Ten Months," CNN Business, October 8, 2019, https://www.cnn.com/2019/10/08/business/ransomware-attacks-trnd/index.html.

17. Thomas Brewster, "Five Arrested as Cops Hunt Two of the Biggest Ransomware Strains Ever," *Forbes*, December 20, 2017, https://www.forbes.com/sites/thomasbrewster/2017/12/20/ransomware-arrests-for-cerber-and-ctb-locker/#4da8f3f9315a.

18. Jerome and Marilyn Murray, *Computers in Crisis* (New York: Petrocelli, 1984); reissued by McGraw-Hill under the title *The Year 2000 Computing Crisis* in 1996.

19. Anthony Cuthbertson, "Bitcoin: Millions of Dollars of Cryptocurrency 'Lost' After Man Dies with Only Password," *Independent*, February 5, 2019, https://www.independent.co.uk/life-style/gadgets-and-tech/news/bitcoin-exchange-quadrigacx-password-cryptocurrency-scam-a8763676.html.

20. Amanda Macias, "Legendary Drug Lord Pablo Escobar Lost $2.1 Billion in Cash Each Year—And It Didn't Matter," *Business Insider*, September 24, 2016, https://www.businessinsider.com/pablo-escobar-and-rubber-bands-2015-9.

21. Kayla Hawkins, "Pablo Escobar Reportedly Buried Millions of Dollars and this TV Show Wants to Find It," Bustle, November 3, 2017, https://www.bustle.com/p/was-pablo-escobars-money-ever-found-the-drug-kingpins-fortune-is-a-subject-of-major-fascination-3213996.

22. Nick Bilton, *American Kingpin* (London: Portfolio, 2017), http://www.americankingpin.com/.

23. Lily Hay Newman, "How a Bitcoin Trail Led to a Massive Dark Web Child-Porn Site Takedown," Wired, October 16, 2019, https://www.wired.com/story/dark-web-welcome-to-video-takedown-bitcoin/.

24. Michael Martinez, John Newsome, and Rene Marsh, "Handgun-Firing Drone Appears Legal in Video, but FAA, Police Probe Further," CNN, July 21, 2015, https://www.cnn.com/2015/07/21/us/gun-drone-connecticut/index.html.

25. Kelsey Piper, "Death by Algorithm: The Age of Killer Robots is Closer Than You Think," Vox, June 21, 2019, https://www.vox.com/2019/6/21/18691459/killer-robots-lethal-autonomous-weapons-ai-war.

26. Bonnie Docherty, "We're Running Out of Time to Stop Killer Robot Weapons," *Guardian*, April 11, 2018, https://www.theguardian.com/commentisfree/2018/apr/11/killer-robot-weapons-autonomous-ai-warfare-un.

27. David Rivers, "Killer Robots Poised for 'MASS PRODUCTION' as Campaigners Urge AI to be Made ILLEGAL," *Daily Star*, August 21, 2018, https://www.dailystar.co.uk/news/latest-news/robots-artificial-intelligence-killer-war-16879356.

28. "'KILLER ROBOTS' WILL START SLAUGHTERING PEOPLE IF THEY'RE NOT BANNED SOON, AI EXPERT WARNS," *Independent*, November 20, 2017, https://www.independent.co.uk/life-style/gadgets-and-tech/news/killer-robots-ban-autonomous-weapons-toby-walsh-ai-artificial-intelligence-un-amandeep-gill-a8065216.html.

29. "2018 Group of Governmental Experts on Lethal Autonomous Weapons Systems (LAWS)," United Nations Office at Geneva (website), accessed September 23, 2019, https://www.unog.ch/80256EE600585943/(httpPages)/7C335E71DFCB29D1C1258243003E8724. See also "Report of the 2018 Session of the Group of Governmental Experts on Emerging Technologies in the Area of Lethal Autonomous Weapons Systems," October 23, 2018, https://undocs.org/en/CCW/GGE.1/2018/3.

30. "Country Views on Killer Robots," Campaign to Stop Killer Robots, November 22, 2018, https://www.stopkillerrobots.org/wp-content/uploads/2018/11/KRC_CountryViews22Nov2018.pdf.

31. António Guterres, "Remarks at 'Web Summit,'" United Nations Secretary-General, November 5, 2018, https://www.un.org/sg/en/content/sg/speeches/2018-11-05/remarks-web-summit.

32. Samuel Gibbs, "Musk, Wozniak and Hawking Urge Ban on Warfare AI and Autonomous Weapons," *Guardian*, July 27, 2015, https://www.theguardian.com/technology/2015/jul/27/musk-wozniak-hawking-ban-ai-autonomous-weapons.

33. "Lethal Autonomous Weapons Pledge," Future of Life Institute (website), accessed September 23, 2019, https://futureoflife.org/lethal-autonomous-weapons-pledge/.

34. Campaign to Stop Killer Robots (website), accessed September 23, 2019, https://www.stopkillerrobots.org/.

35. Robert J. Marks II, *The Case for Killer Robots: Why America's Military Needs to Continue Development of Lethal AI* (Seattle: Discovery Institute Press, 2020).

36. Stop Autonomous Weapons, "Slaughterbots," YouTube video, 7:47, November 12, 2017, https://youtu.be/9CO6M2HsoIA.

37. Paul Scharre, "Why You Shouldn't Fear 'Slaughterbots,'" *IEEE Spectrum* 22 (December 22, 2017), https://spectrum.ieee.org/automaton/robotics/military-robots/why-you-shouldnt-fear-slaughterbots.

38. Scharre, "Why You Shouldn't Fear 'Slaughterbots.'"

39. Scharre, "Why You Shouldn't Fear 'Slaughterbots.'"

40. Sarah Seguin, "EMPs Could Combat Vast Drone Swarms Better Than Weapons," interview by Robert J. Marks, August 23, 2021, Mind Matters News, Walter Bradley Center for Natural & Artificial Intelligence, podcast, 25:26, https://mindmatters.ai/2021/08/emps-could-combat-vast-drone-swarms-better-than-weapons/.

41. Guterres, "Remarks at 'Web Summit.'"

42. Minyvonne Burke and Andrew Blankstein, "Tesla Driver Charged with Vehicular Manslaughter in Fatal Autopilot Crash," NBC News, January 19, 2022, https://www.nbcnews.com/news/us-news/tesla-driver-charged-vehicular-manslaughter-fatal-autopilot-crash-rcna12724.

43. Dylan Matthews, "Thirty-Six Years Ago Today, One Man Saved Us from World-Ending Nuclear War," Vox, September 16, 2019, https://www.vox.com/2018/9/26/17905796/nuclear-war-1983-stanislav-petrov-soviet-union.

44. Paul Scharre, introduction to *Army of None* (New York: W. W. Norton, 2018).

45. Will Knight, "The Pentagon Inches Toward Letting AI Control Weapons," Wired, May 10, 2021, https://www.wired.com/story/pentagon-inches-toward-letting-ai-control-weapons/.

46. "USA and Israel in Crisis over China Harpy Deal," Flight Global, January 4, 2005, https://www.flightglobal.com/news/articles/usa-and-israel-in-crisis-over-china-harpy-deal-191940/.

47. "Boeing X-45," Wikimedia Foundation, last modified July 3, 2019, 03:53, https://en.wikipedia.org/wiki/Boeing_X-45.

48. Kirstie McCrum, "US Army Building 'Intelligent Drones' to Map Inside of Buildings During Times of War," *Mirror*, September 7, 2016, https://www.mirror.co.uk/news/world-news/army-building-intelligent-drones-map-8784030.

49. "Autonomous Underwater Vehicle," Wikimedia Foundation, last modified September 14, 2019, 03:46, https://en.wikipedia.org/wiki/Autonomous_underwater_vehicle.

50. Aaron Mamiit, "Rain or Snow? Rock or Plastic? Google Driverless Car Can't Tell," Tech Times, September 2, 2014, https://www.techtimes.com/articles/14625/20140902/rain-or-snow-rock-or-plastic-bag-google-driverless-car-cant-tell.htm.

51. T. S., "Why Uber's Self-Driving Car Killed a Pedestrian," *Economist*, May 29, 2018, updated January 18, 2022, https://www.economist.com/the-economist-explains/2018/05/29/why-ubers-self-driving-car-killed-a-pedestrian.

52. Rory Cellan-Jones, "Uber's Self-Driving Operator Charged over Fatal Crash," BBC News, September 16, 2020, https://www.bbc.com/news/technology-54175359.

53. In the Asimov story, the laws were published in the fictional regulatory document *Handbook of Robotics*, 56th ed., 2058 AD.

54. Will Knight, "AI Is Biased. Here's How Scientists Are Trying to Fix It," Wired, December 19, 2019, https://www.wired.com/story/ai-biased-how-scientists-trying-fix/.

55. George Montañez et al., "The Futility of Bias-Free Learning and Search," Cornell University, arXiv.org (July 13, 2019), https://arxiv.org/abs/1907.06010.

56. Tom D. Mitchell, "The Need for Biases in Learning Generalizations," Rutgers University CS Tech Report CBM-TR-117 (May 1980), https://www.cs.cmu.edu/afs/cs/usr/mitchell/ftp/pubs/NeedForBias_1980.pdf.

57. Cullen Schaffer, "A Conservation Law for Generalization Performance," in *Machine Learning Proceedings* (San Francisco: Morgan Kaufman, 1994): 261, https://doi.org/10.1016/B978-1-55860-335-6.50039-8.

58. William A. Dembski and Robert J. Marks II, "Conservation of Information in Search: Measuring the Cost of Success," *IEEE Transactions on Systems, Man and Cybernetics A, Systems & Humans* 5, no. 5 (September 2009): 1051–1061. William A. Dembski, Winston Ewert, and Robert J. Marks II, "A General Theory of Information Cost Incurred by Successful Search," in *Biological Information: New Perspectives*, eds. R. J. Marks II et al. (Singapore: World Scientific, 2013), 26–63. R. J. Marks II, W. A. Dembski, and W. Ewert, *Introduction to Evolutionary Informatics* (Singapore: World Scientific, 2017).

59. Tom Simonite, "When It Comes to Gorillas, Google Photos Remains Blind," Wired, January 11, 2018, https://www.wired.com/story/when-it-comes-to-gorillas-google-photos-remains-blind/.

60. James Vincent, "Google 'Fixed' Its Racist Algorithm by Removing Gorillas from Its Image-Labeling Tech," Verge, January 12, 2018, https://www.theverge.com/2018/1/12/16882408/google-racist-gorillas-photo-recognition-algorithm-ai.

61. Denyse O'Leary, "Google Engineer Reveals Search Engine Bias," Mind Matters News, Walter Bradley Center for Natural & Artificial Intelligence, July 27, 2019, https://mindmatters.ai/2019/07/google-engineer-reveals-search-engine-bias/.

62. IEEE Code of Ethics, https://www.ieee.org/about/corporate/governance/p7-8.html.

63. Daniel Payne, "Berkeley Scientists Developing Artificial Intelligence Tool to Combat 'Hate Speech' on Social Media," College Fix, December 17, 2018, https://www.thecollegefix.com/berkeley-scientists-developing-artificial-intelligence-tool-to-combat-hate-speech-on-social-media/.

64. Michael M. Grynbaum, "Fox News Drops 'Fair and Balanced' Motto," *New York Times*, June 14, 2017, https://www.nytimes.com/2017/06/14/business/media/fox-news-fair-and-balanced.html.

65. Quoted in Lee Rainie, Janna Anderson, and Emily Vogels, "Experts Doubt Ethical AI Design Will Be Broadly Adopted as the Norm within the Next Decade," Pew Research Center, June 16, 2021, https://www.pewresearch.org/internet/2021/06/16/experts-doubt-ethical-ai-design-will-be-broadly-adopted-as-the-norm-within-the-next-decade/.

66. Anthony D'Amato, "Can/Should Computers Replace Judges?," Northwestern University School of Law Scholarly Commons (1977), https://scholarlycommons.law.northwestern. edu/cgi/viewcontent.cgi?article=1128&context=facultyworkingpapers.

67. Quoted in Rainie, Anderson, and Vogels, "Experts Doubt."

68. Tyler Vigen, "Spurious Correlations," https://www.tylervigen.com/spurious-correlations.

69. Sema K. Sgaier, Vincent Huang, and Grace Charles, "The Case for Causal AI," *Stanford Social Innovation Review* (Summer 2020), https://ssir.org/articles/entry/the_case_for_causal_ai.

70. I suspect the problem could be solved using data clustering. See Lei Meng, Ah-Hwee Tan, and Donald Wunsch, *Adaptive Resonance Theory in Social Media Data Clustering* (Cham, Switzerland: Springer International Publishing, 2019).

71. Quoted in Rainie, Anderson, and Vogels, "Experts Doubt."

72. "ERCOT Is Raising Temperatures on Smart Thermostats," Geek News Central, June 21, 2021, https://geeknewscentral.com/2021/06/21/ercot-is-raising-temperatures-on-smart-thermostats/.

73. Quoted in Rainie, Anderson, and Vogels, "Experts Doubt."

74. "Smart Cities," Wikimedia Foundation, last modified January 16, 2022, https:// en.wikipedia.org/wiki/Smart_city.

75. Reuters, "Teenager Caned in Singapore Tells of the Blood and the Scars," *New York Times*, June 29, 1994, https://www.nytimes.com/1994/06/27/us/teen-ager-caned-in-singapore-tells-of-the-blood-and-the-scars.html.

76. The caning incident was soon whimsically treated in the Weird Al Yankovic song "Headline News."

77. "Is Chewing Gum against the Law in Singapore?" World Atlas, accessed January 6, 2022, https://www.worldatlas.com/articles/singapore-laws-to-know-before-you-get-there.html

78. Casey Lein, "Gov. Abbott Outlaws Red-Light Traffic Cameras in Texas," *US News*, June 3, 2019.

79. I have gotten a few speeding tickets I deserved.

80. Anna M. Tinsley, "Intersections with Red Light Cameras 'Likely to Be Among Most Dangerous,' Study Says," WFAA, August 11, 2018, https://www.wfaa.com/article/news/local/texas-news/intersections-with-red-light-cameras-likely-to-be-among-most-dangerous-study-says/287-582109796.

81. See, for example, Chris Buckley and Paul Mozur, "How China Uses High-Tech Surveillance to Subdue Minorities," *New York Times*, May 22, 2019.

82. Mark Urychi, "How Ohio's Cuyahoga River Came Back to Life 50 Years After It Caught on Fire," NPR, June 18, 2019.

83. International Union of Operating Engineers Local 18, http://www.oe18.org/.

15. THE AI CHURCH

1. Mary Shelley, *Frankenstein* [1818] (New York: Bantam Books, 1981), 39.

2. Yuval Noah Harari, *Homo Deus: A Brief History of Tomorrow* (New York: Random House, 2016).

3. Neuralink home page, https://neuralink.com/.

4. Lulu Chang, "Want to Live Forever? Ray Kurzweil Thinks That Might Be Possible Very Soon," Digital Trends, March 27, 2016, https://www.digitaltrends.com/health-fitness/ray-kurzweil-immortality/.

5. Ray Kurzweil, *The Singularity is Near: When Humans Transcend Biology* (London: Penguin, 2005).

6. Kurzweil, *The Singularity.*

7. John Rennie, "Ray Kurzweil's Slippery Futurism," *IEEE Spectrum* 47, no. 12 (November 29, 2010): 24–28, https://spectrum.ieee.org/ray-kurzweils-slippery-futurism.

8. Rennie, "Ray Kurzweil's Slippery Futurism."

9. Deuteronomy 13:5.

10. Mark Harris, "Inside the First Church of Artificial Intelligence," Wired, November 15, 2017, https://www.wired.com/story/anthony-levandowski-artificial-intelligence-religion/.

11. Harris, "Inside the First Church."

12. Harris, "Inside the First Church."

13. "Former Uber Executive Sentenced To 18 Months in Jail for Trade Secret Theft from Google," United States Department of Justice, August 4, 2020, https://www.justice.gov/usao-ndca/pr/former-uber-executive-sentenced-18-months-jail-trade-secret-theft-google.

14. "Anthony Levandowski: Ex-Google Engineer Sentenced for Theft," BBC News, August 5, 2020, https://www.bbc.com/news/world-us-canada-53659805.

15. Lauren Good, "UC Berkeley Alumnus Anthony Levandowski Pardoned by Former President Donald Trump," *Daily Californian,* January 21, 2021, https://www.dailycal.org/2021/01/21/uc-berkeley-alumnus-anthony-levandowski-pardoned-by-former-president-donald-trump/.

16. Eric Holloway, "The Creative Spark," Mind Matters News, Walter Bradley Center for Natural & Artificial Intelligence, January 21, 2019, https://mindmatters.ai/2019/01/the-creative-spark/.

17. Selmer Bringsjord, Paul Bello, and David Ferrucci, "Creativity, the Turing Test, and the (Better) Lovelace Test," *Minds and Machines* 11 (2001): 3–27. See also Robert J. Marks II, "The Turing Test is Dead. Long Live the Lovelace Test," Evolution News and Science Today, Discovery Institute, July 3, 2014, https://evolutionnews.org/2014/07/the_turing_test_1/.

18. Chang, "Want to Live Forever?"

19. See Roger Penrose, *The Emperor's New Mind: Concerning Computers, Minds, and the Laws of Physics* (Oxford: Oxford University Press, 1989); Roger Penrose, *Shadows of the Mind* (Oxford: Oxford University Press, 1994); Stuart Hameroff, "Quantum Computation in Brain Microtubules? The Penrose-Hameroff 'Orch OR' Model of Consciousness," *Philosophical Transactions-Royal Society of London Series A Mathematical Physical and Engineering Sciences* (1998): 1869–1895; Roger Penrose, Roger and Stuart Hameroff, "Consciousness in the Universe: Neuroscience, Quantum Space-Time Geometry and Orch OR theory," *Journal of Cosmology* 14 (2011): 1–7; and Robert J. Marks II, "Quantum Randomness Gives Nature Free Will," Mind Matters News, Walter Bradley Center for Natural & Artificial Intelligence, December 6, 2018, https://mindmatters.ai/2018/12/quantum-randomness-gives-nature-free-will/.

20. This includes today's quantum computers that use different properties of quantum mechanics.

16. Parting Thoughts

1. Alan J. Perlis, "Epigrams on Programming," SIGPLAN Notices 17, no. 9 (September 1982): 7–13, http://pu.inf.uni-tuebingen.de/users/klaeren/epigrams.html.

2. Justin Bui, "Artificial General Intelligence: The Modern Homunculus," interview by Robert J. Marks, Mind Matters News, Walter Bradley Center for Natural & Artificial Intelligence, November 4, 2021, podcast, 33:17, https://mindmatters.ai/podcast/ep159/.

3. I first read about this fun idea in the science fiction short story "Martian Odyssey" in an anthology edited by Robert Silverberg, *The Science Fiction Hall of Fame, Vol. 1: 1929–1964* (New York: Orb Books, 2005).

4. George Gilder, "George Gilder on Blockchain and Carbon Computing," interview by Robert J. Marks, Mind Matters News, Walter Bradley Center for Natural & Artificial Intelligence, November 12, 2020, podcast, 23:09, https://mindmatters.ai/podcast/ep108/.

5. Latchesar Ionkov and Bradley Settlemyer, "DNA: The Ultimate Data-Storage Solution," *Scientific American*, May 28, 2021, https://www.scientificamerican.com/article/dna-the-ultimate-data-storage-solution.

6. Samantha Allen, "Is a Pig With a Human Brain Still a Pig?," Daily Beast, April 13, 2017, https://www.thedailybeast.com/is-a-pig-with-a-human-brain-still-a-pig.

7. Brett J. Kagan et al., "In vitro Neurons Learn and Exhibit Sentience When Embodied in a Simulated Game-World," BioRxiv preprint, https://www.biorxiv.org/content/10.1101/2021.12.02.471005v2.

8. Tony Tran, "Researchers Teach Human Brain Cells in a Dish to Play 'Pong,'" Futurism, December 17, 2021, https://futurism.com/the-byte/brain-cells-play-pong.

9. Eric Holloway, "Are the Brain Cells in a Dish That Learned Pong Conscious?," Mind Matters News, Walter Bradley Center for Natural & Artificial Intelligence, December 27, 2021, https://mindmatters.ai/2021/12/are-the-brain-cells-in-a-dish-that-learned-pong-conscious/.

10. Holloway, "Are the Brain Cells."

11. For an overview of the mind-brain problem, also called the mind-body problem, see "Mind-Body Problem," Wikimedia Foundation, last modified February 27, 2022, https://en.wikipedia.org/wiki/Mind%E2%80%93body_problem. Also see Jonathan J. Loose, Angus J. L. Menuge, and James Porter Moreland, eds., *The Blackwell Companion to Substance Dualism* (New York: John Wiley & Sons, 2018).

12. René Descartes, *Discourse on the Method* [1637] in *The Philosophical Works of Descartes*, vol. 1, trans. John Cottingham et al. (Cambridge: Cambridge University Press, 1984), 127.

13. I am working with Brian Krouse and Angus Menuge on editing a book whose working title is *Minding the Brain*, which dives deeper into such questions. It's due to be released in 2023.

14. "New Navy Device Learns by Doing," *New York Times*, July 8, 1959, https://www.nytimes.com/1958/07/08/archives/new-navy-device-learns-by-doing-psychologist-shows-embryo-of.html.

15. Oren Etzioni, "Artificial Intelligence Will Empower Us, Not Exterminate Us," TEDx, Seattle, February 2, 2017, YouTube, video 13:17, https://youtu.be/H9Ddd1H9uLE.

ACKNOWLEDGMENTS

To my fetching wife, Monika, for her patience during the ordeal of her husband's seemingly endless polishing and repolishing of this book. Especially when I was infected with writer's block and got grumpy. Thanks to John West for guiding me through the numerous hoops of getting this book to print. John's width and breadth of knowledge in all matters continues to amaze me. And thanks to Amanda Witt for her expert editing of my often clunky prose. I was often irritated by her thoughtful edits but only for a while. After forcibly wrestling my ego into silence, I found she was always spot-on. In terms of technical content, I have been most influenced herein by the big brains of Selmer Bringsjord, Gary Smith, William Dembski, Roger Penrose, and Gregory Chaitin—all masters of their domains. Their work is cited many times in the book. And lastly thanks to the Discovery Institute. I am honored to be associated with such an amazing organization that continues to make a big difference in our world.

FIGURE CREDITS

Figure 2.1. Nikola Tesla. "Nikola Tesla, with His Equipment." Photograph by Dickerson V. Alley, circa 1899, Wikimedia Commons. Public domain.

Figure 4.1. Guitar faces. Photographs courtesy of Pat Kelley.

Figure 4.2. The AI-generated portrait Edmond de Belamy. "Edmond De Belamy," Wikimedia Foundation, July 29, 2019. Public domain.

Figure 4.5. Elsie Wright and a Cottingley fairy. Photograph by Frances Griffiths, 1917. Public domain.

Figure 4.6. Frances Griffiths and the Cottingley fairies. Photograph by Elsie Wright, 1917. Public domain.

Figure 4.7. Montana's giant grasshopper. Photography by Cole Studio, 1937. Public domain.

Figure 4.8. A non-existent person from ThisPersonDoesNotExist.com.

Figure 6.1. Sophia the Robot. "Sophia (robot)." Image by ITU Pictures, June 8, 2017, Wikimedia Commons. CC-BY-SA 2.0 license.

Figure 10.1. Gödel is a dangerous guy to question. Cartoon by XKCD, date unknown, https://xkcd.com/468/. Used by permission.

INDEX

Made in the USA
Monee, IL
09 September 2023

42250996R00236